REAW~~AKENED~~
BY HIS
CHRISTMAS KISS

JESSICA GILMORE

THE RANCHER'S
BEST GIFT

STELLA BAGWELL

MILLS & BOON

First Published in Great Britain 2019
by Mills & Boon, an imprint of HarperCollinsPublishers,
1 London Bridge Street, London, SE1 9GF

Reawakened by His Christmas Kiss © 2019 Jessica Gilmore
The Rancher's Best Gift © 2019 Stella Bagwell

ISBN: 978-0-263-27273-4

Printed and bound by CPI Group (UK) Ltd, Croydon, CR0 4YY

REAWAKENED BY HIS CHRISTMAS KISS

JESSICA GILMORE

For Rose, Rich, Ol and Jake.
Thank you for everything.

PROLOGUE

FINN HAWKIN ACCEPTED a glass of champagne from a passing waiter and surveyed the scene before him, his lips curving into an appreciative smile. Fairy lights and gossamer white drapes, elaborate costumes and a vast ballroom might be wasted on him, but his small nieces would want to hear about every single detail of the night. The Armarian Midsummer Ball was like every one of their favourite fairy-tales brought to life.

A masked and cloaked figure paused beside him. 'Having fun?'

'Laurent!' Finn turned to greet his old friend with genuine delight. His presence here might be more business than personal, but it was good to see his host. 'Thanks for the invite.'

'You are more than welcome. I'm glad you could come.'

A hint of sympathy tinged the other man's voice; Finn didn't confide in many people, but Laurent knew how difficult the last year had been, the hard choices Finn had been faced with.

'How are your nieces?'

'Tired out after a week of enjoying your glorious beaches. Not that they'll admit it. Tonight they are most put out at not coming with me to a real-life royal ball. I've promised to smuggle cake back to the villa. Hopefully that will mollify them.'

'Bring them to the palace,' Laurent offered. 'It'll still be chaotic tomorrow, but maybe the day after? We have puppies in the stables they can meet, and I'll take them to the highest turret and tell them grisly stories about how my ancestors repelled would-be invaders.'

'They'll like that. Thanks, Laurent.'

'And we can catch up properly. It'll be easier when I'm not hosting several hundred people.'

'Perils of being a prince.'

But Finn couldn't help noticing that Laurent seemed more at ease than usual. He was usually so reserved, so rigid when in public, but this evening he was like a different man, his smile genuine and easy, his whole being infused with a lightness and joy that Finn couldn't imagine feeling.

'Who's the girl?'

'What girl?' Laurent's grin only widened, his eyes softening as they rested on a slim figure in yellow and silver, standing to the side of the ballroom, directing a group of waitresses.

'The girl you haven't been able to take your eyes off all night. When you haven't been disappearing outside with her, that is.'

It was unlike Laurent to be openly seen with a woman—and, although his costume gave him a degree of anonymity, it wasn't enough of a disguise to ensure complete privacy. No, if Laurent was dancing, flirting and holding intense, smouldering conversations so publicly, then his intentions must be pretty serious, and that was unexpected from a man who had seemed reconciled to a sensible marriage of convenience.

'That's Emilia. She's the party planner. She put this whole ball together in less than a month.' Laurent might have been aiming for offhand, but the pride in his voice was a dead giveaway; he was in deep.

'She's done a great job. The whole evening is magical.'

'Says the man standing on the side alone. I didn't expect you to use your plus one, Finn, but there are plenty of beautiful women here who I'm sure would love to dance with you. Would you like me to introduce you to anyone? How about the Contessa, over there?' Laurent indicated a haughty blonde waving a fan as she ignored an eager crowd of young men.

Finn laughed. 'She looks a little above my pay grade.'

'Modesty doesn't become you, Finn. You're young, active, and you still have all your own hair and teeth. That puts you above half the men in this room, and that's before we take into account your very successful company and the small fact that you've just bought your own castle. Even the Contessa would think that makes you very suitable for one dance at least.'

'Blakeley hardly compares with a royal palace,' Finn protested, but pride swelled through him at the thought of the ancient old building, currently being restored to make a home for his nieces and a base for his rapidly expanding business.

He hadn't inherited the castle, he'd bought it with money he'd earned the hard way. Although he'd grown up on the Blakeley estate, nothing had been handed to him. His success was down to pure hard work and some lucky—and canny—decisions.

'I'm happy for you,' Laurent said softly. 'You've achieved your goal. How many men can say that?'

Finn sipped his drink. Laurent was right. He was barely thirty and he'd hit every one of the goals he'd set when they were students in Paris: to found his own business, make a fortune, and live on an estate like the one he'd grown up on. Only this time he'd be the one in the big house, not the gardener's boy, doffing his cap to his so-called betters.

'We never stop setting goals, Laurent, we just change the goalposts. Now my nieces come first. Giving them the kind of happiness and security they need…that's my priority.'

'If anyone can, you can.'

They stood there in silence for a moment, watching the opulently adorned dancers waltz around the dance floor until Laurent's gaze strayed once again to the girl in the yellow dress. Finn followed his gaze. She had moved away from the waitresses and was talking animatedly to a tall, elegant woman dressed in a demure black dress, her light brown hair elegantly coiled into a chignon.

Recognition punched him. It couldn't be…

Or could it? Was this the girl he'd searched for in vain through the years, right here in a ballroom hundreds of miles away from the place where they'd grown up?

Last time he had seen her, her hair had been bleached platinum blonde and cut into a choppy bob which had instantly spawned a thousand imitations. She'd been a decade younger, coltish and angular, with cheekbones sharp enough to cut through butter and a knowing, slanting gaze that had pouted down from billboards

and magazine covers across the globe—before she had
disappeared from public view and from his life, as if
she had never been.

'Lola?' he half whispered. And, as if she'd heard him,
the woman looked up, alert, scenting danger.

He must be imagining things. Lola Beaumont was
gone, disappeared into the ether. He knew that. He'd
looked for her for long enough. He blinked and refo-
cussed. He must be mistaken. The woman was clearly
working at the event, and Lola was always the guest
of honour, not the help. It was a passing resemblance,
that was all.

He'd thought he'd cured himself of seeing Lola at
every corner years ago. But Finn couldn't stop himself from turning to Laurent. 'Who is that? Talking to
Emilia?'

'Who? Oh, that's Alex—Alexandra Davenport. She
co-owns a party planning agency with Emilia and two
other women. She arrived yesterday, I think, to oversee
things tonight so Emilia could attend the ball. Why?'
Laurent's smile turned sly. 'Would you like an introduction to her?'

'No, thanks. Just curious.'

But Finn's mind was working furiously. Alexandra
was Lola's middle name, wasn't it? Surely it was a coincidence—a similarity of features, a shared name, that
was all. But as he gazed across at the woman he couldn't
help feeling that there were no such things as coinci-
dences and now, just as his life was exactly where he
wanted it to be, Lola Beaumont had returned to disrupt
it all over again.

The question was, what was he going to do about it?

CHAPTER ONE

WITH A HERCULEAN effort, Alexandra Davenport managed to wait until she had passed through Passport Control before she turned on her phone. Pulling her small case behind her, she headed towards Customs and the exit, impatient as her phone whirred through its settings and began to process all communications from the last eight hours.

All around her people staggered past, eyes red, clothes wrinkled from the overnight flight. Alex, on the other hand, felt surprisingly well-rested. Thank goodness she'd packed a washcloth and a clean top in her overnight bag, and had freshened up just before the fasten seat belts sign came on. She was refreshed, she had slept, and she was ready for anything.

She glanced at her phone, not surprised to see every notification symbol jostling for space at the top. There was always a crisis somewhere. Which for her was a good thing; promotional PR paid the bills, but it was managing the unexpected and spinning disaster into gold where she excelled.

She dialled up voicemail and waited for the first message to come through.

'Alex? It's me.'

Alex smiled as she heard the voice of Amber, her colleague and, more importantly, her friend. With just three words she was home. Home. A place she had stopped believing existed. After all, hadn't she trained herself not to rely on people or places?

'Hope you get this in time. What am I saying? Of course you will. There's no way you don't have a fully charged phone ready to switch on the second you land! So, we've had a last-minute booking. It's a residential stay and the client is very much demanding that you get there asap. So you need to head straight there. I've arranged for a car to pick you up and take you. Give me a call when you're on the way and I can go through everything with you. Don't worry, I packed up some clothes for you and they've been collected. Well done again on New York. You rocked it. Can't believe we're properly international! Talk soon!'

The voicemail ended and Alex frowned as she saved it. She hadn't been expecting to head straight out again—after a week away she was more than ready to return to the Chelsea townhouse she had inherited the year before and turned into both a home and the business premises for her three closest—and only—friends. Together they had set up the Happy Ever After Agency, offering regular, one-off and consultancy support in everything from admin to events, PR to bespoke jobs.

Only eight months after opening they already had a strong reputation, backed up by glowing testimonials from previous clients. Glowing testimonials thanks to their ability to react quickly. Exactly as she needed to do right now, she reminded herself. Her feelings didn't matter. The client always came first.

Of course it didn't hurt their reputation that one of

their previous clients, Prince Laurent, Archduke of Armaria, was currently courting Emilia, their events specialist, whilst tech billionaire Deangelo Santos was engaged to Harriet, his former PA and their head of admin.

Alex suppressed a sigh. They'd been open less than a year and already it was all change. Next year Harriet would marry Deangelo and officially move out of the townhouse, and they all knew Laurent would propose to Emilia any day now.

Harriet intended to carry on working once she was married but, although Emilia would remain a business partner, there was no way she would be able to take on any jobs once she became Archduchess. Alex was absolutely delighted for her friends, but she couldn't help wishing they'd had more time together first. Time to really build the agency.

She swallowed, not wanting to admit even to herself that the ache she felt deep inside wasn't just down to the changes in the business. She'd been so happy these last few months, living and working with her friends. She'd trained herself to enjoy her own company, but the house felt alive with the four of them in it. It was welcoming. Would it seem empty when there were just two?

Pushing the dark thoughts away, Alex walked swiftly through Customs, checking her emails as she did so and flicking through her clients' social media feeds to make sure there was nothing requiring immediate attention.

She was just aware enough of her surroundings to make sure she didn't crash into anyone, otherwise she zoned out the noise and hubbub as she exited into the Arrivals Hall. She stopped for a moment, scanning the waiting crowds for a sign with her name on it, but before she could spot it her attention was snagged by a teenage girl running past her to launch herself into the arms of a middle-aged couple, whose wide smiles and bright eyes showed how very glad they were to see her.

No one had ever waited for Alex unless they'd been paid to be there, like the driver today. She watched as the couple enfolded the girl in their arms, unable to help noticing other reunions, some loud, some tearful, and one so passionate she felt like a voyeur.

She straightened. Enough of this nonsense. She had just had a very successful few days, turning the agency into an international proposition, and she was heading straight into another job. Success, security, everything she was working towards was within reach. That was where she needed to focus.

With a jolt of relief, she spotted the sign with her name on it and headed towards it. The sooner she was out of the airport the better.

Ten minutes later Alex found herself ensconced in the back of a comfortable saloon car, her laptop purring to life beside her, a notebook on the folded-out tray table, a chilled bottle of water and a pot of fruit beside it. She read through her emails again quickly, but there was nothing from Amber to indicate where she was going and what she would be doing once she was there.

The driver had volunteered the information that the journey would take around an hour and a half, depending on traffic, but hadn't mentioned the destination. No matter. Amber would fill her in.

Despite the earliness of the hour the roads were busy and the car crawled along. Looking out of the darkened windows into the pre-dawn winter gloom, Alex noted how low and heavy the skies were. The temperature had dropped as well, now closer to the New York chill she'd just left than the autumnal mildness she'd flown away from just a week ago.

It was easy to believe that Christmas was less than three weeks away and winter was well and truly settling in.

A sign caught her eye and she winced at the realisation that they were heading out to the M40. Hopefully they'd turn off soon. She normally avoided the area around the Chilterns. It was far too full of memories.

She checked her phone and decided that it was late enough to call Amber. Barely had she pressed the call button when her friend answered, sounding, as always, far too chipper for first thing in the morning.

'Hi, Alex! You got my message?'

'I did. Which is why I am in the back of a car heading *out* of London and not into it. Who's the client and what's so urgent that I'm needed on site straight away? A threatened exposé? PR disaster?' Her mind whirled. The thornier the problem the more she loved it.

'Nothing so exciting. I'm sorry. But hopefully you'll still enjoy the brief. Have you heard of Hawk?'

Alex thought for a moment, the name niggling at her. 'It sounds familiar.'

'It's an outdoor lifestyle brand, all rugged clothing, popular with those people who like to leave their city pad in their four-by-four to go for a ten-minute walk on the beach, but the clothes are the real deal as well, you know? They're worn by loads of serious climbers and explorer types. They have that cute hawk symbol on all their clothes. Like my winter coat?'

'Yes. I know who you mean.' She didn't own any of their clothing personally, but she was aware of the company's stellar reputation. 'What's happened? Why do they need me?'

'A broken leg.'

Alex blinked. Maybe she wasn't as refreshed as she thought. 'A broken leg?'

'Their PR manager has managed to break her leg in several places. She's confined to bed with her leg in a cage.'

That made more sense. 'I see.'

'They've just moved their headquarters to some kind of stately home out towards Swindon, I think. That's where you're headed.'

Alex let out a breath she hadn't quite realised she was holding. Swindon was past the danger area. 'Okay...'

'The owner is opening up the whole estate as an outdoor activity and nature destination. You know the kind of thing: adventure playgrounds and forest trails, all in line with the whole Hawk brand. They're running the business out of converted barns, or stables, or something suitably rustic. They're officially opening at the end of the week, with a ton of Christmas-themed events. Apparently the house and grounds were all neglected and it's the kind of area where jobs are sparse, house prices sky-high and lots of incomers are buying second homes, so there's a whole rejuvenating-the-village and local-jobs-for-local-people thing going on as well.'

'Very worthy,' Alex said drily. 'But any Communications and PR plan for all that will have been agreed months ago. What do they need me for?'

'To look after things while the PR manager is on bed-rest.'

Alex shifted, staring out of the window at the pinkening sky. 'Amber, that's not a difficult job. Any of our temps could take a plan and implement it. They don't need me for anything so simple. It's not like I'm cheap.'

'They were adamant they wanted you. It's a big deal, Alex. Opening up the house after all this time is a huge undertaking, and it's very different to anything they've done before. They see the estate as the embodiment of their brand. They're really big on sustainability and corporate responsibility, which fits in with the job creation and community stuff. They need a safe pair of hands to make sure it's properly publicised. Besides, they hinted that there might be bigger work coming our way if they were happy. Maybe this is some kind of test.'

'Maybe…' But Alex had entered PR for a reason. She knew when someone was spinning a story and this situation just didn't ring true. 'Send me the brief, will you?'

'I don't have it. They wanted to talk you through it all in person. But, honestly, they are opening with a whole Christmassy bang. You'll be kept suitably busy, I promise.'

All Alex's senses tingled. As soon as she finished the call she planned to find out every last bit of knowledge she could about Hawk and its owner. If it was in the public domain—or semi-public—then she would find it. Maybe she was wrong, and this situation was all absolutely legitimate, but she needed to be prepared for any and every eventuality.

'Alex, before you go… Dalstone sent over their press release for you to work your magic on and they want it back before nine this morning. Can you take a look now?'

'Of course. I'll send it right back. Is everything else okay?'

'All's good. Harriet's working from home today.

Deangelo just got back from an oversea trip so she wants to see him. Emilia's event went really well, but she didn't get in until after two so I think she'll be sleeping in.'

Amber sounded wistful. She thrived on the company of others and was happiest when they were all together. It didn't help that Christmas was so close. For the last few years the four of them had spent Christmas together, but this year Deangelo was taking Harriet back to his native Rio De Janeiro for the holiday, and Emilia would be spending two weeks in Armaria. All three of them expected their friend to come back sporting an engagement ring.

'I was thinking,' Alex said with an impulsiveness that surprised her. 'You and I should do something this Christmas. Skiing, maybe? Or we could have a city break somewhere wintry, like Vienna?'

'Really?'

'Absolutely. Why don't you look into it? After all the hard work we've had over the last few months we deserve a short break.'

'It will have to be short,' Amber reminded her. 'Your contract with Hawk lasts until Christmas Eve, and we have the Van Daemon New Year's Eve charity ball, but we could do three days in between without any problems.'

'Three days sounds perfect. Okay, I'll get the press release straight back. Speak later.'

'Give me a call when you're fully briefed and settled in. I'm sorry you had to head out on another job without coming home first.'

'It's fine. It's what we're here to do. It's a good sign, Amber. A sign we're where we want to be.'

Alex finished the call and opened her laptop, connecting it to her phone's data so she could access the press release Amber had mentioned. And then, she reminded herself, it would be time to investigate her new employers and check just why her every hackle was up and sensing danger.

But the press release needed far more work than she had anticipated, and between the pull of her work and the lull induced by the car's steady process she soon got lost in it, any thought of research flying out of her head.

She didn't notice the car turn off the motorway long before Swindon, and nor was she aware as they drove through a succession of idyllic villages, more like a film set than real places, with a succession of village greens, quirky pubs and thatched cottages.

It wasn't until the car slowed and turned in at a pair of elaborate gates that she realised she'd arrived at her destination.

'Already?' she muttered, glancing at the time on her laptop.

Only an hour had passed. There was no way they had made it to Swindon in that time. Which meant they were somewhere else entirely; somewhere an hour west of London. Inhaling slowly, Alex looked up. There was no need to worry. She was in control; she was always in control.

Repeating the mantra, she looked straight ahead at the gates, taking in every detail of the ornate gilt-covered iron, the curlicues and symbols, time stilling as she noted every familiar detail. Her breath caught painfully in her throat, and her mouth was dry as the old, unwelcome panic, banished for a decade, thundered through her.

She hadn't just arrived. She'd returned. She was at Blakeley. Ten years after swearing never to set foot here again. Ten years after renouncing her way of life and starting anew.

Calm deserted her. She couldn't do this. Wouldn't. The car would have to turn around and take her straight back to London.

Hands shaking, she began to bundle her phone back into her bag, snapping her laptop shut. But she couldn't find the words to tell the driver to stop. Her chest was too tight, her throat swollen with fear and long-buried memories.

And still the car purred inexorably on. Every curve of the drive, every tree and view was familiar. More. It was part of her soul. Alex sat transfixed, fear giving way to nostalgic wonder, and for a moment she saw the ghost of a fearless long-limbed girl flitting through the trees.

But that girl was long gone. Lady Lola Beaumont had disappeared the day the Beaumonts' fortunes had crashed and in her place Alexandra Davenport had appeared. Any resemblance was purely superficial.

Besides, who would recognise flamboyant Lola in demure Alex? Alexandra didn't party or flirt, she didn't dance through life expecting favours to be bestowed upon her, and she didn't try to shock or crave publicity. She worked hard; she lived a quiet existence. Her clothes were fashionable and stylish, yes, but on the sensible side. Her hair was coiled neatly, her jewellery discreet. And it was Alexandra Davenport who had been employed to do a job. The fact that the job was at her old family home must be one awful coincidence.

It *had* to be. After all, no one knew who she once had been. Not even her best friends.

Alex sat frozen, still undecided. Turning tail and running wasn't her style, but she had stayed clear of this entire region for a reason. She might not feel like Lola any longer, might not act like her, but what if someone recognised her?

Her hands folded into fists. She managed the story; she was no longer the story herself. She'd left her tabloid headline existence in the past, where it belonged, but she knew her reappearance at her childhood home would create nothing but speculation and the kind of publicity she'd spent a decade avoiding.

If she turned around now she wouldn't be running away, she'd be making a prudent retreat. She could claim a double booking and send one of her many capable temps in her stead, with a discreet discount and an apology. It was the right—the only—thing to do.

Only at that moment the car swept round the last bend and there it was, gleaming gold in the winter morning sun. Blakeley Castle. Alex could only stare transfixed at the long, grand façade, at the famous turrets, the formal gardens, now autumnal in browns and oranges and red, the trees bare of leaves, their spindly branches reaching high to the grey-blue sky. Her breath quickened and she leaned forward as if in a trance.

Blakeley Castle was beautiful. There was nowhere like it. Nowhere as steeped in myth and legend and history. Kings had fallen in love within its walls; queens had fallen from favour. Dukes had lost their hearts, and sometimes their heads, and the Beaumonts had gambled their fortunes, their titles, their freedom, their looks and their marriages on games of chance, of love, of treason.

Until one had gambled too much and lost it all. His freedom, his family, his home.

And now his daughter, the last Beaumont, was returning to Blakeley. But as an anonymous employee, no longer the spoiled darling of the house.

Alex took a deep breath, straightening her shoulders. She might have changed her name and changed her destiny but the old ancestral cry of 'Semper porsum', always forward, ran through her veins. This was just a job. And Blakeley was just a house—well, a castle. But it was still bricks and mortar. There were no ghosts here apart from the few that still haunted her dreams. And she made sure they vanished in the cold light of day.

She wasn't Lola Beaumont. She was Alexandra Davenport. She was calm and capable and she always saw her commitments through. Her life was sensible and measured and it was ridiculous to think of upsetting any aspect of it because of an old link to a mere place. A link that had been severed ten years ago. Nobody here knew her. She would do her job to the best of her ability and leave without looking back once. No regrets. She'd had too many of them.

Mind made up, Alex sat back as the car swept into the parking area at the side of the house, checking herself in her mirror. Her lipstick was in place, her hair neat, her expression coolly inscrutable. All was as it should be. The panic had gone. It was back in the past where it belonged. Nothing fazed her, nothing touched her, and her walls were firmly back in place.

She couldn't help noticing the changes in the familiar. Everything looked better cared for, and the flag flying from the highest turret bore a bird of prey, not the Beaumont crest. The car park was freshly laid, not a pothole to be seen, shielded from the castle by a tall hedge. She glimpsed the grand front entrance as the car turned. Doors stood open, the old faded steps were now gleaming, and the rug half covering them sported the same golden bird as that flying overhead on the flag.

Alexandra Davenport had never been to Blakeley Castle before. She would wait for the driver to open the door and then look around her in curiosity as she exited the car, asking if she should go in through the back door or report somewhere else. All would be unfamiliar, all new. She would be focussed on the task ahead. The beauty of the old house and grounds were of secondary importance, and her curiosity about the new owners confined to a moment's idle speculation before work took over, as it always did.

One deep breath and any dangerous traces of Lola disappeared as Alexandra stepped out of the car, her expression bland, her smile practised, and turned to face the person who had appeared to greet her.

The smile only wavered for one infinitesimal second as she took in the tall, broad-shouldered man, his dark jacket and jeans showcasing lean, powerful muscles, his hair swept back off his face, dark eyes as cold as the December air.

'Hello.' Her voice stayed calm and in control as she held out a hand. 'Alexandra Davenport.'

The man's gaze only grew more sardonic as he took her hand in his. His clasp was strong, almost too strong, as if he had something to prove.

'Finn Hawkin. But you knew that. Didn't you, Lola?'

CHAPTER TWO

FINN LOOSENED HIS grip and Alex withdrew her hand from his in a smooth gesture.

'I go by Alexandra now.'

'I know. Alexandra Davenport, I believe? Of course Alexandra *is* your middle name.'

He noted her slight blink of acknowledgement with satisfaction. Maybe she wasn't quite as calm as she seemed. 'Where's the Davenport from?'

'My grandmother's maiden name.' She stepped back and looked around before her cool gaze rested on him once again, understanding in her grey eyes. 'Hawkin… hawk. Of course. I see. You always did say you'd earn enough to own somewhere like Blakeley some day. I didn't think you actually meant Blakeley itself, but that wasn't the first time I underestimated you. Congratulations, Finn, you've obviously done very well.'

Finn had been rehearsing this meeting for the last few hours. Ever since he'd heard about his Head of PR, Penelope, having an accident. No, longer than that. Since the summer, when he had glimpsed Lola across the ballroom floor and done some digging into the agency which had organised the Armarian Midsummer Ball and its four founders. From the moment he'd realised that Alexandra Davenport was exactly who he thought she was.

Lola Beaumont was unfinished business. Business he needed to resolve in order to move on once and for all—especially now that he was master of Blakeley and all that entailed. He had to focus on the future, on his nieces, and let go all the regrets that still haunted him. And he could only do that by confronting the past—and the woman who dominated it.

And then the fates had aligned, for good or for ill, and he had taken advantage of them. Penelope's accident was more than unfortunate, coming at such a very crucial time. The castle would be opening to the public for the first time in its history this weekend, and he needed an experienced pair of hands to manage all the resulting publicity. Who better than the woman who had grown up here? Who now worked as a PR consultant?

The Lola he'd known would have reacted to her homecoming in some dramatic fashion, with tears or laughter equally likely, but this new version radiated a disconcerting cool calmness. A calmness he hadn't anticipated, hadn't prepared for. Nor had he missed her slight emphasis on the words 'underestimated'.

His mouth tightened. He didn't reply, not at first, taking a moment to observe the woman who had been his oldest friend—and his first love.

'You didn't know I founded Hawk?'

He didn't hide his polite disbelief. Maybe she'd walked away and never so much as typed his name into a search engine or on a social media site, but his business was a global brand, and as founder and CEO he had been extensively profiled.

Alex was a PR professional. It didn't seem possible

that she had no idea of who he had become and what he'd achieved.

But her smile was apologetic. 'Sorry. Outdoor pursuits aren't my speciality and nor is clothing. I'm aware of Hawk, of course, but you've never been a rival of any of my clients, so I haven't ever needed to investigate further. That was why I was so surprised when Amber said you had requested me specifically. I have to say I am even more surprised now I'm here. Finn, obviously it's flattering that you would like me to cover your PR. But, given everything, I don't think that our working together is in any way a good idea.'

'Everything?' He kept his voice icily smooth, but she still didn't react, her expression unruffled.

'Our shared history.'

He raised an eyebrow. 'Shared history? That's one way of putting it, I suppose.'

He stopped himself from saying anything else, from letting the bitter words he'd been holding back for ten years come spilling out. He was no longer a young man with no idea how to handle his emotions, how to cope with accusations and betrayal and heartbreak.

'However, that's exactly why you're perfect for this job. After all, you know the castle better than anyone else.'

Again, just a blink as her reaction. Finn folded his arms and waited for her to respond, refusing to allow her calmness to throw him. After all, whether she called herself Alexandra Davenport or Lola Beaumont, there was one thing he knew for sure: she didn't just know Blakeley Castle, she loved it with every fibre of her fiery being.

But, he conceded as he studied her, this woman

wasn't fiery. Gone was the platinum blonde hair and dramatic eyeliner, the cutting-edge fashion and almost fey wildness. Instead Alexandra's hair was her natural light brown, neatly pinned up, her make-up discreet, her clothes professional. There was nothing wild in the way she stood, nor in her eyes. Instead Finn noted her absolute air of control. Was there any trace of Lola trapped inside this stranger?

'The castle, yes. Your brand, no.'

'But you specialise in short-term jobs, in getting up to speed quickly,' he pointed out silkily. 'I have a whole team who can manage Hawk's PR work. What I need is someone to help me launch Blakeley Castle as a destination. Your expertise and knowledge make you the logical choice. Your colleague, Amber, didn't think there would be any problem.'

'Amber doesn't know that I have any personal connection to Blakeley—or to you,' she added in a low voice. 'So of course she wouldn't foresee any conflict of interest. But there are conflicts, and it's my professional opinion that you would be better off with one of our excellent consultants instead of me. I can think of at least three who would be perfect. I propose I go back to London now and send you their profiles. I can make sure your preferred candidate is with you by the end of the day. I'm sorry you have wasted your time. It's unfortunate that I was out of contact when you called.'

She picked up her bag and took a decisive step back.

'I'm glad to see you've done so well, Finn. I look forward to our companies working together. I'm sure it will be a successful partnership.'

Not so fast. He hadn't got her back just to watch her drive off into the sunset with nothing resolved.

'You've signed a contract.'

Her eyes flickered. 'And we'll honour that contract…'

'The contract specifies you, Alex. That *you* will work here at Blakeley Castle until Christmas Eve. Not one of your consultants, however excellent they may be.'

'Yes, but—'

'It's you I have employed, your expertise I want, and your exorbitant rates I have agreed to.'

'We can, of course, offer a discount to offset any inconvenience.'

'I don't need a discount. Either you fulfil the terms of your contract or I sue you for breaking them. Your choice. I'm sure you'll be happy to stand up in court and tell everyone why you didn't feel able to work for me.'

Her silence and stillness were absolute. 'I see. I'm sorry that you hate me this much, Finn…'

'I don't hate you, Lola. I have absolutely no feelings at all towards you. This isn't personal. This is business. So what will it be?'

He held her gaze, conscious of the lie. Of course it was personal, but his business reasons were more than valid. And he didn't hate her. He never had.

She sighed. 'If you're absolutely adamant that I stay then of course I will, but I'd like to make it clear that I think you would be better letting me assign someone else to this job. Are you sure this is what you want?'

'I'm sure. Come along and I'll show you to your desk. Not that you need me to show you anywhere. I'm sure you remember your way around.'

Her eyes dipped briefly and she laid a hand on his arm, her touch light. Even her touch had lost its fire.

Or maybe he was immune, their past having inoculated him against any spells she might cast.

'Finn, I need to get one thing straight. If you really want me to work for you then please forget you ever knew me. Forget I ever lived here. Lola Beaumont is gone. I left her behind a long time ago.'

'Shame. There was a lot of good in Lola behind it all.'

'That's neither here nor there. Do I have your word that you will respect my anonymity? The reputation I have built up? I don't know how you tracked me down, Finn, but if you really have brought me here to do my best for your business and not to create a whole other kind of publicity then you'll forget about Lola.'

She fixed her disconcerting gaze on him. Still no trace of visible emotion in their grey depths. No longer could a lovestruck boy compare them to stormy seas or windswept skies. Instead they were more like a glossy pebble, smooth and unreadable.

'Unless, of course, it's other publicity that you are after? Not my expertise but my past?'

Finn stared at her, incredulous as her meaning took shape. 'You think I brought you here to expose you?'

She shrugged. 'It would be excellent PR. The last Beaumont back at Blakeley… The papers would love it. They'll rake up the old scandal anyway, you know that—you must be counting on it. Everyone loves the idea of an old, proud family brought down, and now they can stand on the spot where it happened. I am quite happy to facilitate that, Finn, but I am no longer personally part of that story.'

His hands curled once more into fists as he fought to match her calmness. 'I don't expect you to be the story. Blakeley is mine now. I prefer to concentrate on the future and on building prosperity for everyone who works here.'

'Thank you. I'm glad we understand each other.'

Even with the toned-down make-up and hair, the professional clothes, he could still see traces of the vibrant girl he had known in the tilt of Alexandra's pointed chin, the curve of her cheekbones, her elegant posture. But any resemblance was purely skin-deep.

Lola was gone, and with her all that fire and passion. It might have got her—and all who knew her—into trouble sometimes, but she had at least known how to live. He got the impression that the woman in front of him didn't really live a single day of her ordered life. Rather she sleepwalked through it, merely existing. Of all the tragedies that had hit the Beaumonts, this seemed like the biggest tragedy of all.

But whether she called herself Alexandra or Lola one thing was clear—she still thought he would use her, expose her for his own personal gain, just as she had believed ten years ago. No matter what he had achieved, to the woman opposite he was still the boy she thought had betrayed her. Well, his word might not have been good enough then, but she would have to believe in it now.

His future awaited him, and once Christmas was over Lola/Alexandra would be out of his life and his memories for good.

Control had been at the centre of Alex's life for many years now, but she had never had to fight so hard for it as she did right now. Standing beside her old home, with its turrets reaching up into the skies, standing opposite the man she had once given her whole heart and trust to, only for him to rip them—and her—to pieces, had whipped up feelings and emotions she had long thought buried and gone. Nausea swirled through her and her hands shook, but she fought to keep her voice even and her expression bland.

Finn could never know the effect he had on her. She would never give him—or anyone—that kind of power again.

'I think I'd better get started. Where shall I set up? I would usually arrive fully prepared, but I was told I'd be briefed when I got here.'

She allowed the merest hint of accusation to hang in the air. Finn had deliberately allowed her to turn up unprepared and wrong-footed. Although, she allowed, if she hadn't been too absorbed in her work to do the background check she'd promised herself, then she wouldn't have been quite so unprepared. She couldn't blame Finn for everything. Not this time.

'I'll take you to meet your team and brief you on the way. Leave your bags. One of the staff will take them to your rooms. The Hawk offices are in the stables. This way.'

Finn indicated the freshly laid woodchip path which wound away from the car park into the small copse which separated the newly refurbished offices from the castle. Alexandra hefted her leather laptop bag onto her shoulder and followed him—as if she didn't know the way to the stables just as well as he did.

'Amber said you're planning to open the castle up to the public and the launch is this week—is that right?' She barely waited for his nod before continuing. 'So, will you open all year round or just for Christmas? Seasonally? Weekends? What about the gardens? Will they have different opening hours and prices? Obviously I should have researched this before I started, but I only got off my flight a couple of hours ago.'

Every question was direct and to the point. Information-gathering for her job, no more. She had to treat this like any other job, Finn like any other client. It was the only way she was going to get through this.

'My apartments are in the top two floors of the west wing, and private, but the rest of the castle, including the grounds, will be open every day. Houses like this should be for everyone, not just for the privileged few.'

Alex swallowed, tightening her hold on her bag. Finn was living in her home, her beloved castle. Once she had daydreamed of such a situation, only in her dreams she had been living there alongside him. Was there a woman living with him? He wasn't wearing a wedding ring but that didn't mean anything. Not that she cared. She just hoped he'd learnt loyalty in the last decade. How to love, not how to use.

Although, judging by the way he was using her right now, she wouldn't bet on it.

'I assume all the paintings and furniture are still here? I know the castle was bought complete.'

She fought to suppress a dangerously revealing wobble in her voice. This was a job, not personal. Blakeley and all its treasures meant nothing to her. She couldn't think about the old oak furniture that dated back to Tudor times, or the famous collection of Pre-Raphaelite paintings. She couldn't remember the old dolls' house or Strawberry, her beloved pony.

Finn nodded. 'Luckily for me the castle was bought by an oligarch who never actually visited the place. Rumour in the village is that he wanted a hunting lodge and didn't realise the estate wasn't suitable for the kind of stag-hunting he'd planned. I don't think he even set foot in the place. Blakeley hadn't been touched since the day you left.'

Alex allowed herself one dangerous moment of memory. One flashback to the desperate girl with tears streaming down her face, the police tape still flickering around the lake, the hardness on Finn's face, the paparazzi pressed up against the gates. And the last look back before she had slipped out of the secret door in the wall and out of her life, leaving Lola in the headlines and her heart in Blakeley's keeping.

And then she pushed that memory firmly back down and picked up the pace. 'So, Finn,' she said as brightly as she could. 'Tell me more about your plans and what you need me to do.'

Work was the answer. Work had always been the answer. And for the next few weeks she suspected it was going to be her salvation.

CHAPTER THREE

ALEXANDRA DREW IN a deep breath and stared fixedly at her laptop screen, refusing to let the letters in front of her blur or her mind wander. She was focussed and busy, just the way she liked it, with all messy emotions kept at bay.

All around was a low hum of activity: the sound of a contented, productive office. Sitting here, it was hard to imagine that this building had once been ramshackle stables. There wasn't a whiff of straw or old leather to be found. When she'd first walked in she'd passed the place where her old mare, Strawberry, had been stabled, and for one terrifying moment had been catapulted back in time. Luckily, the receptionist had spoken to her and pulled her back to the present.

She didn't want to go back. She couldn't…

No, better to focus on the present. And if she concentrated hard she could do exactly that.

It helped that the once familiar room was now so unfamiliar. The architect had done an amazing job of transforming the dark old buildings into a light, airy and modern space. On the ground floor was a spacious reception area, meeting rooms, and what Finn had described as 'creative space', filled with sofas, board games and a kitchen area.

The executive offices were also housed on the bottom floor, but she hadn't been shown them. Instead Finn had taken her upstairs to the general offices, making it very clear what her position was.

Upstairs was one big office area, with pale wood desks blending in with old oiled beams, the walls matt white, the floor gleaming parquet, and wide windows showcasing breathtaking views of the parkland and estate gardens.

Alexandra had barely given them a glance. There was a reason she'd moved to London. Not only did she prefer the anonymity of the city, she also liked the way the noise and hubbub gave her so little space to think. London was overwhelming, and that was exactly how she liked it. There was no space to be an individual. The city assimilated you and you just had to be swept away.

Finn had introduced her to the team and his marketing director before leaving her with a curt nod. For a moment, watching him stride away, she had almost felt lost. She'd swiftly shaken that absurdity from her mind, but now, as she read through her handover notes and began to get to grips with her workload, it began to dawn on Alex just what Finn had achieved. Her childhood playmate, her first crush, the boy she had naively thought she might love, had achieved his dream.

She tapped a pencil absentmindedly on the desk as she looked around at the comfortable space filled with people hard at work. He had always proclaimed that one day he would travel around the world, that he'd own his own company and make a fortune, and live in a place like Blakeley, not just work there. And she'd believed him, that fierce determined, skinny boy with his messy dark brown hair and chocolate eyes. Even though he'd never even travelled as far as Oxford, and his father and grandfather and every generation before them had been born, had worked and died within the castle grounds.

But for a while it had looked as if his dreams had stagnated—a pregnant sister, an alcoholic father demanding all his time and attention. The boy who had dreamt of the world had found himself bound to one place, and meanwhile her burgeoning modelling career had taken her around the globe. How he must have resented it. Resented her.

The pencil stilled and the old questions once more flooded her mind. Was that why he had done it? Betrayed her when she had already been as down as a girl could be? The money from those photos must have freed him. And look what he had achieved with that freedom. Did he ever consider that he'd purchased it with her innocence and happiness? Or did he think that it was a fair trade for the generations of Hawkins who had been trampled on by generations of Beaumonts?

Another inhale. Another exhale. Push it all away. All those inconvenient feelings. Concentrate on the job in front of you.

She'd been Alex for so long there were times when she forgot that Lola had even existed. She needed that blissful ignorance now. She had to treat this as any other job, forget she knew Finn, not allow herself to speculate on how he'd found her and why he had gone to such trouble to bring her here. Forget everything but the task at hand.

She put the pencil down firmly, pulling her laptop

closer, and as she did so a pretty dark-haired girl approached her desk.

'Hi, is it Alex or Alexandra?'

'I answer to both.' She smiled in welcome as she desperately searched her mind for the girl's name. Katy? Kitty?

'I'm Kaitlin.' The girl smiled shyly back. 'I doubt you'll remember anyone after that quick introduction. I've never known Finn to be in such a hurry. I thought you might want to get settled in today, but I'll make sure you get properly introduced to everyone tomorrow, so you know what they actually do. I'm the PR Assistant, so technically I report to you. I suggest you ask me anything you need to know and I'll do my best to point you in the right direction.'

Kaitlin's friendliness was disarming—and a relief after the frosty civility Finn had shown. 'That's good to know. Nice to meet you properly, Kaitlin.'

'Penelope asked me to talk you through her strategy and plans so you can go to her with any questions before things get too manic. Is now good?'

'Now's great, thanks.'

Alex looked at her neat notes, perfectly aligned, finding the long to-do list its usual balm. At first she had been at a loss as to why she was so urgently required. Penelope, Hawk's laid-up Head of PR was organised and had clearly taught her junior staff well. Looking through her notes, strategies and task lists, Alex saw that it appeared that there was little left for Alex to actually do, apart from follow instructions. A job anyone with half a brain could manage. It didn't seem worth her substantial fee, and her lurking suspicion that Finn had tracked her down and employed her simply to gloat about their reversal of fortune had deepened.

But as she read on it became clear that the plan Penelope had put together would need careful tweaks and adjustments as the castle was finally opened to the public, and the potential press interest needed to be handled by someone with experience. It was a job she was confident any of the temps on her books could handle, but she could see that Finn genuinely needed outside help, and as it was unlikely he'd manufactured Penelope's accident her presence here was in some way coincidental, even if her concern as to how he had tracked her down remained.

After all, if he could then so could any of those journalists who still ran occasional stories on the fall of the Beaumonts.

Kaitlin pulled a chair up to the desk. 'So, the first thing is the media launch party. May I…?'

Alex nodded permission and the younger woman manipulated the mouse on the PC Alex had been allocated and brought up the appropriate file.

'Here are the notes and the event plan. It's on Thursday night, and the party is for journalists, local dignitaries and VIPs. The castle will then have a soft opening for two weeks and will officially celebrate with a second, bigger party on the twenty-fourth of December. That party will include locals, colleagues, suppliers, partners…everyone, really.'

Alex inhaled as she read the timeline.

The official opening of the castle and grounds will be marked with a traditional Christmas Eve party.

'Christmas Eve?' Somehow she kept her voice calm.

'Apparently it's a real tradition at Blakeley. I hear the parties here used to be wild. Full of every kind of celebrity from pop stars to princes.'

'Right. Then we need to make sure we publicise that angle.'

Her heart began to thump; her hands felt damp. Christmas Eve. Her birthday. More than that, the day Blakeley had always celebrated Christmas.

For generations, friends and lovers, enemies and rivals had descended on Blakeley on Christmas Eve to feast and dance, intrigue and plot.

As a child Alex would spend the afternoon hosting a sumptuously over-the-top party for her friends—and then spend the evening darting through the dancing, flirting adults, sipping champagne from discarded glasses and sneaking canapés. No one had ever told her to go to bed. Instead she had been the spoilt princess of the house, petted and indulged, falling asleep on a chair or a sofa, where she would wake on Christmas morning to find herself covered with some discarded jacket.

In her mid-teens the two parties had been combined, with lithe, knowing teenagers far too at home amidst the glamour and heady atmosphere of the adult affair. At least they'd pretended they were at home. Alex had been very good at pretending. Until the night of her eighteenth birthday, that was, when her world had become real for the first time—for a few blissful hours, until the moment when it had stilled and stopped for ever.

She tried to inhale again, to take those sweet, calming breaths that kept her pulse even, her heart still, her head clear. But her breath caught in her throat.

I can't do this, she thought, panic threatening to flood through the walls she had built so carefully, so painstakingly, solid walls, covered in ivy and thorns, ready to repel all invaders. *I can't.*

But she could. She had no choice. Stay and deal with it or leave and run the risk of exposure.

She was stronger than this. Nothing and no one could hurt her now. Blakeley was just a place, Christmas Eve was just a date, her birthday would go unremarked. She would show Finn that he hadn't won. Not then, not now. And she would do so by making sure his planned launch ran absolutely perfectly.

Gradually her pulse returned to normal, her emotions stilled, and she calmly made another note.

Check the invite list for the Christmas party.

'Okay,' she said, her voice as steady as ever. 'What's next?'

The conversation with Kaitlin was illuminating in several ways, taking up the rest of the morning and lunch. It had been a long time since her airline breakfast, and Alex had had no chance to get anything to eat, but Kaitlin ordered a working lunch, which the two ate at the desk as they finished going through the notes. Alex's to-do list was getting satisfactorily ever longer.

At some point in the afternoon the younger woman finally returned to her own desk and Alex sank thankfully into work. There she could forget that Christmas Eve had once meant something, meant everything, deep in the absorption that working out how to craft and manipulate a story gave her.

As always, she lost track of time, and when she finally stretched and looked up she realised it was now dark outside, the office lights bright against the gloom. The room was almost deserted. Just a few people were left at their desks and they seemed to be packing up. Alex leaned back and stretched again, glad that the weeks ahead looked interesting but achievable.

She would give Finn no reason, no excuse to find fault with a single thing she did. He had the power and the influence now. With one word he could tell everyone who she was—who she'd used to be—and trash her fledgling agency's reputation. She wouldn't have thought him capable once. She knew better now.

'Alex?' Kaitlin hovered by her desk, her bag already on her shoulder. 'I'm off now. Is there anything you need before I leave?'

'No, I'm fine. Thank you. You've been so helpful.'

'I hope so.' The younger woman looked pleased, brushing her thick dark hair away from her face as her cheeks turned a little pink.

Alex looked around at the gleaming new office. 'I guess you haven't been based here very long?'

'No, Finn's been here since the summer, but the rest of us moved in October. There's still a London office, but the plan is to scale it right back. For now some people are splitting their time between there and here. It's easier for those of us without families, I guess. Finn has converted an old mill into flats and a few rent there. One or two rent in the village and quite a lot of us are in Reading—we're not ready for a totally rural life just yet!'

'It's impressive that so many of you were ready to uproot yourselves.'

'Finn's so inspiring…his whole ethos. I wouldn't want to be anywhere else.'

'That's reassuring to hear. I hope I'll feel the same way.'

'I hope so too.'

The deep masculine tones made both Alex and Kaitlin jump, the latter's cheeks going even redder as Finn sauntered towards them.

'Loyalty is very important here at Hawk.'

But it wasn't Finn's unexpected appearance that made Alex's pulse speed up, and nor was it the sardonic gleam in his eye as he looked at her. It was the two small girls holding on to his hands. Finn had *children*? He had security, money, her old home and a family? Everything she had lost. Everything she would never have.

The oldest girl looked, to Alex's inexperienced eye, to be about nine, the other around five. They were both in school uniform, their dark hair so like Finn's own in messy plaits, and the same dark, dark eyes fixed on Alex.

'It's the Sleeping Princess,' the younger one said, pointing at Alex. 'Look, Saffy, it's the Princess from the painting.'

Finn suppressed a grin as Alexandra's startled gaze flew to his. Turned out the lady could show surprise after all.

'Alex…' The name felt clumsy on his tongue. 'I'd like you to meet my nieces. Saffron, Scarlett, this is Alex. She's working here for a little while.'

'No, Uncle Finn.' Scarlett tugged at his hand. 'She's a princess in disguise.'

Wasn't that the truth?

'Nice to meet you.' Alex smiled uncertainly at the

girls. 'But I'm afraid it's a case of mistaken identity. I'm not a princess, although it's lovely to be thought one.'

'You *are*,' Scarlett insisted.

Kaitlin nodded. 'I see what you mean, Scarlett. You're thinking of that painting, aren't you? The one of Blakeley Castle and the Sleeping Beauty? She does look a little like Alex.'

Alex's cheeks reddened, just slightly. Finn was certain she knew exactly which painting Scarlett was referring to; it was a Rossetti, part of the castle's famed Pre-Raphaelite collection. Alex's great-great-grandmother was the model: a woman who in her youth had been as scandalous as her granddaughter several times removed.

What would the Pre-Raphaelite muse and late-Victorian It Girl think of her descendant? Would she recognise this poised, apparently emotion-free woman sitting in an office chair as if she were made for it, the very model of efficiency? Finn barely recognised her himself. It was all too easy to think her who she claimed to be.

'If you say so, but I can't see it myself,' he said, taking pity on Alex, even though her resemblance to the woman in the painting had been notable when she was younger and was still remarkable, despite her decidedly un-Pre-Raphaelite appearance. 'I'll take it from here, Kaitlin.' He nodded at the dark-haired girl. 'You get off now or you'll miss the last bus.'

'Bus?' Alex watched Kaitlin leave before swivelling back to face him. 'Since when was there a bus?'

'If I want my employees to come and bury themselves in the depths of the Chilterns then I have to make it manageable for them,' Finn pointed out. 'Some live on the estate in the Old Corn Mill, but that didn't suit everyone, so a mini-bus goes between here and Reading several times a day. It picks up at the train station too. Not everyone is ready to leave London just yet. And when the employees don't use it, the villagers do.'

'How very Sir Galahad of you…riding to the rescue with your jobs and renovations and buses.'

Alex's voice and face were bland, but Finn felt the barb, hidden as it was. The situation was getting to her more than she was letting on, and he had to admit he was relieved. It didn't seem normal for anyone to be so serene when confronted with their past in the way she had been.

'The village must be very grateful.'

He shrugged. 'Relieved more than grateful. Goodness knows it needed a Sir Galahad to swoop in after the Beaumonts' reign of benign neglect, followed by a decade of an indifferent and absent landlord.'

His barb wasn't hidden at all, and he saw her flinch with some satisfaction. The Beaumonts had adored being the Lord and Lady of the Manor but they hadn't been so interested in the people who lived and worked on the estate.

Blakeley might be situated in a wealthy commuter county, but the village itself was very rural, its twisty roads and the Chiltern Hills making even a short journey as the crow flew lengthy. Plus, it was a place where more than half the houses were owned by the castle, but where the jobs that had used to come with the houses had disappeared over the years.

Picturesque as Blakeley village was, not everyone wanted to rent a home where the colour of their front door and guttering was prescribed by the estate, public transport was non-existent and the nearest town a long, windy ten miles away.

'The locals are just happy to see new life breathed into the place, and enough staff are renting to make the local businesses and the school viable. My village is breathing again.'

'*Your* village? You wear Lord of the Manor pretty well.'

Another barb. Interesting.

Finn didn't react, simply nodded towards the door. 'Are you done here? The girls are ready for their dinner and I need to show you where you're staying.'

'There's a lot to do, but I can work in my room.' Alex folded her laptop closed and slipped it into its case. 'Look, if there's a bus to the train station I might as well go back to London. The train's only half an hour or so, right? Save you the problem of putting me up.'

'It's no problem. Besides, it's not just the train. You need to factor in the half-hour journey to Reading—and that's assuming you haven't missed the bus, which you have. Then say another fifteen minutes through traffic to get to the train station. Half an hour to Paddington and then your journey at the other end. You'd rather endure a four-hour return journey than stay here?'

Her gaze flickered away. 'I don't want to put anyone out.'

She didn't want to spend the night surrounded by her past, no doubt.

'You're needed evenings and weekends until Christmas. The contract says we expect you to be on site and that's exactly where you'll be. Unless you still want to walk away.'

He allowed the hint of a threat to linger in his voice,

hiding the doubt he'd spent the afternoon trying to dispel. Would it be better, after all, to take her advice and let her choose a consultant to come and work here? She could still advise from London. He'd wanted her here to resolve the past, but this woman wasn't Lola. She was a stranger.

Finn hardened his heart. He needed to give his nieces a place where they belonged, the security they hadn't had until now. He'd earnt a fortune, but a lot of his profits were ploughed back into the company and the foundation he'd set up. For the reopening of Blakeley he needed the best. And everyone agreed that Alexandra Davenport *was* the best. Her expertise and inside knowledge of the castle and estate meant she was exactly what he needed—whether she liked it or not.

Alex stood up decisively. 'I never walk away from a job, Finn, not until the client is happy. I'm fine staying here if that's what you want. Whatever's easiest. You're the client.'

Finn rubbed his chin, feeling the rasp of stubble under his fingertips, suddenly weary. 'Come on, then,' he said brusquely. 'I'll show you where you're staying.'

He rounded up the girls and made his way down the stairs, all too aware of Alex following behind, the tapping of her heels on the wooden treads. He'd called the last of the Beaumonts home to Blakeley. It was up to him to control the situation. He was the boss now, and the sooner Alex accepted that, the better.

CHAPTER FOUR

NEITHER SPOKE AS Finn led Alexandra out of the stable and onto the dimly lit path. The castle reared up, lit up against the winter dark sky, and he noticed Alex turn away from it. So she wasn't as impervious to coming home as she seemed. The girls skipped ahead, oblivious to the chilly atmosphere, which was colder than the rapidly lowering evening temperature.

'Do you think it might snow?' Alex said, looking up at the clouds overhead.

'It's early yet.'

'But it has snowed this early. Remember that year—' She broke off, sentence unfinished.

But he did remember. Snowball fights and sledging, hot chocolate in the kitchen and the skiing lesson she'd given him. They'd been children, no older than Saffy, still mesmerised by the wonder of snow.

A minute went by before Alex made another attempt to break the increasingly charged silence. 'Kaitlin mentioned that you'd converted the old Corn Mill into apartments. Is that where I'm staying? Or does the village pub still have rooms?'

'Yes, no and yes.'

Now it came to it, Finn felt profoundly uncomfortable. His decision on where to house her had seemed purely pragmatic at the time. Now he wasn't so sure that his thinking had been as rational as he'd told himself, with every step provoking memories.

'The Corn Mill doesn't have any space, but it isn't the only building we've renovated. For instance, we've turned the barns at the bottom of the estate into bunkhouses. Places where inner city school kids can come so they can get a chance at the outdoor life. Hiking in the Chilterns, orienteering around the estate, building shelters, that kind of thing.'

Her mouth quirked into a half-smile. A real half-smile, like the girl he'd used to know had had, and his pulse jumped at the sight.

'You're putting me in a bunkhouse?'

'No, that's just an example. We've also renovated some of the old estate cottages for holiday lets. As you know, we'll be running outdoor activities throughout most of the year, so it made sense to give people the chance to stay here.'

'Estate cottages? Not the ones in the village? The ones in the grounds? The Lodge, I suppose, and the Dower House, and…' Her voice trailed off.

'And the Gardener's Cottage. Yes.'

'I'm sleeping in the Gardener's Cottage.' It wasn't a question.

'It's the smallest so it made sense. Four of us lived there for years, Alex. I'm sure you won't find it too much of a squeeze. And don't worry. It's been done up since you last saw it. You won't have to endure my mother's taste in wallpaper or the sofa my father used to pass out on.'

'That's not what I…' She paused and then, voice

bright, said, 'It sounds very charming. I can maybe do some short videos for all the social media accounts about staying there. One weekend I'll do a full day's story—fresh eggs for breakfast in the café, a walk in the woods, that kind of thing. You're right; it makes complete sense for me to stay in a holiday cottage and I'd rattle around in the Dower House. Are the others booked yet?'

'The others?'

'The Dower House and the Lodge? I guess the Foreman's Cottage and the Blacksmith's Cottage are also holiday lets? Because if they're not let out yet then it might be worth offering them to journalists the night of the press party. And then to some influencers in the run-up to Christmas, maybe over Christmas Eve, with invitations for the party. I know the perfect people.'

For a moment, when she had said the words 'Christmas Eve' he could have sworn her voice wobbled. Just a little.

'They are all free; letting starts in the New Year. Invite whoever you'd like. Kaitlin can put you in touch with the letting team. Girls! It's getting dark. Stay close.'

Alex shot him a quick glance and he suspected she was curious about the girls' presence. But before she had a chance to ask any questions his nieces ran back, chattering on about a rabbit Scarlett was sure she'd seen in the wood, and they hadn't exhausted the topic by the time they reached the gate to the cottage.

As they neared the gate a security light was triggered, and Alex stopped just outside the fence and stared. 'It's exactly the same,' she said softly.

Finn inhaled. From the outside nothing much had

changed. His father had always kept it immaculate, even at his worst—on the surface respectable, behind the perfectly painted front door a secret drinker and despot.

'Not quite the same, I hope.'

The first sight of the house still gave Finn a sucker punch to the chest every time he walked through the gate. He'd thought buying Blakeley Castle and turning it into the place he had dreamed it could be would put some of his ghosts to rest, but sometimes they haunted him even more.

'I've put in new windows and fencing and the garden needed a lot of work.' He shot a quick look at the girls, but they were playing hopscotch on the path. 'In the end Dad stopped pretending to function—I suppose there was no one here to judge. Things were in a sorry state when I took over.'

'When did your father die?'

Alex had lowered her voice. She must have noticed he didn't want the girls to overhear. Finn couldn't help remembering just how empathic she had been, especially where his family were concerned. She was the only person living who knew the whole truth. There was a strange freedom in their conversation, in not having to watch what he said, how much he revealed.

'Two years ago. He refused to leave the cottage, refused to let me pay for anyone to help him. Sacked the cleaners I sent, left the groceries I ordered outside to rot in the rain. He died as he lived. On his own terms and with difficulty.' He snapped his mouth closed. He'd never said those words aloud before, not to anyone.

'I'm sorry,' Alex said softly. 'How about your sister? Where is she now? The girls are hers, I suppose?'

But Finn had already said too much, shown too

much—and his sister and her actions was a topic he wasn't ready to share. Not yet. Although he'd need to talk about both with Alex at some point.

'Here's a key,' he said instead. 'Your bag should be inside.'

Alex took the hint, made her voice efficient again. The moment of shared memory was gone and with it an intimacy he'd not realised he'd missed.

'Right. Is there anything I need to know about the boiler or hot water?'

'It should all be working. If not, then there's an information book in the kitchen.'

'Great. Just one more thing: is there any milk or bread in? Because I came straight from the airport and I'm not as prepared as I usually like to be.'

She looked slightly embarrassed, as if she would usually turn up at a work assignment with a week's worth of groceries on her, just in case. And maybe she would.

Finn winced. The Gardener's Cottage was the first to be completely ready. All the linen and towels were there but, because they hadn't started letting, welcome hampers were yet to be organised—and they'd only known for sure that Alex was coming late the night before. The fridge and cupboards were emptier than Mother Hubbard's.

He had meant to ask Kaitlin to sort out the basics, but once he'd seen Alex to the office he had headed out onto the estate and spent the day rebuilding a wall, not questioning why he'd felt the need for hard physical exercise. The mental note to email Kaitlin had uncharacteristically slipped right out of his mind.

'Once we're up and running we'll be leaving welcome hampers, of course, but we haven't started yet. Sorry.'

'Okay,' she pulled her phone out of her pocket. 'Look into sourcing hampers,' she said clearly, before smiling at him—a brisk, businesslike smile that reminded him just what a stranger she was now. 'Believe me, if I'm going to be inviting journalists and influencers we need highly photogenic hampers. Don't worry, I'll get on to it.'

'Right. Of course.' This efficiency was why he had employed her.

She took the key and pocketed it. 'You'd better get the girls back and fed. I'll head down to the village shop.'

Ah... 'It closes at six.'

'Or the pub...'

She bit her lip on the last word and he understood her hesitation. If she was going to be recognised anywhere it would be the pub, with its loyal clientele of locals who had known her since she was a baby. But not tonight.

'They don't serve food on a Monday night.'

'Oh.' Her smile got even brighter, but there was no warmth, no light in it. 'In that case a takeaway it is.'

Finn didn't have the heart to tell her that the only takeaways available to the village were at the weekend, when a fish and chips and pizza van set up on the green for a couple of hours.

'Look, this is my fault, so I had better fix it. Come over to the castle and I'll make you some food.'

As soon as the words were said he wanted to recall them. It was too much, too soon. There were things to say, but not tonight, not when he was still trying to work out just who Alex was.

And she clearly felt the same way, stepping back, away from him, away from his invitation. 'You don't have to do that.'

'I do,' he said drily. 'Your only alternative is water. There's not even any tea bags in the cottage as far as I know.'

'But you cooking is too much,' she protested. 'Honestly, it's been a long day, and I have a lot to be getting on with. I can just grab some eggs and beans or something and bring them back here. I don't want to be any trouble.'

'Once,' he said, in a voice so low he didn't know if she could hear him, or if he wanted her to hear him. 'Once you said trouble was your middle name.'

She looked up at him then, eyes bright. 'I was wrong. Trouble was the family curse. That's why I avoid it whenever I can.'

Finn stared back at her. At a face at once as familiar as his dreams but also that of a stranger. The same almond-shaped grey eyes, the same high cheekbones and full mouth. The same pointed chin and high forehead and look of determination. But the spark that had made Lola so irresistible was gone, and he couldn't tell if it was extinguished entirely or just slumbering, waiting for someone to rekindle it. For one soul-aching moment he wanted to find out, to take this beautiful yet lifeless woman and kiss life back into her.

'Uncle Finn! I'm hungry!'

Now it was his turn to take a step back in denial, and the cold early winter evening breeze was a welcome wake-up call. Finn couldn't believe what had just nearly happened. Kissing Lola Beaumont or kissing Alexandra Davenport—no matter which woman she was, any personal contact was a terrible idea. After all, look what had happened last time.

Even worse, he wasn't alone. The girls were right here. Weren't they damaged enough? He had promised them, promised himself, that they would only ever have love and stability in their lives, had vowed to himself that there would be no women flitting in and out. They'd only meet a girlfriend if he was pretty damn sure she'd be permanent.

'Sorry, Scarlett.' He threw her an apologetic smile and noted with a pang the pinched look on Saffy's face. 'I was just trying to persuade Alex to eat with us, I forgot to put food in her house.'

'Yes, then you can look at the picture,' Scarlett said with a beaming grin.

But Saffron's scowl just tightened further and Finn's heart ached for the small girl. With a jolt of surprise, he noticed a look of understanding cross Alex's face as she looked at his eldest niece, her expression relaxing with compassion.

'It's been a long day, so if it's okay I will just grab some bread and milk, maybe some cheese, and bring it back here,' she said, smiling at Scarlett. 'I'll see the picture some other time, though.'

'Promise?' Scarlett asked.

Alex nodded. 'Promise.'

As he turned to walk back to the castle Alex fell behind. Finn was preoccupied with Scarlett's chatter, and it wasn't until they reached the lights surrounding the castle that, looking back, he realised Alex was making determined conversation with Saffron. The girl wasn't answering—she was always slow to warm to strangers—

but her posture was less defensive and for one moment he thought he saw a slight smile on her face.

So Alex still had the old charm, when she wanted to use it, and he was absurdly grateful she was using it on his prickly niece.

And then he saw it, in the lowering of her gaze, the slight hunch in her posture—the reason Saffron's wariness had always seemed so familiar. It *was* familiar. It was the same wariness he had seen in Alex throughout her childhood—on the rare occasions when she hadn't been performing, being the bright, glittering Beaumont girl everyone had expected her to be.

He'd have done anything to protect his nieces, no matter what, but was the reason he had stepped in so very firmly, before things could go from difficult to toxic, because he had recognised the warning signs in Saffy's eyes?

He hadn't been able to protect Lola. Not from the consequences of her parents' selfishness and not from his own family's part in her downfall, and he'd been too full of his own bitterness to reassure and help her when she'd come back demanding answers at the time. No wonder he was making damned sure that Saffy was as protected as she could be. He knew the consequences.

He'd searched for Lola for years, dreading that he'd find her struggling and alone, and equally dreading that he'd find she'd moved on in true insouciant Beaumont style, not caring about the havoc she left behind her. But now he realised with blinding clarity that all he had wanted to do was put things right. And now she was finally here he had no idea if it was possible. She had her life, and he had the girls.

Maybe it was better to leave the past where it belonged. Lola was gone and Alex was a stranger. He
could finally move on.

'So, if he proposes—and he will—Emilia will be a real-
live princess. Well, an archduchess, but she'll be called
Princess Emilia.'

Saffron's dark eyes widened. 'And she didn't know
who he was when they met? It's just like a fairy-tale.'

Alex looked up and caught Finn watching them, the
rather cold expression he'd been wearing much softer.
Her breath caught. He really cared about his niece. Of
course he did. He had always been someone who cared
deeply. Which was why she had never understood why
he had done what he did—to her, of all people. How he
could have exposed her so publicly, sold her for thirty
pieces of silver.

The old sense of betrayal caught at her heart and she
swallowed back the bitterness. She couldn't indulge.
Not here, not now, not ever.

But as she looked at the warmth in his eyes she
couldn't help but wonder why he'd betrayed her so com-
prehensively. Money, she'd assumed then—and goodness knows he'd needed it—but it still felt wrong, just
as it had back then.

She'd headed straight to him at the time, desperate
for answers, for a way out of the dark labyrinth she'd
found herself trapped in. But there had been no comfort, just cold anger. He'd been the last person to turn
on her—and he would stay the last person. She'd vowed
it then, and she needed to remember it now.

But she couldn't punish the girls for their uncle's
transgressions.

Alex forced a smile as she nodded at the eagerly listening child. 'It is. And then she'll live in a castle too. Just like you.'

Not that living in a castle was any indicator of happiness. She knew that better than anyone. But maybe the curse had disappeared with the Beaumonts. She hoped so for the girls' sake, if not Finn's.

'But I'm not a princess,' Saffron said sadly. 'Princesses are beautiful and clever.'

'Some are. But a real princess, a true princess, has a big heart and she fights for what's right.'

'She does?'

'Absolutely.'

Alex managed to stop herself rushing in to tell Saffron that she was beautiful. It wouldn't be a lie—the little girl was very pretty, with her tangle of dark hair and darker eyes—but, having been brought up knowing that her appeal lay in her looks and her precociousness, Alex had no intention of laying that burden on another Blakeley child.

Smiling reassuringly at Saffron, Alex looked up at the castle looming overhead and stifled the panic rearing inside her. This wasn't a good idea. She wasn't prepared. How could she be prepared?

But it didn't matter whether she was prepared or not because she was here. Here with the man who had administered the final kick ten years ago, making sure she was both down and out.

She had to remember that no matter how disarming his smile, how familiar the warmth in his dark, dark eyes, how protective he was of his nieces, it was all deceptive. All she could do was protect herself the way she always did. Concentrate on the job at hand and block out all other emotions.

And right now her job was getting some food and getting out of the castle as quickly as she could.

But, try as she might to stay cool and collected, she felt her heart start to beat a frantic and painful rhythm as they neared the side door leading into the boot room. From there, the well-trodden path led to the old scullery and then into the kitchen. The heart of the castle. Not a place either of her parents had ever ventured, unless her father had reverted to his school days and crept in to steal a still-warm cake from the huge walk-in pantry.

Ruled over by Mrs Atkinson, the kitchen had been a refuge, a stage and a home. Once ensconced at the kitchen table, Alex had known that she would be ordered to do her homework and sent off to bed at a reasonable time. It had been oddly satisfying.

'Is Mrs Atkinson still here?' she asked as she and Saffron joined Finn and Scarlett at the side door, after checking that the girls weren't listening. She didn't want them suspecting that she and Finn had a prior friendship, or that she wasn't the stranger to Blakeley she pretended to be.

'No, none of the castle staff stayed on afterwards.'

The word hung there. *Afterwards.* Just three syllables to sum up the dissolution of her entire life.

'I tried to persuade her to come back to run the café, but she wasn't tempted. Too many ghosts, apparently.'

'That's a shame.'

Alex was split between relief that someone who would most definitely recognise her wasn't there to blow her cover and a surprisingly deep disappointment that she wouldn't be seeing one of the few people who had seemed to care about her when she was being just a normal child, not a precocious ingénue or a reckless daredevil.

She forced a smile. 'Her shortbread was legendary, and she'd never tell anyone the recipe. Your café would be a guaranteed success with her in the kitchen.'

She didn't usually chat so much, but talking helped mask the nerves tumbling through her body as Finn typed in a code on the back door and pushed it open, ushering her inside after the racing girls.

Alex blinked, recognition tingling in every nerve. Nothing had really changed. The same pegs on the walls, the same deep butler's sinks. The walls were a fresh white, the flagstones on the floor clean and oiled, and there were no dog bowls lining up against the far wall, but otherwise she could have been stepping back in time.

She swallowed as she followed Finn through the scullery, now a smart-looking utility room, and into the kitchen.

'The oligarch really didn't remodel,' she managed to say through the ever-increasing lump in her throat.

Again, the kitchen was almost untouched. Buffed and painted and fresh, but with the same wooden cabinets and vast stove chucking out welcome heat. The same huge table dominated the centre. The table she had eaten at, drawn at, cried at more times than she could remember.

'No, he never came here. Everything was left as it was.'

'Until you came along to make it a new and improved model.'

She didn't want or mean to sound bitter. It was better that the castle was looked after. Of course it was. But why did it have to be Finn doing the looking after? And why did she have to be here, witnessing his success? Here on his payroll, her professional reputation in his hands, dependent on him for her evening meal.

None of it matters, she told herself, as she had so many times in the past. *None of it affects you.*

But the mantra didn't work. Not while she stood with the past all around her. The past in front of her. Finn had shed his winter coat and stood there in jeans and a close-fitting cashmere long-sleeved T-shirt. He'd filled out in the last few years. The snake-hipped passionate boy was now a lean but muscled man, eyes as dark and intent as ever, hair still falling over his brow.

For one treacherous moment something stirred inside her. Maybe her heart, maybe long-dormant desire. But she stood firm and pushed the feeling away. After all, hadn't this man hurt her the most? She couldn't, mustn't forget that. Ever. She'd worked too hard to move on.

She'd do her job to the best of her ability and leave, reputation and secret intact. No more cosy walks with Finn through the woods, no more trips down memory lane, and no recognising kindred spirits in small girls. It wasn't safe. The only time she would set foot in the castle after this evening would be to work.

Stick to the rules and she'd survive this. She had before and she'd do it again. She just needed to remember exactly who Finn Hawkin was.

CHAPTER FIVE

FINN LOOKED AROUND the crowded room, satisfaction running through him. All these people were here because of him. Journalists, influencers, local dignitaries, a scattering of celebrities. All drawn to Blakeley Castle once again.

Oh, he knew that many of them had only a passing interest in Hawk, in adventure trails, reinvigorating rural economies and bringing inner city kids into the countryside. They just wanted to set foot in the Blakeley Castle's legendary ballroom. To imagine they were one of the fabled generations of Bright Young Things who had danced, flirted, betrayed and seduced on this very floor.

Sometimes, at night, Finn would come in here and just for a moment catch a glimpse of a wisp of silk, a hint of taffeta, a flash of brocade. Every generation had its scandalous youth—whether they were Cavaliers, Regency beaux or jazz kids—and whatever the generation, whatever the scandal, they could all be found here at Blakeley.

But no more. His reign might be duller and more benign, but it would usher in a new tradition. One that was more inclusive. One with less misery in its wake.

Talking of which…

'Finn, here you are.'

Alex was playing the role of professional pen-pusher hard tonight. Finn knew that she hadn't lost her eye for fashion, or her taste, but there was no evidence of that eye or that taste tonight in the simple knee-length grey dress and matching jacket she wore. Her hair was tightly pulled back into a severe bun, a pair of black-rimmed glasses perched on her nose. She looked like a stock photo of a librarian rather than an attendee at a sought-after social event.

But Finn knew that her sartorial dullness was absolutely deliberate. After all, if her real identity was to be discovered then this was the time and place: back in her ancestral home surrounded by journalists. Not for the first time Finn wondered if he had done the right thing in bringing her back. Only this time it wasn't his peace of mind he was worried about. It was her anonymity. After all, hadn't he recognised her straight away?

But, then again, hadn't he known her better than anyone?

Alex ushered forward a petite woman. 'Can I introduce Isma Syed? Isma is the travel editor for the *Daily Courant* and she has a great blog as well—really inspiring and always ahead of the crowd. She's one of Blakeley's first guests too. She's spending the night in the Dower House.'

'Pleased to meet you.' Finn smiled at Isma, whose dark eyes were bright with interest. 'I hope you've enjoyed the day so far—and that the accommodation is up to your expectations?'

'It's very comfortable, thank you. And, yes! I wasn't sure that a treetop trail was really my thing, but I enjoyed it far more than I expected. So, Finn, how does it feel to come home? You grew up here, didn't you?'

It was no secret. 'My family have lived here for generations,' Finn agreed.

'But not in the castle itself? Do you know how the Beaumonts feel about the gardener becoming the Lord of the Manor?'

Finn sensed rather than saw Alex stiffen beside him. 'I haven't had an opportunity to discuss it with them, but I hope they would be pleased to know that the castle is being looked after by someone who loves it as much as they did…someone who has an ancestral affinity for the place.'

'Of course.' Isma leaned forward, her voice lowered confidentially. 'Lord Beaumont is dead and there were no male heirs. That's why the castle was for sale in the first place. But what about Lady Beaumont and her daughter? Do you have any idea where Lola Beaumont is right now?'

Lying didn't come easily to Finn, but he hadn't brought Alex here to embarrass her or, worse, to expose her to the media, no matter what he had said earlier that week when persuading her to stay.

'As far as I know Lady Beaumont is still in California. As for Lola, I haven't heard from her for many years. So, how does the Dower House compare with other holiday cottages you've seen? Any suggestions on how we can improve things?'

'Ah, you'll have to wait for my review. I hear you're also reviving the famous Christmas Eve party?'

Finn nodded. 'It is a Blakeley tradition.'

'But do you think it's wise? After all, the last party ended with the drowning of Lord Beaumont's mistress and that started it all…' She raised her eyebrows in query.

Finn was very careful not to look at Alex as he answered, focusing all his charm on the journalist. 'This is a new era at Blakeley and the party will reflect that. We are planning more of a community affair, including carols sung by the local primary school choir and a village nativity. Have you had a chance to look around the castle yet? Nearly all of it is publicly accessible now, from the servants' quarters to the room where Elizabeth I is reputed to have had a secret liaison, and it's all exactly as it has been for the last four hundred-odd years.'

Isma stepped forward, her phone in her hand, no doubt ready to record, her expression avid. 'Of course Blakeley is famous for its liaisons. When you lived here before did people know about what went on at the parties the Beaumonts held? The wife-swapping, the orgies, the drugs? The mountain of debt their lifestyle was built on? I mean, you were right here. You must have seen things? Heard things? What about Lola? You were around the same age. Did she ever pull a Lady Chatterley with the staff?'

Finn tensed. *Great.* The travel reporter was hot on the scent and Finn couldn't blame her. The drowning of a pop star's model wife at one of the most famous events in the social calendar had been the scandal of the year ten years ago.

The Blakely Christmas Eve party had always been filled with an eclectic mix of aristocracy, minor royalty, actors and musicians, a mecca for the rich, beautiful and cool. When it had been revealed that the dead woman was Lord Beaumont's lover—and that his own wife had been having an affair with the much younger pop star—the scandal had blown sky-high. Stories of years of excess had circulated, and at some point Lord Beaumont's debts had surfaced. Facing ruin, he had shot himself, and his wife had fled to LA with her lover, leaving her daughter alone to deal with the debts, with the press, with the scandal.

At that point Lola might have turned things round. She had been young, beautiful, and making a name for herself as a model, an It Girl. If she'd wanted to she could have ridden out the storm and kept her influential friends, her endorsements and her contracts. But then the photos had surfaced. Photos of her at that very same Christmas Eve party on her eighteenth birthday. Photos not meant for the public to see.

Photos for Finn's eyes only.

It was strange how she had been able to pose in a barely-there bikini, her almost nude body up on a billboard, and nobody had blinked. That was *fashion*. But private photos, in which she exposed more or less the same amount of skin, were salacious just because of their private nature.

And they'd been everywhere. Front pages, comedy panel shows, opinion pieces. The sins of her parents had been put squarely on her shoulders. She had become a symbol of everything that was wrong in a world that at the time had been facing a recession. The Beaumonts' excessive consumption had been held up as an example of a world that needed fixing.

Still she might have stayed and fought. If it hadn't been for the fact that only one person had had access to those photos.

Finn.

He glanced across at Alex, standing by the journalist's side, her face absolutely impervious, as if none of the things the journalist had said affected her at all. As if she really was someone completely different not just in name but in every way. Someone so closed down there was no knowing what, if anything, she was thinking. It was as if she was sleepwalking through life.

'I'm sorry, I didn't really take much notice of anything that happened in the castle. Too busy focusing on my future.'

His smile was tight as Alex turned to the journalist, as ever the consummate professional. Did none of this affect her at all? But then she hadn't asked to be put into this position. He had put her there. How could he judge her for the way she handled it?

'Isma, can I introduce you to Desiree?' Alex was saying. 'She's got over two hundred and fifty thousand Instagram followers and is thinking about writing a book about her love of travel. I said that you were absolutely the person to speak to. Your book about your year travelling solo was my favourite read last year... it was so inspirational. Thank you, Finn.'

And with a polite but firm smile Alex steered Isma away.

Finn took a glass of Prosecco from the table next to him and drank it down in one long gulp, closing his eyes briefly. He hadn't had a chance to talk to Alex about the photos, to make the explanation he should have forced her to listen to back then. At the time he'd been so angry and hurt that she'd believed him capable of such betrayal he hadn't been able to see how devastated she was, unable to see the wood for the trees as her world collapsed around her. Everyone and everything she had known was a lie. No wonder she'd thought him a lie as well.

It was too late to repair the damage. But it wasn't too late to tell her the truth.

Finn watched Alex as she introduced Isma to a striking young woman dressed in an eye-catching jumpsuit. The two women immediately fell into animated conversation and Alex stepped back, her clear gaze sweeping the room, making sure everyone was having a good time, talking to the right people, looking for anything that might need to be explained or contained.

Her disguise was completely effective. No one spared her a second glance.

It wasn't the glasses. They couldn't hide her long lashes or her large grey eyes with their provocative tilt, as if she was smiling at a joke only she could see. The severe bun couldn't disguise the glossiness of her hair, and her tall, lean curves weren't diminished by the unflattering cut and colour of her suit.

No, her beauty was as stunning as it had ever been, and no amount of stereotyped frumpy clothes could change that. It was inside. She was switched off. There was no vibrancy lighting her, no animation, and that was why she could slip through the crowds unseen.

But Finn saw her. He always had.

Alex inhaled as she looked around. Everything was in order. The ballroom was festively decorated, with fairy lights strung around the panelling, and a large Christmas tree dominated the far corner, tastefully blazing with white and silver lights, wrapped presents clustered at the bottom. So the presents were empty boxes? It didn't matter. This evening, like all this kind of occasion, was an illusion. The journalists, influencers and assembled celebrities were there to be charmed and to spread the word: Blakeley Castle was open once again.

Of course conversation turned again and again to the last owners. Who were Elizabeth I or Charles II or Beau Brummel compared to the disgraced Viscount and his family? But no one gossiping about the events of ten years ago really thought about the cost—about the two people who had died, about the families torn apart. The Blakeley scandal was like something out of a novel, not real life.

Only she knew all too well just how real it had been. No one else could ever know or understand what it had been like in the centre of that hurricane, with her life whirling more and more out of control, everyone wanting a piece of her.

Alex shivered, aware that she was being watched. Looking up, she saw Finn's dark gaze fixed unwaveringly on her. As if he saw *her*, not the woman she had worked so hard to be but the girl she had left behind her. That needy creature who had thought beauty and praise worth having, who hadn't understood how fleeting and insubstantial they were.

How dared he look at her that way? He had lost the right to see her the day he had betrayed her. What game was he playing anyway? How had he tracked her down? And how could she trust him not to betray her again?

The room was too hot, too busy. She needed to regroup. Slipping out of a side door, she let her feet lead her unerringly through the maze of corridors, up the stairs, until she reached the long picture gallery, still hung with portraits of her ancestors.

Alex stood in the cool, dim light and looked around.

Thank goodness that oligarch had bought the castle complete with all its contents—she would have hated for the pictures to have been sold off and separated, to hang in museums and private collections, even though the money raised would have been enough to pay off her father's debts and give her a nest egg to rebuild her life.

The gallery had been included in the tour of the house laid on for the party guests, and she had stood here in this room several times already today, but she hadn't allowed herself to look up, to be distracted, to remember how she'd used to come here and chat to her favourite pictures. Now, alone, she walked slowly from picture to picture. There was the Gainsborough, the Reynolds, the Holbein... Every ancestor had the same smile, the same sleepy cat eyes she herself had inherited, the same pointed chin.

'Hi,' she whispered softly to the spaniel hiding in one lady's skirts. 'Sorry I haven't been to visit for a while. Hello, handsome.' She reached a hand up to a grey horse, not quite touching it. As a child these painted animals had been her confidants and playmates. These animals—and Finn.

She wandered slowly up the long panelled gallery, reuniting with old friends, stopping to say hello to her favourites until she reached the end, where she stilled, barely breathing, her heart squeezing in on itself until her whole chest ached.

The huge painting of a nude with long red hair and a slanting smile dominated the room. Some had called her the most beautiful woman in the world. She could have married royalty or wealth, a Hollywood star or a business king, but she had chosen a boy with a minor title and a castle, and she had reigned over that castle with whimsical tyranny.

Alex stared up at the painting, at the creamy skin, the curve of perfect pert breasts, the come-hither glance in green, green eyes. 'Hi, Mum,' she said.

The portrait stared impassively back. No different from its sitter. Alex could count on one hand the conversations she had had with her mother since that last tragic Christmas Eve.

After breaking up with her pop star lover, the former Lady Beaumont had married an actor some years her senior. They now lived on a ranch with their two children, where her mother ran an online health and well-being empire. A disgraced daughter who was a living reminder of a past much better left behind didn't fit with the brand she'd so painstakingly built up.

Occasionally, very occasionally, Alex would scroll through her social media feed, full of nutritious home-made food and yoga poses, outdoor living and glowing, laughing children, and search for clues. Were her unknown half-siblings really happy, or did they too spend their lives waiting for a nod or a smile, desperately trying to please their capricious beautiful mother? Trying to be the perfect child and always, always falling short?

She didn't really want an answer. She would hate for them to be raised the way she had been, but on the other hand, if her mother genuinely loved her new family, did that mean there was something wrong with Alex? That she was fundamentally unlovable?

History tended to bear that assumption out.

Swallowing, she turned her back on her mother, smothering a gasp as she saw two white figures at the far end of the gallery. 'Saffron! Scarlett, you startled me,' she said, half laughing with nerves. 'Aren't you supposed to be in bed? You must be freezing,' she added as she took in their bare feet and thin white pyjamas.

'Not as cold as that lady.' Scarlett giggled as she pointed at the portrait of Alex's mother.

'True. At least you're wearing *some* clothes.' Alex managed to keep a straight face.

'Who is she? Is she a princess? And why isn't she wearing any clothes?'

'Not a princess, but she used to be married to someone who lived here. It's considered artistic to paint people without clothes, for some reason, and she was a very famous beauty.'

'I think she looks mean,' Saffron said suddenly. 'Like a wicked witch or a bad godmother who casts an evil spell.'

Alex swivelled to look back at the portrait, at the sensuous look in the famously hooded eyes, the knowing expression. 'Yes,' she said slowly. 'I suppose she does.'

'Alex, Alex, come and look at your picture!'

Before Alex could make her excuses and head back to the ballroom, Scarlett had run up to slip one small, cold hand in hers and begun to tug her towards the small antechamber where the castle's prized collection of Pre-Raphaelite paintings hung.

'Quickly,' she agreed. 'But then straight back to bed. It's far too cold—and late—for you two to be running around the castle.'

Hypocrite, she told herself. As if *she* hadn't spent many nights roaming the castle when other children her age had been fast asleep. But she would have loved someone to scoop her up and order her back to bed. Freedom palled when it was mixed with indifference.

'Will you read us a story?' Scarlett asked.

Alex looked down at the small heart-shaped face and the pleading expression in her dark eyes. She didn't know any children, and rarely needed to interact with them. Amber loved nothing more than organising a child's party or entertaining their younger clients, but Alex never knew what to say to them…how to be.

'I really need to get back and do my job,' she said.

'Don't be silly, Scarlett. Alex is far too busy to bother with us.'

There was a resigned loneliness in Saffron's sneer, one Alex recognised all too well.

'Let me check for messages,' she said. 'If no one has tried to contact me then one story. Okay?'

For once her phone showed no urgent messages or red-flagged emails.

'One short story,' she warned them. 'Before I'm missed.'

'Picture first,' Scarlett said.

Alex allowed herself to be towed into the dimly lit room where the Beaumont collection of Pre-Raphaelite paintings was displayed. She couldn't help but gasp in recognition as she looked at the jewel-like colours on the six perfectly displayed paintings. They weren't the best known, or the most critically well regarded, but it didn't matter because they were all set here at Blakeley.

The nymph in the lake eying up a young Narcissus was standing in Blakeley water. The goddess hiding from Actaeon's gaze stood in the woods Alex had walked through today on her way to the office. And the sleeping maiden, her hair falling to the floor, her nightgown dipping below one perfect white breast, a rose in her hand, slumbered in Alex's old bedchamber, on the Victorian bedstead where she had once slept.

'See, she looks like you,' Scarlett said triumphantly.

Saffron nodded. 'She does. If you weren't wearing glasses and if you grew your hair really long.'

'And I wore a see-through nightie and forgot to do it up properly? Sorry, girls. I'm a more of a scrunched-up ponytail and yoga pants kind of nightwear person.'

To her surprise both girls laughed at her weak attempt at humour, and the bell-like sound echoed off the panelled walls, warming the frigid air.

'Come on,' she said, taking Scarlett's hand and touching Saffron's shoulder. 'If you want me to read a story before I have to go back to the party—and before you both turn into blocks of ice—then we need to get you back to bed.'

But before she went she allowed herself one last lingering glance at the slumbering girl. At the stained glass in the window behind her and the way the light played across her supine figure. At the little dog curled up at his mistress's side. At the anticipation on the sleeper's face, the way her lips were parted ready. At the shadow at the window, the glimpse of thorns and the determined man ready to slash through them.

Some people thought the story insipid—a heroine who merely fell asleep and waited to be rescued—but Alex had always thought it the ultimate romance that no matter how lost you were, someone would find you. That you could be hidden behind one hundred years' worth of trees and thorns and someone would still see you, know you and fight for you.

She no longer felt like that. Now she knew better. Now she knew the only person to fight for you was you. And that sometimes the only way to do that, the only way to save yourself, was to retreat and keep all the things that could hurt you at bay. No hope, no love, no dreams.

But for one moment, as she walked through corridors she knew better than she knew her heart, listening to the chatter of two over-excited girls, she allowed herself to wish, just briefly, that she still believed in fairy-tales.

CHAPTER SIX

'Alex!'

Alex turned at the sound of the high-pitched voice and saw a small child speeding towards her. It had turned even colder over the last few days and the trees glistened with morning frost, the grass crunchy white underfoot.

'Good morning, Scarlett.' She caught the small girl before she barrelled into her, suppressing a smile at the layers of clothing, the thick padded jacket, hat and gloves and the bright orange wellies on her small feet. 'Living the Hawk brand, I see.'

'Of course.'

Finn caught up with them and her breath caught in her throat. It was most unfair that he had turned out even more attractive than the boy she had loved, especially with his chin coated with overnight stubble, his hair tousled and his expression relaxed.

'Thanks for the other night,' he added. 'The press party seemed to go very well.'

'I'm never satisfied until I see all the reviews but I'm cautiously optimistic,' Alex agreed. 'Thank goodness the weather held for the afternoon. I'm not sure treetop treks and biking woodland trails would have been so much fun in the rain. It's just a shame the nature walk looks so bare at this time of year, but the interpretation was really good, so they got the gist of what you want to achieve.'

'The tweaks you made really enhanced the whole experience, especially housing some of the journalists here—even the ones in the Bunkhouse seemed to have fun, judging from the comments I heard at breakfast yesterday. Thank you.'

'Just doing my job.'

'It wasn't your job to return these two scamps to their bed, though.' Finn glared mock sternly at his nieces, and they shrieked and rushed along the path ahead. 'Thank you for keeping them out of trouble. That was above and beyond.'

'It was no problem. They're nice girls.' She paused, not wanting to prolong the conversation or bring up any more shared memories, but her curiosity overran her good sense. 'They must miss their mum. Where is Nicky? She was pregnant when I...'

Dammit, this was where curiosity took her. Right back to that night. And there were so many reasons not to go back to that night. Self-preservation for one.

Self-preservation took many routes. It meant not thinking about watching her father stagger out of the lake with a lifeless body in his arms. It meant not remembering the media storm, the reporters at every gate. It meant not reliving her rigid fear, sitting in the back of a police car as she was taken in for questioning, camera flashes blinding her.

And self-preservation meant not thinking about the photos or the moment she saw them all over the front pages. It meant remembering that this man couldn't be trusted, no matter how warm his gaze as it fell on his nieces, how attractive his crinkled smile.

A smile that was currently playing around his mouth as he watched Scarlett gravely hopscotching along the path leading through the woodland.

'Nicky finally signed over custody to me this summer.' As he spoke the smile disappeared and Finn's jaw set firm, his mouth a grim line, his eyes unreadable.

'Custody? You mean she isn't around at all?'

'She's flitted in and out of their lives for years. Every time she swears she's made a change. So I set her up in a house, make sure there's enough money for the girls, and then she meets another loser. Next thing I know he's moved in or she's moved out, and six months later the girls are returned to me for another "holiday" while she sorts herself out. It might be two weeks, it might be a month, or longer. I've had enough of enabling her. They need stability. Especially Saffy.'

'Yes. I see. She does seem fragile.'

They walked a little further in silence before Finn spoke again, his words tense and clipped. 'I should have done something sooner, said something sooner, but I didn't want to alienate Nicky. They were her daughters... what if she banned me from seeing them? And, despite everything, I wanted to believe that her heart was in the right place. She protected me, you know, from the worst of my dad's drinking. Even when she did something wrong her motives were good. I had to keep giving her the benefit of the doubt. But then Saffy...' He stopped and rubbed his hand against his jaw.

'Then Saffy what?'

Finn sighed, and she could see the indecision in his eyes as he weighed up whether or not to answer.

'She reminded me of you,' he said at last.

Alex's breath caught at his words, chills numbing her every nerve.

'That look you had when your parents would go away and you'd be waiting for them to come back, or when your mum barely knew you were there. That hopeful look. It used to break my heart then, but seeing it replicated on Saffy...' He shook his head, lost in some memory. 'I was no longer a boy. I have money, and a home, and I can give her the stability she needs. I thought Nicky would fight me for them, and I was prepared to involve the courts if I had to. Even though I know she loves them. But she just gave in.'

'Maybe she gave in *because* she loves them. Because she knows it's for the best.'

But Alex's heart was hammering so loudly she could hardly hear herself speak. She'd always thought she'd hidden her fear of rejection from everyone, including Finn. She'd worked so hard to be the smiling, impetuous, devil-may-care child her parents had wanted. Never cried, never sulked, never followed the rules. Charming, wild and beautiful. A Beaumont through and through.

Beaumonts didn't need or ask for approval and they felt stifled by rules and stability. Alex had done her very best to feel stifled too. But if Finn had seen it was all a pretence had others seen it too? Her parents?

'Maybe,' said Finn. 'I'd already bought Blakeley and I started to invest in turning it into the kind of outdoor centre I wanted it to be, decided to stop travelling so much. Moving my life here properly made perfect sense. The girls can go to the local schools. Stop chopping and changing, stay in one place.'

'And Nicky doesn't see them at all?'

'She's in India right now, but she can see them whenever she wants for as long as she wants when she's in the UK. So long as it's here. She has a bedroom here that's hers alone—not that she's even seen it. But the girls stay with me until they are out of formal education. That's the agreement.'

'Wow. That's a big commitment.'

'I didn't have a choice. I couldn't let them down. I've done enough of that. Letting people I care about down.'

His words hung in the air until Alex could hardly breathe. Did he mean his father, belligerent and difficult, refusing all offers of help? Or his sister, searching for an elusive happiness even her children couldn't provide? Or was he talking about back then? When he'd promised to be her knight but ended up her betrayer?

'No, you had a choice and you chose them. Even with money and a home that's an unselfish choice to make. Being a single parent is hard even when children have always known love and stability.'

'Which is why they come first. Their happiness is paramount.'

'Of course.'

Despite everything that hung between them, all that lay unsaid, all the secrets and lies and betrayals, she couldn't help but admire Finn for his dedication—and she allowed herself one tiny wish: that someone had put her first when she'd still needed somebody to care.

Once again Finn found Alex almost impossible to read. She had been curious about the girls, understandably, and she had sounded sympathetic whilst asking questions, but there was still an otherworldly air around her, as if she were miles away from here, in a different existence entirely.

That was probably what made her so good at her job. That sense she was somehow remote, untouched, that nothing really affected her. He'd seen her at work during the press party. Always watching, introducing, stepping in with a cool smile and a light but steely touch, making sure every message stayed on brand, that the assembled journalists experienced what she wanted them to experience. So unlike the girl he'd known, who had felt everything so very deeply a harsh word could cut her.

But only he had known that. She had been so adept at hiding her true nature. Did she still hide now? It was impossible to tell. But for a moment he badly wanted to find out.

'Uncle Finn, can Alex help us choose our tree?'

Scarlett appeared at his side, her cheeks the same colour as her name, her hair once again a tangled mess.

He passed a rueful hand over the curls. 'I need an uncle school to teach me how to do plaits,' he said.

'I told you. Emily's dad watched online videos and he can wind ribbons through her hair. You just have to try harder,' Scarlett told him.

He tugged one messy plait. 'Message understood.'

'So can she?' She turned eagerly to Alex. 'We get to choose our very own tree from our very own woods and then we take it back and decorate it. And Uncle Finn has all these amazing Christmas tree ornaments; he collects them everywhere he goes.'

Alex stilled, her cheeks paling. 'I used to collect Christmas tree ornaments,' she said softly.

'Do you still have them?'

'No. Not any more. I had to leave them behind when I left home. And some I gave away.'

Finn curled his hand into a loose fist as she stead-fastly avoided looking at him, but he knew they were thinking of the same time. Of her first modelling job in New York, when she was barely fifteen and barely chaperoned by her mother. She'd brought him back an ornament from a world-famous department store: a per-fect glass apple. Far too delicate for his Christmas tree, and far too beautiful for a seventeen-year-old boy whose focus had been on school and getting out. But he had thanked her, and from then on, on every trip to every place, she had brought home two Christmas tree orna-ments: one for him and one for her to keep.

He still had every one.

'So, can she?' Scarlett asked.

Finn searched for an excuse, a reason to let Alex off the hook, but before he could speak Saffy mooched up to them, her thin shoulders hunched under her anorak.

'Are we going to choose this tree or not?'

'I was just explaining to Alex what we are doing,' Scarlett said with extraordinary dignity. 'And inviting her along to be one of the party.'

Finn looked at Alex, startled into a shout of laugh-ter, and saw answering laughter soften her grey eyes, her mouth grow full and sweet with the natural curve of her smile. His breath caught in his throat. She had been a beautiful girl, but she had grown into a glorious woman. When she allowed herself to be natural. When her smile had meaning.

His pulse began to thud as he stared, unable to look away, drinking in the sight. He didn't care what she called herself, this was the only woman who had ever made his blood thrill; the only woman to make his heart thump so loud he was convinced it could be heard back at the castle; the only woman his hands ached to touch so badly the pain was physical. He knew how she tasted. Sweet and fresh and lush, like nectar. How she felt. Warm silk and soft velvet. And she knew him as well. For all she denied it.

'Uncle Finn!' Scarlett's insistent voice brought him out of his reverie and he stared at her and blinked. 'Ask Alex to join us.'

And Finn realised that he wanted nothing more. Not just because of that shared conspiratorial moment of amusement, or because of the sudden visceral memories that had blindsided him, but because he suspected that Alexandra Davenport was even lonelier than Lola Beaumont had been.

'Of course,' he said easily, taking Saffron's hand. 'If you have nothing better to do.'

'I...'

'You might as well,' Saffy said, staring down at the ground, and Finn saw Alex's expression soften with recognition.

'Only if you're sure I'm not intruding.'

'Yay!' Scarlett started dancing around, hair flying. 'Come on, Alex. After we choose the tree we're going to decorate it and have hot chocolate with cream and it's going to be the best day ever.'

She flew off down the path, tugging a startled-looking Alex with her, and Finn followed on more sedately, still holding Saffron's mittened hand.

'Do you mind, Saffy?' he said gently. 'I know today is meant to be a family day...'

A life filled with 'uncles' and 'new daddies' had left

Saffron wary of outsiders, especially ones who tried to step into her inner circle. But to his surprise Saffy shook her head.

'Alex is nice. She's really good at reading stories too. She did all the voices. Even though it was a baby-ish story of Scarlett's she made it seem really funny.'

'That's good. As long as you're okay, Saffy.'

His niece rolled her eyes in the pre-teen way she had perfected recently. 'I'm fine. Come on, Uncle Finn, bet I can beat you.'

And she was off, too-long skinny legs pumping furiously as she sped down the path, ponytail flying out behind her.

With a mock roar of rage Finn took off after her, but underneath a beat of anxiety pounded insistently. The girls had been hurt enough. It was good that they liked Alex, but she would be leaving at Christmas. He had to make sure they didn't get too attached.

And it wasn't just them he needed to watch. Having Alex back at Blakeley felt too right, too easy, especially when he saw glimpses of the girl he'd used to know. But they were both different people now, with very different lives, and far too old to believe in happy-ever-afters.

It was surprisingly easy to find and agree on the right tree, and before an hour had passed they were all back in the castle for the promised hot chocolate, the tree cut and delivered by one of the estate hands.

Alex paused as they left the kitchen, uncertainty on her face as the girls rushed into the sitting room. 'Are you sure it's okay for me to be here?'

'More than sure. I need someone to help carry these mugs.' Finn nodded at the large mugs filled with hot chocolate he'd just made, topped with cream and sprinkles, and slipped a packet of shortbread into his pocket before picking up two of them.

'Biscuits not served on plates? Mrs Atkinson would be horrified,' Alex said. 'Shop bought as well.'

'If you want to make some from scratch you're very welcome to try.'

Finn grinned as she shook her head.

'Amber's the baker in our house. She bakes to relax, which means there is always fresh bread and cakes and biscuits all over the kitchen. I'm dreading Emilia and Harriet moving out, leaving me to face temptation all alone.'

'Send her to me. Feeding two growing girls is exhausting. I feel like a mother bird, constantly pushing worms into open mouths.'

'What a lovely analogy.'

She picked up the remaining two mugs and slipped through the door he held open with his foot and into the sitting room, pausing uncertainly as she reached the threshold of what he knew was a room once familiar to her.

In her day this had been the family room, a space used only by Alex, Finn and Mrs Atkinson. Her parents had rarely set foot in the domestic quarters. They had used the entire castle with careless entitlement, sitting on sixteenth-century chairs and sleeping in beds older than entire family trees. They had thought nothing of dancing on priceless carpets or leaving glasses on Chippendale tables.

But the rooms and their contents had all been painstakingly cleaned and restored, and now the whole castle was open to the public. All except the west wing, which he'd turned into a spacious, comfortable home.

'This looks amazing.' Alex halted as she stepped into the sitting room. 'I can't believe the difference. Look how beautiful the floor is!'

Finn had opened the room up into the old dining room beyond to create a large, welcoming space, with grouped sofas and chairs, a huge fireplace, and filled bookshelves in every alcove. Cushion-covered window seats ran the length of the room, and the pale grey of the walls showcased the bright, modern paintings he'd chosen.

All the furniture in their living space had been bought especially, and every room was newly painted, every floor stripped and polished. He'd wanted a blank canvas, a new start, with no hint of the old aristocratic family imposing on his.

The only part of the west wing that hadn't been renovated was the long picture gallery which ran the entire second floor of the wing. That he *hadn't* opened up to public view, despite the fame of some of the portraits.

He hadn't allowed himself to wonder why. But seeing Alex here, back in her home, he knew why. He hadn't wanted to rake up the old scandal again with every visitor. He hadn't wanted them to look at the cat-shaped eyes and pointed chins of her ancestors and remember her, gossip about her. Without knowing it he'd protected her, as he had failed to do so long ago.

He set the mugs on a small table and looked over at the huge tree set in a corner of the room. 'Okay,' he said, trying to push the past back where it belonged. 'Who wants to decorate the tree?'

'Me! Me!'

The girls nearly upset their hot chocolate in their bid to get to the box of ornaments first.

'Thank goodness John put the lights on when he brought the tree in,' said Alex, her eyes narrowed in amusement as she watched the girls delve into the large box Finn had brought down from the box room earlier. 'They might have combusted if they'd had to wait any longer.'

She wrapped her hands around the large mug, lowering her nose to the fragrant chocolate and inhaling deeply.

'Thank you, Finn.'

'For what? The hot chocolate? I was making it anyway.'

But she didn't respond to his teasing smile. 'For not telling anyone who I am.'

'Alex…' Her name felt natural now. It suited this new incarnation. It was a name as anonymous as she seemed to be, yet with so many different layers and interpretations. 'It is completely within my interests to keep your secret. I want people to talk about Blakeley—of course I do. But I want them to talk about the local produce in the farm shop and the scones in the café, the treetop trail and the treasure hunt in the house, not to be sidetracked by old gossip. I'd much prefer that no one has the faintest idea who you are.'

'Then why hire me? And how did you even track me down?'

Finn inhaled, the scent of chocolate mixing with the pine tree and permeating the room. So, they were going to have this conversation. Well, maybe it was time. Maybe it was time he finally told her the truth. Maybe it was time to set the past free.

'Finn? I think I deserve some answers.'

'Yes,' he agreed. 'You do.'

CHAPTER SEVEN

'How DID YOU find me?' Alex repeated. She fixed her gaze on him firmly and waited.

Finn slanted a look towards Saffron and Scarlett, but they were intent on the tree, deliberating over where a Christmas angel Alex recognised as one she'd picked up in Prague should go. She'd never expected that he would still have the ornaments she'd bought him. Never expected to see them hung on a tree in Blakeley Castle. It shook all that she'd thought she knew. About him, about them.

She swallowed and waited some more. He set his hot chocolate down on a side table and leaned against the sofa arm, looking out of the window at the white mist swirling along the frost-covered lawn.

'Returning to Blakeley brought back old memories,' he said abruptly. 'But I had my own personal reasons to return. Reasons that have nothing to do with you. My ancestors are as much a part of this castle as yours, even if no one really cares about the people who spent their lives in the kitchens and the gardens, no matter how many generations they dedicated to serving the castle.'

'I care. And I don't dispute your claim on Blakeley.

If I can't be here to look after the castle, then there's no one I'd rather it should be than you.'

'Really?'

His eyebrows rose in disbelief, but she nodded, reinforcing her statement.

'Finn, how can anyone *own* history? We're only ever custodians of a place like Blakeley. Now the castle has a custodian who loves her and knows her, respects her. That's a wonderful thing.'

She meant every word, but her chest ached with loss and regret as she spoke. She hoped he didn't sense her wistfulness, saw only her sincerity.

'Thank you. That means a lot.'

'So?' she prompted. 'You're back here and you need a temporary PR person and what? It's a huge coincidence that you chose me.'

'No. Not a coincidence. I've known where you are for six months.'

She froze. 'That long? How? Why? Were you looking for me?'

Damn it, was that hope she was feeling? Hope that he had been searching for her? That she hadn't been lost after all?

'Not straight away.' He stopped abruptly, jaw tightening. 'I should have,' he said, his voice resonant with regret. 'I should have come straight after you at the time…shouldn't have allowed you to walk away without an explanation. But for the first few days afterwards I was too hurt, too angry to speak to you. You were so sure I was guilty. After all we had been to each other, after all we'd said, you thought I'd sell photos of you to the press. *Those* photos.'

The utter disbelief in his expression floored her. Hurt

and anger were still evident in that disbelief. Had she got it so wrong? But who else could it have been? She'd sent the photos to him, not to anyone else…

'I'd have given anything for it not to be you. The papers were full of people who I'd trusted, who I'd thought cared about me, spilling every last sordid detail about my family. You needed money. You said so yourself. To help Nicky, to get to university…'

'And so I sold you for thirty pieces of silver? Did you really believe that? Do you still?'

'I…'

Of course she had. It had been the last revelation. The one that had tipped her from holding on to falling, falling into a dark, dark place. But now? Seeing all he had achieved, and more importantly what he was doing with that success—opening up the estate, working with inner city schools, raising his nieces… These were the actions of a decent man, not a man who would betray someone who'd loved him.

And, truthfully, nothing he had done back then had shown him to be capable of such an act. He'd been her one constant after all.

'Finn…' But she couldn't speak, and the silence thickened, broken only by the chatter of the girls, their words washing over Alex.

'I waited too long,' he said after a while. 'I waited for you to come back and apologise. And by the time I could see more clearly, by the time I understood, you had disappeared.'

'What did you understand?' she whispered; throat thick with fear. She wasn't sure she could cope with his answer.

'I understood that you needed to blame someone for

the way things fell apart. How could you blame your dad when he was no longer around to blame? And you always made every excuse for your mother. You had to blame me. I had to be the scapegoat. I knew that it was up to me, that I had to go to you. But, even though it had been just a few days since I'd seen you last, I couldn't find you anywhere. Not in any of the usual places, not with any of the usual people. In the end I told myself that you would show up eventually. I hoped to see you back in the gossip columns and on billboards within months, riding out the scandal. But months went by and you didn't appear in any headlines or adverts. It was as if you had been airbrushed out of existence and I knew I had lost you in every way possible. It didn't stop me hoping that one day you would turn up, that I would see you again, but finally I had to accept that you didn't want me to find you, that you didn't want anyone. I had to do my best to move on, to build my business and my life.'

Alex stood stock-still, her mind digesting every word he'd said, turning each phrase over and over and trying to make sense of it all. 'You *had* to have sold them,' she said. 'I only sent them to you. You needed money and you had them. There was no one else.'

He folded his arms and said nothing, but she saw his eyes flicker towards the still absorbed girls and clarity almost blinded her.

'It was Nicky.'

'Yes.'

'Nicky...'

Of course. She would have been able to access Finn's phone—goodness knew he'd always been mislaying it. She'd needed money and she'd always disliked Alex.

How had she not realised at the time? Maybe Finn was right. She had had to blame someone and he'd been right there, her one constant. She'd lashed out and driven him away just when she needed him most.

All this time she'd thought he had betrayed her, but *she* had betrayed him. The ache in her chest intensified, constricting her and making it hard to breathe. 'Finn, I—'

But he held up a hand to cut her off. 'Don't. Like I said, you needed a scapegoat. I was there. It's fine. It was long ago. I moved on and moved out, after realising my presence here wasn't going to save my father or change Nicky. I needed to start working for the future I'd always promised myself. To concentrate on university and a life of my own.'

'You've achieved that, all right.' Alex looked around at the original pieces of art on the walls, at the two happy girls, giggling over a bauble. 'Achieved so much. You should be so proud.'

'But I never stopped thinking about you. I've always known I could have done more, should have done more when you needed me. I hoped you were with your mother in the States, happy and fulfilled, but I always knew that was a long shot.' He sighed. 'I just wanted closure, I suppose. This last year, worrying about Saffy, buying the castle, just made me realise I hadn't really moved on, that maybe I never completely would.'

'Did you hire a detective?'

Alex sat on the window seat, her back to the wall, needing as much physical support as she could get. Because if Finn could track her down, then who else could? With the renewed interest in Blakeley it was surely a matter of time before another *Where is Lola?*

piece ran. What if a journalist really wanted answers? Look at Isma, just a couple of days ago, not even suspecting that the woman she wanted was standing right there.

'No. I considered it, several times, especially at the beginning. But back then I couldn't afford it, and later it didn't seem right…not when you had gone to such lengths to disappear. I tried to resign myself to living with the guilt, with never knowing, but I couldn't stop myself looking for you wherever I went, ridiculous as I knew that was. And then I was invited to a ball…'

'A ball?' She couldn't hide her surprise. It so wasn't the answer she'd been expecting.

Alex quickly ran through a mental list of all the charity balls she had helped organise over the last few months.

'A Midsummer Ball. The invite came from a guy I studied with briefly at the Sorbonne—a guy who just happens to be an archduke.'

Alex nodded slowly. All the pieces were coming together. 'Laurent?'

'Laurent,' he confirmed. 'At one point I was talking to him and he was so busy staring at a woman—your friend—he was barely focussing on what I was saying. When I looked over too, she was talking to a tall woman dressed in black. A woman I knew instantly. Although she had a different name, I knew that Alexandra Davenport and Lola Beaumont were the same person.'

'Why didn't you come and see me? Pick up the phone? Why make me come here after everything?'

'Because in just the brief glimpse I had of you it seemed that you had changed fundamentally, Alex. Not just your name, but you. It was as if the fire that used to fuel you had gone out. It got me wondering if I wasn't the only one who needed closure. I spent the next six months wondering what the right move would be—and of course I had the girls to settle into their new schools, the move of the business to manage, the opening up of the castle. Part of me wondered if you would hear about what was happening at Blakeley and contact me. Then Penelope was injured, and it just seemed the time was right. When I phoned that evening I thought I'd speak to you, so when Amber picked up it threw me somewhat. That was why I said I'd brief you when you got here. I wondered if you would simply refuse to come, but it didn't cross my mind that you had no idea I'd hired you.'

As he finished, he picked up their cups and headed back to the kitchen. Alex watched the door swing shut. She shivered. Sitting there in her old family room, with the past excavated, was almost more than she could bear—and yet for reasons she couldn't articulate to herself she was reluctant to leave, although she knew she should.

'Alex, we can't reach any higher.'

Saffron's voice drew her attention back to her surroundings and, shaking off her thoughts, Alex slid to her feet. It was Christmas and she was home again. It might be temporary, but Finn was right. She did need closure—and she also needed to remember the good times. Like the many evenings spent in this room with Mrs Atkinson and Finn. Preparing for Christmas with the scent of spice in the air as she and Finn decorated their own tree.

'Okay. But if I am going to help with a Christmas tree then you know what we need?'

Both girls stared at her wide-eyed and Alex brandished her phone. 'Christmas music, that's what.'

She searched through her library until she found the playlist Amber had shared with them all on the morning of the first of December. A playlist she had barely glanced at, let alone played. She hit the button.

As Mariah began to tell them what she wanted for Christmas, Alex stepped over to the tree and held out her hand for an ornament. 'This is your tree, girls, so you tell me where you want things to go. Okay?'

'Okay!' Scarlett handed her a delicate silver pinecone and stared solemnly at the tree. 'I want that to go there.'

She pointed at a spot near Alex's ear, and equally solemnly, with ceremonial care, Alex hooked the shining ornament onto the branch.

"You've done a great job so far."

Alex stood back and surveyed her handiwork before scanning the opulently decorated tree, laden with delicate baubles and ornaments in every colour and style imaginable. A crystal reindeer hung next to a jolly carved wooden snowman, and a pottery Father Christmas beamed at a gold angel. It was as far from the stylised, professionally decorated tree in the ballroom as possible. It was perfect.

She held out her hand. 'You guys have quite the collection. Next.'

'They're all Uncle Finn's. He always brings us new ones, wherever he goes. Oh, my favourite!' Saffy said, clapping her hands together before reverentially picking up a small wooden box and opening it.

Nestled inside was a perfect red glass apple. Alex caught her breath. Finn still had it all these years later.

'Oh...' Scarlett's lip wobbled as she scanned the bottom of the box. 'Look, Saffy, we're almost done and there's still the whole top of the tree to do. We haven't got enough.'

Alex palmed the small red apple, feeling the cool glass against her skin and cringing for her fifteen-year-old self—of all the things to buy the seventeen-year-old boy you had a crush on. She'd almost died of embarrassment when she handed it over and saw the hastily hidden surprise on his face. She should have bought him a T-shirt or a Yankees hat—but, no, she'd bought him an ornament. Yet he still had it. And all the others she'd picked up over the next two years. Had them and had added to them.

'Don't worry, Scarlett, a place like Blakeley Castle has lots of hidden treasure. Wait here. I bet we can finish this tree off perfectly.'

Finn pushed the door open with his shoulder, balancing the tray carefully. Mrs Atkinson would approve; the crisps and nuts were in glass bowls. He set the tray down and picked up a glass of wine before realising that Alex was nowhere to be seen. Had she slipped away? Had he pushed too hard?

'Has Alex gone?' He made the question as light as possible, as if the answer barely concerned him. The last thing he wanted was for the girls to realise there was anything wrong. 'Is that music yours? I didn't know you two liked The Pogues.' It was great that they had such good taste, but he didn't think this song was entirely suitable.

'What's a Pogue?' Scarlett asked, wandering over to lean on his leg, one small hand straying towards the bowl of crisps.

JESSICA GILMORE   97

Saffron looked up from the ornament she was exam-
ining. 'Alex has gone to look for treasure.'

'For treasure?'

'For the tree. We ran out of ornaments.'

'We did go for the biggest tree we could find. I suppose it was always a possibility.'

Finn suppressed a smile as he walked over to admire
the tree. The bottom two-thirds was so full of decorations there was barely a patch of green to be found, but
the top third was all bare branches, with just one silver
cone and a solitary red apple. He reached one finger out
and sent the apple spinning.

'Okay, who wants to excavate some treasure?'

Alex backed into the room, her arms full with a
large, dusty cardboard box, and Finn hastily stepped
over to her, relieving her of the box.

'Thanks. It's not heavy, but it is large.'

'Where did you find that?' Saffron asked.

Alex smiled. 'I followed the clues to the attic. Now,
shall we see what's inside?'

Carefully the girls lifted the lid and peered inside.

'Ornaments!' Scarlett yelled. 'Look!'

But Saffron just looked at Alex, her forehead pinched
suspiciously. 'How did you know where to find them?'

'I've been here before,' Alex said. 'A long time ago.
It's okay, Saffron. Your Uncle Finn owns everything in
the castle. You can use these. I think the former owner
would be very happy to see them hung on a tree again.'

Saffron considered Alex's words for one long moment and then she nodded. A second later she was on
her hands and knees beside Scarlett, unpacking the treasures and laying them out on the coffee table.

Thank you, Finn mouthed at Alex, unsure whether

he was thanking her for reassuring Saffron, getting the ornaments or just for being there.

'Look!' Scarlett held up a red glass apple. 'It's the twin of yours, Uncle Finn.'

'And so is this angel!'

'And this reindeer.'

'Don't forget I lived here before,' Finn said, his gaze not leaving Alex's.

He couldn't have looked away if he'd wanted to, and the air crackled as he watched her. Her hair had tumbled out of its usual smooth knot and her cheeks were flushed, her eyes soft.

Neither girl found his answer odd, although it didn't really make any sense, and continued to sort the ornaments.

'Here.' He handed Alex one of the glasses and she accepted it.

'Thank you. I can't believe it's got dark already. I used to like the lead-up to Christmas, the dark evenings, but now I'm just holding out for spring.'

'You don't like Christmas?' Scarlett stopped in the middle of unwrapping an ornament, her mouth a perfect O of surprise.

'It's not that I don't *like* it,' Alex reassured her. 'But my Christmases are very quiet.'

'You'll have to come to my school play,' Scarlett told her. 'We're doing it here on Christmas Eve and then singing carols—aren't we, Uncle Finn? I'm a lamb and Saffy is the narrator, which is a really big part. Bigger than Mary, whatever Polly Myers says.'

The last place Alex wanted to spend Christmas was Blakeley, but she forced a smile. 'I need to get back on

Christmas Eve. My friend is waiting for me, and we always spend Christmas together.'

'Invite your friend,' Saffy suggested.

'I'll see. We were thinking of going away for Christmas, so it depends on our flights. But thank you. The party sounds amazing and I bet you two will be excellent.'

'Going away for Christmas?' Scarlett looked up from the box. 'Won't your family be sad?'

'Okay,' Finn interjected. 'Stop cross-examining Alex. Come on, step to it. More tree decorating, less chat. Someone pass me a reindeer.'

Over the next ten minutes Finn finished the tree, after arbitrating a short but fierce quarrel about whether to use tinsel or garlands—a squabble resolved by Alex declaring that she liked both.

'Okay,' he said at last. 'I think we're done here. What do you guys think? No?' His nieces were adamantly shaking their heads. 'We're not finished? What have I forgotten? Can't be the apple…we have two this year. Can't be the tinsel… Scarlett took care of that. Definitely isn't the chocolate because I sorted that…'

'The star!' Scarlett burst out. 'We haven't done the star.'

'The what?'

'The *star*!' Both yelled at once and he covered his ears.

'I think Father Christmas could probably hear that all the way in the North Pole,' he said feelingly. 'Okay. You know the drill. Out!'

Finn sensed Alex watching him as he ushered the girls out of the room. She'd curled up on the sofa, glass of wine in hand. She was contributing little to the conversation, but seemed contented, more relaxed than he'd seen her all week. It was partly the casual weekend clothes—the red sweater dress matched with grey tights and boots, the chunky silver necklace round her neck—and partly the way her smile finally reached her eyes. Maybe it was also partly the way the girls had pulled her into their circle, disarming her defences.

And possibly...probably...the talk they'd had earlier had helped. It had certainly made her presence easier for him, the long overdue clearing of the air, the explaining of misconceptions. The only problem was that without that barrier between them he was remembering all the reasons he'd failed to stay away from her all those years before. Not just her beauty but her empathy, her warm wit. The way she had seemed instinctively to know him better than anyone else. And even now her perceptive glances warmed him through.

Finn had to face the truth: Alex was the only woman he'd ever loved. But that knowledge changed nothing, because in the end she'd walked away.

He needed to remember that. Needed to remember that the girls needed stability. They only had him. Alex had made her choice long ago, and that choice had been to believe the worst of him. Even if she was still interested, even if he wanted to rekindle what they'd had, he couldn't allow anyone with so little faith near his already damaged nieces. Particularly as they both seemed to have taken to her—even the usually wary Saffron.

'Pass me the star,' he said, and Alex uncurled herself, picking up the finely wrought glittering silver star and walking over to hand it to him.

'You're doing a Mrs Atkinson!' Her smile lit up her whole face. 'Oh, how I remember the utter deliciousness of the anticipation, waiting outside, desperate to peek, knowing when I came in the tree would be lit and the star on the top. I think of it every Christmas.'

'You should go and see her. She would love to see you.'

'And I would love to see her. I couldn't before, I didn't want to be anywhere near Blakeley, but maybe now it might be easier.' She pushed his shoulder impatiently. 'Go on, put the tree lights on! I'll switch the main lights off and let the girls back in before they combust.'

Finn obeyed, after making sure the star was straight. The tree lights sprang to life, flickering more brightly as Alex dimmed the overhead lights. She stood silhouetted by the door and Finn had a sudden vision of how his life might have been if she'd believed in him all those years ago…if she'd allowed him to support her through the fallout of her parents' fall from grace.

But that life had disappeared as surely as Lola. All that could ever be was a friendship of sorts. It was all he could risk for the sake of his girls.

CHAPTER EIGHT

ALEX HAD NO idea why people complained about Monday morning. She *liked* Mondays. Too often there was so little purpose to the weekend. She'd clean, run, do some dutiful yoga, maybe cook, occasionally see a film or see a play, but it was all just killing time until Monday, when she could fill her mind and her time with work, reminding herself that she had a purpose, that she was good at what she did. It helped that she worked in public relations and had a legitimate interest in checking her emails and social media channels throughout the weekend, never switching off her phone.

Her life might seem small to some, but it was the life she wanted, the life she'd chosen. Just as she'd chosen London, cacophonous and dirty and full of people. The city surrounded her, protected her. No one saw her there. She was hidden in plain sight, able to sleepwalk through her life untouching and untouched.

Which meant she'd better be careful not to spend too many more cosy evenings with Finn and his cute-as-a-button nieces. There had been moments on Saturday evening when his dark-eyed gaze had rested on her for just a second too long...moments when she'd been über-aware of his every movement...moments when she'd been fixated on the vee of his throat exposed by his shirt, his wrists, the nape of his neck, all those soft, vulnerable spots in such a hard, fit body. A body she'd once had the freedom to love and to explore. The only body she'd ever…

No. She wasn't going there. She couldn't. It didn't matter that Finn hadn't sold those photos—maybe deep down she had always known he wasn't capable of such cruelty. What did matter was that she'd made herself vulnerable and it had backfired spectacularly. She could never allow that to happen again.

With renewed energy, Alex returned her focus to her laptop and the social media plans she'd been reviewing, pausing only to scribble notes and thoughts, the coffee Kaitlin had brought her cooling at her elbow. When she finally looked up the weak winter morning sun had disappeared and the sky had turned an ominous yellowy grey, the clouds low and heavy. A snow sky if ever she had seen one.

The air shifted and Alex knew Finn had walked into the office. She didn't need to look and check if she was right. A sixth sense had shivered through her body, every nerve awake.

'Okay, everyone,' he said. He didn't need to raise his voice. It was clear and commanding it reached every corner of the room. 'The forecast is for snow, and lots of it, so the minibus is waiting outside for those of you who live in Reading and London. I suggest you take work home with you. It may be a couple of days before the roads are passable. I remember being snowed in for a week when I was a boy.'

Alex couldn't stop herself from looking up as he finished speaking, knowing the exact week he was referring to. He was looking directly at her, and their eyes held for what seemed like an eternity as they were caught in their own private world of memories.

It wasn't until someone claimed Finn's attention that she was recalled to her surroundings. Cheeks hot, she checked to make sure no one had noticed their momentary lapse, but everyone was too busy talking about the snow to have paid her any attention.

'Alex?'

Finn strolled over to her desk and she willed her cheeks to cool. 'Hi.'

'I'm aware that you won't have anything suitable for snow with you. I could send you back to London…'

Yes! That would be perfect, and give her exactly the breathing space she needed. So why wasn't she jumping up at his words and grabbing her laptop?

'But if you'd rather ride out the weather here then of course you may,' he continued. 'I can't see the snow lasting too long, and if you do want to stay then I can kit you out. Time you started living the brand.'

Oh, that smile! The way it lit his whole face, turning a slightly aloof handsomeness into something much warmer—and so much more dangerous.

'I'd better stay,' she said, only a little reluctantly. 'There's a lot to do and there's something I want to discuss with you. Work,' she added.

'Of course,' he said lightly. 'What else could it be?'

'Exactly.'

'Give me fifteen minutes to sort everything out and then I'll be right with you.'

'Fine.'

She didn't mean to be so curt, but there were so many things unsaid, so many things she was scared of saying. So many things best left in the past where they belonged.

Alex stayed at her desk as the rest of the staff gathered their belongings, most of them about to leave. She scrolled through various social media feeds, adding notes when something caught her eye, gradually falling back into the absorbed spell of the world she preferred. A world where noise dimmed and people faded and all she knew was her work.

After a few minutes she looked up, aware that the very atmosphere of the room had changed again. It was no surprise when she looked around to see that the office had emptied and there was just Finn, leaning against the wall, watching her.

'You look busy.'

'That's what you're paying me for.'

'So busy that you haven't even noticed the snow?'

He nodded towards the window and Alex turned and stared at the view. The grass had already been covered with a fine dusting of snow, but judging by the big, fat flakes floating down from the sky in ever-increasing spirals it wouldn't be long before the snow was ankle-deep.

'Time to get you some boots. Come on.'

Closing her laptop, Alex followed him down the back stairs. His stockroom was in the old tack room at the back of the stables. It was almost unrecognisable, the rough wood panelling sanded and painted, the tack pegs replaced with neat shelves, the dirt floor covered in grey tiles. Each shelf was filled with folded clothes, labelled by size and type.

'All employees have a generous clothes allowance,' Finn explained as he ushered her in. 'They need to believe in us, live our values and look the part. Hawk isn't just spin and fancy campaigns, it's a way of life. Here, try these.' He held out a pair of sturdy yet oddly elegant leather boots. 'They're lined, waterproofed, and the sole has been especially designed for icy conditions.'

He eyed her up and down in a way that was purely professional and yet still made her feel exposed. She resisted the urge to wrap her arms around herself.

'Okay, and try this, these, this and…let me see… this.'

'So when you say "live the brand", you mean be kitted out from head to toe?' She took the grey trousers and the white shirt, the berry-red fleecy jumper and black down jacket from him. 'I hate to break it to you but I'm a city girl. There's not much use for waterproof trousers in Chelsea.'

'You're back in the country today and you'll be glad to have those trousers by this evening. Try them. They might surprise you. Our Chiltern range combines cutting-edge technology and fabrics with design-led style. And even Chelsea girls need warm hands and feet.' He added socks, gloves and a hat to the pile. 'You know, there's something I've been meaning to ask you since last week…'

'Oh?'

Alex's heart began to hammer, with strong, painful thuds. There had been enough treading old ground at the weekend. She needed to concentrate on moving forward. Being back at Blakeley, spending all this time with Finn, was dangerous. It was reminding her of all she'd used to be, all she'd used to want. They had to get their relationship back on purely professional ground before it was too late.

'Is your agency really called the Happy Ever After Agency? That's its actual name?'

That was his burning question? Alex didn't know whether to laugh or sigh in relief. 'I know. It's unusual, whimsical in some ways, but that was our purpose. We wanted to stand out.'

'You've managed that.'

Alex shifted, balancing the pile of clothes more securely. 'It has a dual meaning. Obviously we want all our clients to have complete peace of mind, and to know that using us means there will always be a successful outcome. But at the same time it's a personal wish. Once none of us had the security we wanted; our futures felt unsure. The agency was our way of taking back control. It's our happy-ever-after.'

Alex looked up and saw such utter comprehension in Finn's eyes it almost undid her. It was as if she were naked in front of him.

She smiled awkwardly. 'Thanks for these, but I'd better get back to work. Let me know when you're ready to have that talk.'

But as she left the room, Finn fell into step beside her.

'There are four of you, aren't there? I did my research before employing you. Obviously the Armarian royal ball was a huge coup, but I needed to know that such a new agency was capable of handling my work. And I have to tell you, Alex, I was impressed. Not only do you have lots of glowing testimonials, but you've also managed to make one archduke very happy. And apparently there's another equally happy billionaire— Deangelo Santos? Not bad work for just eight months in existence.'

Alex couldn't see his expression, but the teasing note in his voice was enough to raise her defensive hackles. 'You're right, our testimonials *are* impressive. And that's because we work dammed hard to make them that way. As for the rest, the love lives of my business partners are really none of your business. What's important is that we offer exemplary service for everyone, whether they are an archduke or a local café wanting some social media advice.'

'As I said, glowing testimonials.' He paused, and when he spoke again there was a curious tension in his voice. 'So how did you end up in Chelsea? Did you stay in touch with your godmother? I often wondered if that was where you went. The two of you were pretty close, I remember. I did try her a few times, but she wouldn't speak to me. It makes sense if you were living there, I suppose.'

They'd reached the top of the stairs and Alex dropped the pile of clothes onto the nearest desk. 'What does it matter, Finn? It's history. None of it is relevant to why I'm here and the job I'm here to do.'

He didn't answer at first, running a hand through his dark hair, expression unreadable. When had he achieved that inscrutability? She'd always been able to read him before.

Shame engulfed her. She should have read him when he'd told her he hadn't sold those photos, should have seen his innocence in his eyes then.

'It matters because I let you down,' he said at last, his voice hoarse. 'You needed me and I let you down. That's why I need to know what happened to you back then. Why I need to know that you were safe and happy. That you fled to your godmother's and were looked after and loved. I need to know that, Alex. Because I failed you. That's why I wanted you back here at Blakeley. I needed to know that you're okay. And I don't think you are, are you?'

The silence was absolute. Just the two of them stood there in the large, cavernous space, his words echoing around them. Alex was still, staring at him, wonder and fear warring in her expression.

'You don't need to worry about me. Not then, and not now,' she said at last.

'That's nonsense. We were best friends. You gave me your virginity, Alex, and I gave you my heart. I loved you, and I think you loved me. And then your life fell apart and I just watched it happen.'

Her mouth quivered. 'You were twenty.'

'I was old enough to do more. Do something.' He should have held on to her, should have offered her refuge and the unconditional love she had needed. But he'd failed her, utterly and completely. 'I let you drive me away because you hurt my pride. What kind of man did that make me? *Does* it make me?'

At that, her eyes softened. 'You were always the proudest boy. You would never accept help with any-thing. I should have trusted you, Finn.'

She touched his cheek: a fleeting caress, burning through him.

'Never question what kind of man you are. Look at your girls, look at the village—I never knew it so pros-perous. And look at this office, full of people willing to move their lives for you and your vision. You're a bet-ter man than I ever deserved.'

'Tell me what happened.' It was as much command as plea. 'Tell me where you've been.'

She regarded him for a long few seconds then sighed, a deep shuddering sigh that seemed to come from her soul. 'I don't talk about it, Finn. I try not to even think about it. It's buried deep inside. It has to be. It's the only way I can keep going. But you are right. You of all people deserve the truth. But not here. I need some air, need to breathe properly if I am going to do this.'

Finn glanced out at the still whirling snow, now ankle-deep on the ground, then nodded at the pile of clothes on the desk. 'In that case it's time you got branded up.'

It took Alex less than five minutes to change, and when she returned to the office she was outdoors-ready, the dark trousers showcasing long, lean legs, the berry-red top just visible under the half-zipped jacket. She'd already laced up her boots, and as she reached him she put on her hat before slipping her hands into the gloves.

'You should be on the front cover of our catalogue!' he said.

He was only half joking, but she shook her head.

'My modelling days are well and truly over. I never enjoyed it, but my mother loved it. Loved people saying I reminded them of her. It was something that bonded us. And I needed that.'

'Do you still see her?'

Her gaze fell, but not before he saw the dark shadows in her eyes. 'She prefers not to be reminded of that time.'

There wasn't anything anyone could say to that and Finn didn't try. 'Come on, let's try out those boots. They're a new model, not due for release until later next year.'

The cold hit them as soon as they stepped outside, fresh and icy, momentarily robbing Finn of his breath. By unspoken accord they walked away from the castle and away from the lake, to the parkland at the back of the castle. It was now officially open for business, with nature trails and hikes winding through, a tree-top walk newly installed, bike tracks freshly laid, but he was sure they'd have it to themselves. The weather was bound to deter all but the most hardened of adventurers, and the snow was swirling more quickly now, blocking visibility.

'You know, these jackets are designed for proper alpine conditions. I didn't think they could be tested so close to home.'

Finn turned to look at Alex as he spoke, blinking the snow out of his eyes. She was transformed, cheeks pink with cold, the snow coating her with white glitter, her smile wide and genuine.

'This is bracing!'

'That's one word for it. I was about to call in the huskies.'

It was easier to walk and talk now they were in the woods. The snow was slowed by the branches overhead, and the trees sheltered them from the worst of the wind. Alex looked so much more relaxed, arms swinging as she tramped through the snow, that Finn almost wanted to forget the purpose of the walk and just let her have this time. But he knew getting her to open up was hard, that this chance might never come again, and the curiosity and renewed regret which had hit him so hard in Armaria needed answers.

He had to move on. Once and for all.

'So,' he said, as lightly as he could. 'Tell me about

your transformation from Lola Beaumont to Alexandra Davenport.'

Her smile instantly dimmed, as though it had never been. 'First I need you to tell me something. If Penelope hadn't had to stop working so suddenly, would you ever have told me that you'd found me? Or after looking me up and researching my agency would you have just walked away and forgotten about me again?'

'I never forgot about you, ever. But as for the rest…? I don't know,' Finn confessed. 'I told myself to leave the past where it was. The girls need me now, so what's the point of dragging up the past? But, Alex, seeing you again was like rediscovering part of myself I didn't know I had lost. I picked up the phone to call the agency time after time, only to realise I didn't know what to say. I wrote dozens of emails I couldn't send. When I finally actually had a genuine reason to call you I don't know if I was more relieved or disappointed when Amber answered instead of you. It was clear Amber had no idea where Blakeley was or what it meant to you. When I said we needed you urgently and offered to send a car for you, she agreed. But it wasn't her agreement I should have sought. It was yours. I'm sorry. I shouldn't have blindsided you the way I did, insisting you came straight here. I shouldn't have threatened you to make you stay. I just didn't want you to leave without knowing that you were okay. That you were happy. *Are* you happy, Alex?'

It was the most important question of all.

'I'm content.'

'And that's enough?'

She shrugged. 'It has to be.'

'I don't believe you,' he said roughly. 'The girl I knew would never settle for "content".'

'That girl is gone. You need to accept that, Finn. Lola Beaumont has gone.'

'No.'

He stopped and turned to face her, holding her loosely by the shoulders. She made no attempt to break free, just stood there, her eyes entreating him. To what? To stop pushing? To let her stay in the dream world she inhabited? The one where she told herself she needed nothing and no one and 'content' was as good as it got?

Maybe it would be kinder to leave her there, to let her sleepwalk through the rest of her life. But didn't he owe it to the girl he'd loved, that sweet and sassy and misunderstood wild child, to help her live again? Because, painful and unpredictable as life could be, it was better than barely living at all.

He couldn't make that decision for her. No one could. But he could help her.

'Lola Beaumont was always a chameleon,' he said. 'Maybe that's why it was so easy for you to leave her behind. Because half the time she was just a costume. You modelled her just as much as you modelled any of those designer outfits and perfumes. But there was always far more to you than that costume. I knew it. Mrs Atkinson knew it. Hell, half the village knew it. I'd say that the only person who didn't know it was you. You fooled your parents and your teachers, and most of those toffee-nosed friends of yours, but you didn't fool me then and you don't fool me now. You can call yourself Lola or Alex or Jane, for all I care. But I still see you. And you are worth seeing. You always were.'

Alex didn't answer. She just stood, mute and compliant under his grasp, her eyes swimming with unshed tears.

The tension stretched until he could bear it no longer. He'd promised himself not to get involved, reminded himself that there was no future here, that the girls came first. But the girls were at school and the future seemed like a distant dream as he looked deep into the ocean of Alex's eyes, no longer pebbles but deep, deep grey and full of passion, suppressed and hidden, but there. He knew it, he saw it, it called to him, and his blood thrilled to it.

With a muttered curse he threw his promises and scruples aside and bent to her.

His kiss was neither gentle nor exploratory, but a deep claiming that sent his blood dancing. Her mouth was warm under his, welcoming him even as she made no move to touch him, to close the distance between them. Emboldened, Finn deepened the kiss, his hands still light upon her, feeling the delicacy of her bones beneath the tips of his fingers.

'No.'

The word sent him reeling back. Had he misread the situation? Misread *her*? Surely she'd come alive under his kiss? Or was that merely wishful thinking on his part?

'No,' she said again. 'You wanted a story and I promised you one. You need to understand who I am now, Finn. And then you'll know. I'm not a chameleon. I'm just empty. I always was.'

CHAPTER NINE

FINN GLANCED AT Alex but she stared straight ahead, her mouth set. There was no trace of the warm, yielding woman in the granite hardness of her face, and her eyes were now like stone. What did she think she could tell him that he didn't know? He knew her truth. Had tasted it and loved it and yearned for it. But he had asked for her story and she was ready to tell him. He owed her the listening.

They hadn't discussed their path, but they didn't need to. There was only one destination, and as they tramped through the still, snow-decked woods it seemed to Finn that, despite Alex's desperate words, her past wasn't as done and dusted as she claimed. How could it be when she knew her way better than he?

Finally, a small cottage came into view, chimney first, and then the rest, curious and crooked, more like something out of a fairy-tale than a real, live cottage.

'You haven't let this out as well.'

It wasn't a question.

'No.' Finn deliberately kept his voice low and his tone matter-of-fact, as if the kiss had never happened, not wanting to scare her. 'It's too impractical all the way out here. Hard for people to get to, too much of a trek for regular cleaning. Besides...' his voice was so low he wasn't sure she heard it '...I didn't want anyone else here.'

She didn't respond. Finn couldn't tell if her heightened colour was due to his words and the memories they evoked, or simply a reaction to the biting cold.

He had the key to the front door in his pocket and she slanted a sideways glance at him as he produced it. 'How very Boy Scout of you. How did you know we were coming here?'

'I always carry it,' he said.

The key stayed on his key ring, the original from before. It was a talisman, a symbol, even more than the key to the castle. That one symbolised his change in status. This key symbolised the moment he had truly found what he wanted. The moment he had lost it.

He opened the door and stood aside to let Alex enter. No one knew when the cottage had been built or who had originally lived there. Right in the middle of the woods, with no garden separating it from the trees around, the stone-built old cottage looked as if it belonged on a film set.

The front door led straight into the one original room, a kitchen and living space, dominated by a wood-burning stove which heated both the radiators and the hot water. A later addition housed the downstairs bathroom and scullery; upstairs was just one large bedroom.

'It's been redecorated.' Alex stood stock-still, her keen gaze taking in every detail.

Finn went over to the stove and began to load it with logs from the filled basket. 'One of the first things I had done when I first bought the castle. It didn't need much; structurally it was surprisingly sound, and the damp was because of the lack of regular heating rather than anything more sinister. A damp-proof course, new plastering and painting and a deep clean and it's perfectly habitable, if a little rustic. I come here sometimes when I need time alone, to think. There's always someone who needs me at the castle or in the office, always decisions to make. I built the business on creativity and sometimes I feel that slipping away. Do you mind? Me using it?'

Her eyebrows arched in elegant if disingenuous surprise. 'Why would I?'

'Because this was your special place.'

'No.' Now it was her turn to be almost inaudible. 'It was ours.'

It didn't take long to light the stove. Alex had taken off her boots and curled up in one of the armchairs, pulled close to benefit from the stove's heat. Finn sat opposite her. He'd come out determined to get answers, closure, and yet he still felt as if he were fighting through thickets to reach her. She was as hidden as ever, only her momentary loss of control in the woods hinting that she was reachable if he just kept pushing.

The stove always heated quickly, and within a few minutes it was warm enough to cast their coats to one side. Alex didn't speak for a long time and Finn sat back, letting her set the pace. It was surprisingly soothing, just sitting, watching the emotions play out on her face. She wasn't as in control as she would have him believe.

Finally, she sighed and turned to him, curling up tighter in the chair as if, like a hedgehog, the curve of her body would protect her. 'What are you doing, Finn?'

'I was about to offer you tea. We might have biscuits somewhere too.'

'Not right now. I mean, why are you here, at Blakeley? You could have made a new life for you and the girls anywhere. Why exhume all these ghosts? Why are we right here, right now?'

It was a good question. One he had asked himself several times whilst negotiating a price for the castle and estate and beginning the extensive renovations and investment: an investment that had made a serious dent in the fortune he had so painstakingly built up.

He stared at the polished stove, at the room with its scrubbed table, the comfy armchairs, the bookshelves. He was a thirty-year-old man and the retreat he had refurbished for himself was no man cave. Instead it was an exercise in nostalgia. Because this had been Lola's place. In those days the armchairs had needed reupholstering, the cottage had often been damp and cold, covered in dust and cobwebs, but to them it had been playhouse, palace and freedom.

When she'd been sent to boarding school she'd solemnly presented him with the key—the key he still carried—knowing he needed a sanctuary, away from his father's anger and his sister's unhappiness.

And this was where they had slipped away, nearly ten years ago to the day, on the night of her eighteenth birthday. Memory of that night was in every line of her defensive body.

'Blakeley is my home. It always was. I wanted the girls to grow up here, free and wild and safe. The childhood we so nearly had? I want that for them.'

She nodded, as if she had anticipated his answer.

'Okay.'

She was tense now, ramrod-straight in the armchair as if she was being interrogated. Her hair had slipped out of its coil while she wore the hat and she had pulled it back into a tight ponytail which accentuated the taut lines of her face and her high, haughty cheekbones. She wore the berry-red fleece as if it were cashmere. Still every inch the lady of the manor.

'What do you want to know?'

'Everything.'

She huffed out a laugh. 'You don't ask for much, do you?'

She looked down at her hands, and when she spoke again it was as if she were telling a story.

'No one knows this, Finn. Not even Harriet or Amber or Emilia. Sometimes even I don't know it. Lola belongs to a different time, a different place. She's a story. A fairy-tale or a cautionary tale.'

He didn't argue, not this time. 'How does it start?'

She smiled, a mechanical curve of her mouth with no life or joy in it. 'How does any fairy-tale start? Once upon a time there was a little girl who thought she was a princess. She lived in a beautiful castle and had everything she wanted: an antique dolls' house, a rocking horse, a real horse. She was spoiled and fêted and allowed to roam free and no one was as exciting or as glamorous as her parents. Everywhere they went people took photos of them, and everyone told the little girl how very lucky she was. And the little girl believed it.'

Finn inhaled, desperate to pull her into his arms and kiss the brittleness away, but he held himself still. 'Go on.'

'Sometimes her mummy and daddy seemed to forget about the Princess, and sometimes it seemed like they only liked her if she was wild and beautiful and fun. But she knew that it must be her fault when they forgot her or were impatient, because her parents were perfect, so she made sure she was always wild and free and beautiful. Sometimes it got her in trouble, but her parents didn't mind. They liked it that way.'

It was almost unbearable, listening to her recite the facts of her life in an almost singsong fashion, but again Finn restrained himself from interrupting. He'd asked, demanded to bear witness. He had to follow through.

'The Princess had one true friend, and when she grew up she knew he was her one true love. And so, on her eighteenth birthday, she sneaked out of her party to be with him. That was the last time she was truly happy. Because that night a curse hit her family, and by the end of the week her father was disgraced and dead and her mother had run away. Neither of them remembered the Princess. Not even in their goodbye notes…'

She paused, her throat working, and Finn's fists tightened, his need to give her comfort more acute than ever.

'No one wanted the Princess to be wild and free and beautiful any more. They wanted her to be humiliated— and she was. Unbearably so. It was like being poisoned. Every part of her hurt. Everything she touched shattered, people turned away from her, and she thought the boy she loved had betrayed her. She didn't know how to carry on. For a while she didn't. She just lay there and hoped it was all a bad dream.'

'Alex…'

'For a long time she thought she was broken. She had ended up by the sea, staying in a cottage in a place where no one knew her. There she decided to stop being a princess. She changed her name and used the little bit of money her father hadn't embezzled and the bailiffs couldn't claim to go back to college and get the qualifications she'd been too wild and free to bother with before. And she decided she was never going to let anyone else tell her story again. She was going to be the one who decided how her story was told and she got a job that helped her do that. No one knew she used to be a princess and that was just how she liked it. And she lived quietly ever after and that was how she liked it too.'

She lapsed into silence, almost unbearably still. None of the tale was new. He'd lived it with her. She'd touched on aspects of it over the last week. But to hear her tell it with so little emotion gave her words a power he hadn't imagined. Finally, he understood how broken she had been. How broken she still was, for all her protestations, and he ached to fix her.

'Where did you go to college? Did you live with your godmother?'

She blinked and the spell dissolved. 'Finn, since I left Blakeley I've worked for everything I've achieved the old-fashioned way. No trading off my name or connections. No trust fund, obviously. The debt collectors took care of that. No home, no contacts—I only saw my godmother a couple of times; she was as keen to disassociate herself from the Beaumonts as everyone else. When I found out that she had left me her house I was shocked. To be honest I almost didn't accept it. I didn't want anything from before. But it wasn't just my life the inheritance would change. We'd been planning the agency for a couple of years, my co-partners and I, and I knew I could give the others the home and stability they needed.'

'And you? Has it given you what you need?'

Her smile was brittle. 'Come on, Finn. You know as well as I do that stability is an illusion and there really is no place to call home.'

'You used to pretend this was your home.'

'That's all any of it was. Pretence. I wasn't the girl my parents wanted me to be, they weren't the great love story they told the world they were, the fortune we spent wasn't ours to spend. Everything I was and everything I knew was a lie. That's my truth.'

'Not everything.'

'Everything,' she whispered, and her eyes filled with tears.

He'd wanted real emotion and here it was, raw and painful. 'We were real. That night was real.'

But she shook her head. 'No. That night was as much an illusion as the rest. It was cursed, like everything else. Those photos plastered everywhere…me plastered everywhere…something sweet and sacred and special reduced to sniggers and scandal. The things I said to you. Accused you of. Believed. If it had been real how could I have said those things?'

'It was real,' he repeated. 'The most real thing that has ever happened to me. You want to know why I came back here? Because this is where I was most alive. I have skied down deadly slopes and climbed mountains and kayaked through rapids and seen some of the most sacred and ancient sights in the world, and not once have I felt the way I felt that night. As if I finally understood my place in the universe. And I let that go. I let you go.'

'I shouldn't have come here; you shouldn't have brought me here. I can't do this, Finn. Not now.' She jumped to her feet and rushed to the door, the tears falling freely now. 'You should have let me stay gone.'

'Alex.' It took three strides to reach her, seconds to touch her, to hold her once again, to pull her in close. 'I'm sorry. But I'm here now. Let me in, Alex. Let me in.'

It was too much. The past was all around her. No matter how hard she worked, no matter how far she ran, no matter how much she buried herself, it wasn't enough. She would never be free of the curse.

But strong arms were around her, pulling her in close. Finn's scent enveloped her, warm and spicy and safe. The low burr of his voice vibrated through her as he murmured words of comfort, of reassurance.

For ten years she had stood alone, needing no one, trusting no one, wanting no one. No dates, no relationships, no one-night stands. Just work and purpose and desperately trying to appease whatever malevolent spirit had taken her world and destroyed it, freezing her in pain and loneliness.

She sometimes thought that if she hadn't met Harriet, Emilia and Amber she just might have given up, slipped away into nothingness. Her friends anchored her, and she allowed herself to care for them—but she accepted nothing in return except some company. And she was right to do so, because Harriet and Emilia would soon be moving on, and she couldn't believe that sweet, warm hearted Amber would stay single much longer. Amber yearned for a family, and she deserved one, deserved to be loved.

And then Alex would be alone once more. She knew it, and she was prepared for it. Accepted it. At times she thought she deserved it. But right now it was hard to remember that. Hard to remember why she needed to stand alone when there was someone giving her strength and support. Someone she could lean on.

Not someone. Finn. The boy she'd loved. No longer a boy, a man. A successful man. A good man. A man with a life and commitments she couldn't imagine. Commitments whose needs superseded hers.

Slowly, reluctantly, Alex disentangled herself from Finn's clasp, blinking back still unshed tears, trying to put her mask back in place.

'Finn...'

But then she made the mistake of looking up. Looking up at a face she knew as well as her own, older, honed by life into something more than handsome, more real than the youthful good looks she'd once crushed on. At a firm mouth she knew to be capable of tenderness, dark eyes full of sympathy, yes, but more than that, blazing with heat and want. Heat and want for *her*.

It had been so long since anyone had looked at her that way. Since *he* had looked at her that way. Right here, in this cottage, when she had slipped out of her dress, feeling like a goddess seeing the awe in his eyes, like a supplicant when he had first reached out to run a finger down her arm and she had really, truly known his touch.

She'd wanted him since she was fourteen, but he'd pushed her away, the two years separating them a chasm. But at eighteen she'd been an adult, and he had been powerless to resist her any longer. And she'd never been able to resist him. So how could she now?

'Finn...' she repeated, but this time it was a plea.

For him to let her go or to hold her tighter? She barely knew herself.

But it didn't matter, because he took it as an invitation. Strong hands cupped her face, fingers burning into her cheeks, branding her, claiming her, as he searched her face. She had no idea what he was looking for or what she was showing him, but whatever it was he seemed satisfied. A wolfish smile spread slowly over his face, his eyes heating even more until she was dizzy with the want slowly filling her, warming her, bringing her back to life.

'Finn,' she said again, and this time it was all plea. A plea for something, anything, to happen. She couldn't take the anticipation any longer. It was twisting her stomach, making her pulse pound through her body, a rhythm of need.

'Welcome back,' he said softly, and bent his head to hers.

The moment their mouths met the years rolled back and she was once again an eighteen-year-old in the fierce grip of first love. His kiss was as firm and as sure, as overwhelming, and she melted into it, into him. And, as she'd known he would, he caught her, his grip solid and real. That kiss in the woods had been one of pity, of solace. This was a kiss filled with desire. And she succumbed to it. All the reasons, the *good* reasons, to pull away had flown. There were no thoughts. Her head was blessedly empty of anything but him.

Slowly, skilfully, he increased the pressure, and her mouth opened to him greedily. Heated back to life, back to action, Alex wound her arms around his neck, angling herself until she could deepen the kiss, her hands gripping the sensitive skin at his nape, pulling him into her. Desperately she moved closer, until every inch of her was pressed to every inch of him, ten years of suppressed need and desire and want spilling out of her. It wasn't close enough.

Finally, finally, his hands slipped from her shoulders, travelling with devastating slowness down her ribcage, caressing the curve of her breasts until they came to rest momentarily at her waist. His mouth left hers to skim butterfly kisses along her jaw, down to her neck, and she tilted her head to allow him access, shivering at his languorous journey.

Couldn't he feel her burning up? She didn't want a slow, sweet seduction. She wanted hard and fast and right now, please. To feel and to live.

Impatient, she wriggled even closer, taking a moment to enjoy his tortured groan before slipping one hand down to where his shirt met his trousers, allowing it to explore the hard planes of his stomach, before dipping it lower to the waistband.

He groaned again. 'Alex. Not so fast.'

'Why? Why wait?' She pulled back to examine him, confused. Didn't he want this? It certainly felt as if he did.

'I've waited ten years to do this again,' he said with a crooked smile. 'I want to savour every minute.'

'But,' she pointed out, 'we could do it fast, and then start again and do it slow.'

His eyes flared and her stomach quivered at the look in them, as if he wanted to devour her whole.

'I knew you were still in there somewhere,' he said, gravelly and low-voiced.

For one second Alex wanted to retreat. To deny the part of her sparking into life, hungry and eager and ready. She had been hiding this girl, this woman, for so long, afraid of what might be unleashed if she allowed her to feel and to do. But she was so tired of hiding her. She had told her story and Finn had borne witness. He had looked into her and found her, denied her emptiness and coaxed her back to life. She would not run and she would not hide. Not today.

'I want you, Finn Hawkin.' Alex spoke clearly, enunciating every syllable.

Slowly he reached out and took her hand, strong, cool fingers entwining with hers. 'I want you too. I think I have since the moment you got out of that car, all professional and cold and so damn desirable. I nearly kissed you that same evening. But you weren't ready...'

'I'm ready now. Less talk and more kissing.'

He looked at her, really looked, as if he could see beyond the practical clothes emblazoned with his trademark, could see inside her skin to her beating heart and thundering pulse and aching need.

'Yes, ma'am.'

Tugging her hand, Finn led her to the door which she knew concealed the staircase leading up to the bedroom. Last time she had led him, overcoming the last vestiges of his doubt, proving that she was grown up, a woman. Now it was him leading the way, but she had no doubts. Her blood thundered round her body as she followed him up the stairs. Home at last.

CHAPTER TEN

'WHAT ARE YOU doing?'

Alex jumped as the clear voice sang through the air, and as she did so her feet slipped in opposite directions. She yelped, desperately trying to get them back under control.

'Have you done that before?' Saffron padded through the snow to peer down at Alex's feet, strapped securely into long, slim skis.

'Believe it or not I used to be very good, but I haven't skied since I was seventeen. I'm hoping it's like riding a bike and that when you get your balance you remember how to do it.'

Alex peered down the gentle but lengthy slope which led from the very back of the formal gardens down to the fields that formed the working farm part of the estate. She'd not skied this slope since she was much younger than Saffron. It had been far too tame for her. Now she wasn't entirely sure she could get all the way down.

'Can I have a go?' Saffron looked wistfully at the skis.

Alex nodded. 'If you look in the cupboard in the boot room, you'll find some boots and skis about your size.'

'How do you know?'

'Your uncle mentioned it. There're several pairs of boots, so make sure you get your size. Go on, go and get them, and if I make it down in one piece I'll show you how I did it.'

The boots and skis were Alex's own, long since grown out of and discarded, just as this pair had been. A fraction of her old possessions, her old life, still here in the castle, reminding her of who she'd used to be.

But the memories didn't hurt the way they'd used to. Being at Blakeley didn't hurt the way she'd expected now she was starting to feel again. Instead there was a kind of peace at being here; she'd come full circle. Come home. Back to Finn.

Oh, she was no longer the besotted teenager she had been back then. She had no romantic dreams or hopes of a happy-ever-after. A few happy hours couldn't change a girl that much. Her life was in London, at the agency, building her career. Finn's was here. He had responsibilities she couldn't imagine: to his nieces, to his employees, to the village. Responsibilities she didn't have any share in and didn't want any part of. Better not to dream of any future and leave on Christmas Eve as planned.

But there were still a few days before that happened. A few days of negotiating her way around Finn.

Alex couldn't stop the smile curving her mouth, and her hands gripped the ski poles as she remembered the taste and the feel of him, the fire and heat and life. It had been five days since their tryst at the cottage. Five days since he had breathed new purpose into her. Five days since she had held and kissed him. Since he had kissed her. Since she had touched and been touched.

Because of course he lived with his nieces, so she couldn't come to the castle, and she worked for him, so he couldn't come to the cottage, and it was much better to chalk their afternoon's lovemaking up to emotion and nostalgia and aim for a mutually agreeable professional friendship. Or something.

Only… Alex had seen the way Finn looked at her when he thought she wasn't looking. And she certainly couldn't stop fixating on his wrists, his throat, the firm line of his mouth…

Their business was still unfinished. She knew it and he knew it. The knowledge gave every interaction between them a certain edge, and she couldn't help thrilling to it just as she had all those years ago, when she had sent him those photos.

Full circle, indeed. Luckily she was older and wiser now. The only photos she would be taking were for the Hawk social media accounts…

'Got them!' Saffy appeared on the path, arms laden with boots and skis. 'What do I do now?'

Alex surveyed the girl critically. 'Good, you're in waterproof trousers. That will make falling down a lot easier.' She laughed as Saffy glared. 'You *will* fall down. A lot! So, first things first. Sit on that bench…'

She pointed with her pole to a bench perched on the top of the hill, so passers-by could sit and enjoy the view in more temperate weather.

'And change your boots. Whatever you do, do not put your foot on the floor in just your socks or you are going to have icy toes. Make sure you do the boots up as tightly as possible and then give me a shout to let me know you're ready. Okay?'

She waited for Saffy's nod and then turned to face the hill again, bending her knees experimentally, tilting her body forward. It instinctively knew what to do.

'Like riding a bike,' she murmured as she pushed herself off, keeping her feet tilted slightly together to slow her down as she found her balance again. 'Oh, yes, that's the way.'

She wasn't going to win any prizes for style or speed, but Alex made it to the bottom in one piece, even turning to stop rather than exaggerating her snow plough.

She looked up to see Saffy waving enthusiastically.

'That was amazing, show me!'

'Okay,' Alex called as she began to make her way back up the slope.

This was a lot harder. She was so out of practice she couldn't help sliding about. Any grace or technique was non-existent, and she couldn't help but think longingly of the days when she hadn't even had to think, her skiing technique utterly innate, as had been her horse-riding ability, also long gone. She hadn't been near a horse since Strawberry had been sold.

'Put the skis onto the ground, one in front of each foot and close together, and put one foot into one of the bindings. It should click in. Leave the other one until I get there. Got it?'

'I think so!'

By the time Alex reached Saffron the girl had attached one boot to a ski. Alex checked the bindings and made sure each boot was properly secure and nodded.

'Good job. Right, take my sticks and use them to balance while you put the other ski on.'

She barely remembered her own first ski lesson; she'd been on the slopes and on horseback from the moment she could walk. But she did remember the insistence on self-sufficiency. A good skier knew how to look after her own equipment.

It took Saffron a few goes, but eventually her foot was in and she stood there, wobbling like a baby duck about to take its first step.

Alex held up her phone. 'Smile! Your uncle won't want to miss this.'

She snapped the beaming face and then, as she returned her phone to a secure inside pocket, where it hopefully would survive any falls, realisation hit her. She hadn't seen such open joy in Saffy over the two weeks she'd been at Blakeley. The girl's smile was infectious, and Alex couldn't help beaming back as she instructed her.

'Okay. Shuffle forward, tiny steps…that's it…to the top of the hill. Now I want you to do what I just did: a controlled, slow glide. If you try and point your skis towards each other it slows you. Now, bend your knees… that's it…and let your weight shift forward.'

'It feels weird.'

'I know, and it's so tempting to lean back, but don't! Right. The main thing is to try and keep your balance, but don't worry if you fall. It's inevitable. We all fall. It's how we get up that counts. Right, on the count of three: one, two, three.'

Alex waited until Saffron set off, in a slow, uncertain half-glide, and followed behind her, shouting encouragement.

'That's it. Nice and controlled. Lovely! Oh, well done. Right, let me show you how to get uphill and then we'll do the whole thing over again.'

Laughter was the first thing Finn heard as he walked around the side of the house. Loud peals of pure and unadulterated laughter. His chest tightened and he stopped to listen. When was the last time he had heard Saffy laugh like that? Like the child she was rather than a solemn miniature adult, weighed down by responsibilities and cares he couldn't persuade her to relinquish. Yet here she was, giggling away.

He walked forward, the snow crunching under his feet, taking a moment to take the day in. The air was still crisp but the sky was an impossible blue, the snow millions of bright crystals under the sun's spotlight.

After a couple of days of typical British travel chaos, with gridlocked roads, cancelled trains and supermarkets running out of bread, the country had returned to sheepish normality. With the temperature cold enough to preserve the snow, but the weather fine enough for the roads to be cleared, Blakeley had enjoyed a steady influx of visitors, coming to enjoy the wintry hiking trails or, for the younger visitors, to meet Father Christmas in his real-life sleigh. Visitors of all ages finished their visit with hot chocolate, coffee or mulled wine and delicious homemade treats in the café.

The school holidays had started today, and as a result Blakeley was buzzing. Not that it was apparent here, where there were no signposts or trails to lure visitors.

'Saffy?'

He reached the top of the terrace and looked over the sloping hill leading to the fields of the tenant farm, now snow-covered and bare apart from a scattering of sheep in the distance. To his amazement he saw his eldest niece gliding to the bottom of the hill on a pair of skis, slowly, but with a confidence he hadn't seen before. Alongside her was Alex, her usually pale cheeks pink, whether with cold or excitement he couldn't tell, her eyes sparkling.

'Hi, there,' he called, and both females stopped and turned. Saffy promptly fell over, clutching at Alex as she did so, who tumbled on top of her. Finn held his breath, relieved when they both started laughing again.

'Don't try and join us, Finn,' Alex warned when she'd sobered up a little and helped Saffy get back to her feet. 'The snow has frozen on top and it's really icy. We'll head back to you.'

'Been having fun?' he enquired, and Saffy lifted a glowing face to smile at him.

'Skiing is the best!'

'Is that so?' He grinned as he looked at the tracks in the snow. 'Did you know that I learnt to ski right here too?' With the exact same teacher.

He risked a glance at Alex, all kitted out against the snow, and his whole body heated at the way her hair was slipping out of her hat and at the natural colour in her cheeks. She looked utterly wholesome and absolutely adorable, and Finn couldn't quite remember just why they had decided not to repeat Monday afternoon's activities.

No. He could. And they were all very worthy and sensible reasons. But the main one was that he knew that it was too dangerous. He'd been in love with her once. He so easily could be again. Maybe he was. Maybe he had always been.

But one afternoon didn't cure a lifetime of hurt. He wasn't naïve enough to believe that—although Alex did seem a lot less brittle, more optimistic. But her future wasn't here, where she would be trapped by her past. And his was. The girls were happy here, and he had promised them stability. If he jeopardised that then he would be no better than Nicky.

'Go on, then,' he said to Saffy as she reached him. 'Show me how it's done. Thank you,' he added to Alex. 'This is really kind of you.'

'There's no need to thank me!'

She smiled at him and Finn's heart turned over. Was she feeling it too? This yearning? This sense of belonging?

'I enjoyed it. She's a really lovely girl. You should be so proud of her.'

'I am. Of them both.'

They didn't speak while Saffy set off, then Finn yelled encouragement as his niece sailed to the bottom of the slope. He applauded her enthusiastically and she gave him a shy wave before starting her journey back to the top of the hill.

'She's doing really well. But of course you are an amazing skier yourself. I'm surprised this slope isn't driving you mad with boredom.'

'I haven't skied in years. To be honest I didn't come here for the sport but for work. I had this idea of doing some really short videos of myself, all in Hawk ski gear, out and about enjoying the estate. From my perspective, so it could be anyone. It would be a double reinforcing of the clothes being used in the snow and also all the Christmas things we have on offer.'

The 'we' warmed him through.

She's just doing her job, he reminded himself.

'That's a great idea.'

'I want to do some filming around the castle too, now it's really open and being visited.'

'The place is buzzing. Loads of people are enjoying the Christmas Through the Ages exhibition in the castle and even more are out and about. I've checked that the treetop trails aren't accessible. With this ice it would be a health and safety nightmare if some kid got up there and slipped. But everything else is very much open for business.'

'It's amazing to see the estate so alive. It used to be so exclusive, and in a way I loved the privacy and secrecy of it. But this is good too.'

'It seemed so sad when I first came home. The village neglected and more and more people leaving. The castle all closed up; the gardens barely maintained. It seemed at times like I'd never hack my way through everything that needed doing to get it open for this Christmas. People advised me to wait until the New Year but I knew it could be done.'

'Why was opening for Christmas so important?'

Finn glanced at Saffy as she padded towards them, panting and beaming, and lowered his voice. 'To tackle the elephant in the room straight on. To show that I know what happened here at Christmas ten years ago and move the conversation on. I didn't want a whole year of the anniversary looming on the horizon.'

Alex didn't betray her intimacy with the elephant by even a flicker of her eyes. 'Very sensible. I probably would have advised doing the same. And it's worked. I've been out and about all week and most people are talking about the amazing Tudor marchpane house or the Edwardian tree, not the Beaumonts. Congratulations, Finn.'

She looked over at Saffy.

'That's brilliant, Saffy. You are doing so well. If I were you, I would try and persuade your uncle to take you skiing. I think a few proper lessons and you'd be away.'

'Can I, Uncle Finn?' Saffy's pleading eyes were huge in her thin face. 'That would be the coolest thing ever.'

Finn reached out and tousled his niece's hair. 'Sure.'

'When? This winter? Can I go these holidays? Christmas isn't for five days. We could go now.'

'And miss the play rehearsals?'

Saffy shrugged. 'We already did the play once. Oh, Uncle Finn, please can I go skiing soon?'

'We'll see.' The quintessential adult response.

Her face fell and he cursed inwardly. Oh, to be nine and think that the world was that simple. That you could just decide to go skiing and go. It had been like that for him once, post-university and pre-Hawk, when he had worked his way around the world, deciding direction and timetable on a whim. In those days he'd been as likely to head to the mountains and ski as to the sea to surf. Not the stable life he had promised his nieces, but fun.

Their life with Nicky had been full of their mother's impulse decisions. Finn had vowed to give them the safety of itineraries and timetables and annual planners. Their schoolwork and activities were plotted out on the blackboard in the kitchen. Every appointment was programmed into his phone. He knew clothes sizes and shoe sizes and the name of the woman who cut their hair. They were safe.

But as his gaze snagged Alex's he knew that wasn't enough. He couldn't keep the girls wrapped up in bubble wrap, much as he wanted to. Alex had wrapped herself up and hidden herself away for all her adult life, and maybe she'd been safe, but her life was only half lived. Never sad, maybe, but never truly happy. His greatest gift would be to teach the girls happiness.

'I have to make a quick work call,' he said. 'Keep going, Saffy. I'll time you when I get back.'

'Can Alex film me? And put it online? I'm all in Hawk clothes.'

Finn had a strict no publicity rule for the girls. He had seen what constant exposure had done to Alex, and that had been in a pre-social media age.

He looked at Alex and she shrugged. 'I could make sure her face wasn't in it. Just the back of her head. But it's your call.'

'Let me see it and then I'll decide. Fair, Saffy?'

'I guess… I need to see it too, Alex. I don't want me falling over online, even if you can't see my face.'

'Understood.'

Finn watched for a moment as Saffy set off with a stylish flourish, Alex filming her. Anyone looking at them would assume they were a family. The situation felt so domestic, so right. With a sigh, half for what might have been and half for what was to come, he headed back around the corner to make his call.

Less than five minutes later he was back, to find Saffy and Alex squinting over Alex's phone. They looked up as he hailed them, and Finn was unable to keep the smug smile off his face.

'Okay, Saffy,' he said. 'I've managed to get us a ski lodge for two nights and lessons for you and Scarlett this afternoon and tomorrow morning. Kaitlin is booking us flights right now. So, you need to go and pack for yourself and Scarlett. Warm clothes. I'll get you ski trousers, a jacket, gloves and a hat, but you need clothes for underneath, PJs, and dresses or jeans for the evening. I'll come and check in an hour. Toothbrushes, too.

Scarlett's over at Polly's so we'll grab her on the way to the airport. What?'

Both Alex and Saffy were staring at him, with identical expressions of surprise on their faces.

'I thought you wanted to go skiing?' he said.

'I… I do. We're really going? Today?' Saffy's face was so full of hope it hurt him to look at her.

'If we're ready and don't miss the flight, yes. You'll only get a couple of hours this afternoon, but all day tomorrow and Monday morning. Oh, and don't forget your cossies—the hotel has a hot tub.'

Saffy threw her arms around him, almost overbalancing on her skis as she did so. 'Thank you, Uncle Finn. Thank you.'

'You deserve it,' he said gruffly. 'You had to change schools yet again when we moved here, and you've done really well. And don't think I don't see you looking out for your little sister. Father Christmas thought you deserved an extra early present and I agreed.'

'Father Christmas?'

'Who do you think I was just talking to? Go on, Saffy, get those skis off and start packing.'

'If you leave the skis and boots here I'll put them away,' Alex said. She smiled at the girl. 'I can't wait to hear all about it.'

'Why don't you come too?' Saffy said. 'Can she, Uncle Finn? Alex hasn't been skiing for ages, and she's really good.'

'Oh, I don't…'

'I'm not sure she'd…'

They both spoke at once, and Finn gestured for Alex to go first.

'It's a family trip, Saffy, but thank you for thinking

of me. Besides, I have my work here. I was planning on filming, remember? It will be good to have lots of footage for the next few days.'

'Scarlett and I won't mind you being there,' Saffy reassured her. 'Nor would Uncle Finn.' She looked up at Finn imploringly.

His first instinct was to agree with Alex. She did have work to do, and it was a family trip. But the words wouldn't come. She hadn't skied for years...why not invite her along?

Because you're supposed to be maintaining some boundaries, especially around the girls.

He looked over at Alex and knew that, although she was hiding it really well, possibly even from herself, she wanted to come.

'There's plenty of room for one more. And you could get lots of great footage of Hawk ski-wear. We'll be back Monday afternoon, so you can film here then.'

'I have been meaning to talk to you about featuring you much more prominently online. After all, the brand is all you. You named it after yourself. It's based on your lifestyle. Footage of you out on the slopes would be a great start. But...'

'No buts. That's settled. I'll let Kaitlin know, email her your passport details. Help yourself to anything you need from the stockroom. I'll see you out front in an hour.'

She stood there, bottom lip caught between her teeth as she considered, evidently torn.

'Please, Alex,' Saffy begged from the bench where she was wrestling with her skis.

Alex nodded, more to herself than them. 'Okay.'

'Okay?'

'Yes. Yes, I'll come. Thank you, Finn. Saffy, hand me those skis. Pack warm things. I'll see you soon.'

With a swish of her ponytail she was gone, handling both pairs of skis and boots effortlessly. A small hand stole into Finn's and he looked down at Saffy.

'I like Alex,' she said, with a little wistful sigh that tore at Finn's heart. 'I wish she wasn't leaving at Christmas.'

'Me too, kiddo. Me too.' He ruffled her hair again. 'Come on, let's get going.'

And as Saffy skipped towards the house, her movements graceful on the firm snow, Finn knew that by inviting Alex along this weekend he was making her inevitable departure harder for everyone. But he wanted to give her something to remember. He wanted to remind her just what fun life could be. That was his gift to her.

He just hoped the personal cost wouldn't be too high.

CHAPTER ELEVEN

'THAT WAS THE best day ever!' Scarlett couldn't stop yawning as she spoke and Saffy joined in. Both girls' heads were drooping onto the table.

Alex laughed. 'I have never seen two such tired girls. You've not even finished your chocolate cake.'

'Bed for you two as soon as you finish your dinner.' Finn reached out and snagged a piece of cake off Scarlett's plate. She only half-heartedly swatted him away.

'I'm not tired.' She yawned again.

'I am,' Alex said frankly. 'A whole day of skiing when you're not used to it would exhaust anyone. And isn't Anton meeting you two bright and early for your last lesson? You want to be well rested so you can show him how much you've learnt.'

'Yes!' Scarlett brightened.

Both girls had taken immediately to their handsome and engaging young instructor, who was clearly used to children and beginners. After an anxious first hour Finn had relaxed enough to allow Alex to coax him up to the slopes, secure in the knowledge that the girls were in experienced hands.

'Maybe I *will* go to bed, Uncle Finn.'

'Right...'

Finn looked so discombobulated it was hard for Alex not to laugh.

'If I'd known you were going to say those words I'd have had my phone ready to record them, as proof that Scarlett Hawkin chose to go to bed of her own volition. You heard her.'

'You are silly.' But Scarlett didn't demur when Finn lifted her from her seat. 'G'night, Alex.'

'Night, Scarlett. Sweet dreams.'

'I'm off too,' Saffron said, sliding off her chair. 'Night.'

To Alex's surprise Saffron gave her a small, clumsy hug before joining her uncle and sister. From the look on Finn's face, he was as surprised by the girl's display of spontaneous affection as Alex had been—and as moved.

As Finn shepherded the girls out of the room Alex managed to get to her feet, muscles pressed into action all day after being unused for too long protesting at the movement, and gathered the girls' plates to carry through to the small galley kitchen. A kitchen that was mostly for show, as the cluster of lodges situated by a icy lake were supplied with all meals by the hotel to which they belonged.

Small but comfortably designed, the lodges had a heated outer room, for skis, jackets and other winter clothing to dry overnight, and one huge sitting and dining room, with windows at the back looking out over the lake. The floor was heated, but a huge oil burning stove still dominated the room, chucking out impressive amounts of heat. A staircase at the side led up to two bedrooms, both with their own bathrooms, and a further bedroom, where the girls slept, was tucked into the attic. The décor was very minimalist and tasteful, all greys and creams, with splashes of colour, but comfortable and cosy as opposed to stark and modern, and enhanced by the silver and cream Christmas tree in the corner and other seasonal decorations.

After rinsing and stacking the plates, Alex collected her barely touched wine and moved over to the vast sofa, tucking herself into the corner from where she could see the lit-up lake and some intrepid ice skaters in the distance. She listened to the almost inaudible giggles and talk from above as Finn chivvied the girls into bed. Any minute now he'd be down, and then they would have the whole evening together. Alex's stomach clenched at the thought of the torturous intimacy. Of looking but not touching.

Last night hadn't been too bad. After managing three hours on the slopes they'd all headed to the hotel to use the pool and the hot tubs, and had eaten there with a contact of Finn's who owned the resort—and stocked Hawk clothing in his hotel boutique. They'd stayed on to watch the entertainment, and by the time they'd got back to the lodge they'd all been ready to head straight to bed, knowing they had an early start.

But even with the exercise, fresh air, good food and wine it had still taken Alex far too long to get to sleep, knowing that Finn was just over the corridor. All the reasons for staying in her room were as valid as they had been back at Blakeley: the girls, her own imminent departure, the knowledge that the more time she spent with him the harder moving on would be. But his proximity had made those excellent reasons seem less and less persuadable.

Today was no better. All evening she had been hyper-aware of his proximity, of his every word, every movement, her body reacting to each accidental touch. She wanted him. That afternoon in the cottage in the woods hadn't slaked her desire, it had heightened it.

Maybe she should plead tiredness and head up herself, or go out for a walk…

'I've been thinking.'

Alex jumped as Finn spoke. She hadn't heard him come back downstairs, so lost in her thoughts.

'Why don't we go out for dinner? The hotel offers a babysitting service.'

'It might be too late to get someone,' she said, but the thought appealed. Out. Where there were lots of other people. No intimacy, but crowds. 'But it would be nice to see something of the village while we're here. Gorgeous as the hotel is, I'd like to explore a little further.'

'In that case I'll see what I can do.'

Alex took a sip of her wine and gazed out at the lake while she waited for Finn to return. If he couldn't get a babysitter then she needed a plan: she'd order something quick and light off the extensive menu, talk about work until it arrived and then go straight to bed. No more wine, no lingering glances, and no personal chat. It would be fine. She could absolutely do this. Even if she didn't want to.

'All sorted.' Finn stood opposite her, phone still in his hand. 'I'll just go and tell the girls; I'd hate for them to be alarmed if they wake.'

'Great. I'd better put on some lipstick if we're heading out. Maybe a dress.'

She looked down at her jeans and jumper, both from the Hawk range and both chosen for comfort rather than high fashion. Her friends would barely recognise her. She had a reputation for being exquisitely and tastefully dressed, no matter what her budget. But being with Finn and the girls made her feel comfortable, as if she didn't need her usual armour.

When she re-joined Finn downstairs, twenty minutes later, her armour was firmly in place. She'd picked a long-sleeved red flowery midi-dress, nipped in at the waist, teamed with wool tights—it was cold out, after all—boots and a chunky gold necklace. After some deliberation she'd let her hair stay loose, merely brushing it and tucking it behind her ears.

'You look lovely,' Finn said as she picked up her coat.

His tone was mild, but when she turned to smile her thanks the look in his eyes made her shiver.

'So do you. Nice to see you in a suit, not a fleece.'

'When we start a tailored menswear division I'll wear more suits.'

'I'll look forward to it.'

Before he could answer there was a soft knock at the door and Finn opened it, ushering in a capable-looking young woman who, in a strong Australian accent, introduced herself as Michelle, one of the seasonal workers who enjoyed bed, board and ski passes in return for bar work, waitressing shifts and other duties, such as babysitting.

Alex gave Finn five minutes to question Michelle on everything from first aid to fire safety, her stomach twisting all the time. She had thought going out would be the better of two evils, but they both looked so smart it felt more like a date.

Well, why couldn't it be? In just two days it would be Christmas Eve. She'd go home and this time they'd part as friends. But part they would. Why not enjoy one date first, as if they were living that alternate might-have-been life?

The Alex who had first set foot in Blakeley would be horrified by the idea. But that Alex wouldn't be here, in a ski resort in the Austrian Alps, in the first place. She'd been left behind in that cottage in the woods, and her newer, braver incarnation was taking her first cautious steps into the future. Why not start with an evening to remember?

'Come on, Finn.' She slipped an arm through his and smiled at Michelle. 'You have both our numbers? We won't be far. And do order anything you want. There's tea and coffee in the kitchen, and obviously there's room service for food or soft drinks.'

It was cold out, but fresh, and Alex was glad of her Hawk down coat, even if it wasn't as stylish as the long wool coat she wore in London. Her feet were snug inside her lined boots, her hands protected by gloves.

Although snow lay all around, thick and deep, the paths had been either cleared or gritted, making walking easy throughout the hotel grounds and into the small Alpine village. It had been dark for several hours and streetlights lit the pretty chalet-lined streets. Lights beamed out of hotels, cafés, shops and bars, where the après-ski hour was well and truly going strong, ensuring the town buzzed with activity. Christmas lights were strung across the streets, adding a festive air to the surroundings, and as they neared the village square Alex saw a huge Christmas tree, glaring with red, gold and cream lights and baubles.

As they had left the house Finn had taken her hand in his, and after a startled moment she had let him. They were both in thick gloves, no skin to skin at all, yet she fancied she could sense his pulse beating in time with hers.

'So, what do you want to do first? A drink? Or go straight to eat?'

'I don't mind. It's not often I have time to just wander. It's quite nice.'

Finn squeezed her hand. 'Then let's wander.'

They walked slowly through the packed centre of the village, browsing the enticing shop windows and eventually stopping in front of a shop selling traditional dirndls.

'I can just imagine my friends' faces if they opened parcels with those inside on Christmas Day,' Alex said as she took in the intricate embroidery and lace. 'They'd think I'd gone mad. But they're so pretty. I'd love to have an excuse to buy one. Would the girls like them?'

Finn shrugged. 'Where clothes are concerned I have no clue. A T-shirt can be the favourite thing one moment and the most despised the next. I defy the most accomplished data scientist to forecast Scarlett's sartorial choices.'

'I'll still have a look, if that's okay with you? I'd like to get them something and I've been so busy I haven't had a chance.'

The shop was filled with traditional costumes and accessories of all colours and types, and after some thought Alex bought traditional filigree silver heart necklaces for the girls. Scarlett's on a red ribbon and Saffron's on bright yellow.

'I never thought I'd be so clichéd as to match ribbon colours to names,' Alex said as she paid. 'But they can always change them if they hate them. Are you sure you don't want some lederhosen? I'm happy to get them for you?'

'That's very kind, but a gentleman always buys his own lederhosen.'

Tucking the two necklaces into her bag, Alex followed Finn out of the shop, freezing as she looked into the window of the next shop along. The window dazzled, showcasing glass and crystal, wine glasses and vases—and hundreds of Christmas tree ornaments.

She glanced at Finn to find him looking at her, his expression one of nostalgia and regret. 'Do you want to go in?' he asked.

'I haven't bought a Christmas tree ornament since I left Blakeley,' she said, unable to maintain eye contact, fixing her gaze on the sparkling display instead. 'I love it that you did, though. You wouldn't let me buy you lederhosen, but maybe I can buy you an ornament instead. How about that one?' She pointed to a little mouse holding a pair of skis.

'Yes, the girls will like that one. But I have one condition.'

'A condition?' She still couldn't look at him, feeling unaccountably shy.

'That I choose one for you. But you can't open it until Christmas day.'

That didn't sound like too much of a condition. Amber was bound to have put up a Christmas tree in the office. It would be nice to have something of her own to put on it. 'Okay.'

She turned to walk into the shop and Finn put a hand on her arm.

'And one more condition.'

She looked up at him then, and her breath caught at the tenderness and desire in his eyes.

'That you let me thank you properly.'

His kiss was light but, oh, so sweet, and after a moment's surprise Alex kissed him back, uttering a small cry of protest when he drew away, her fingers still entangled in his hair.

'I thought we'd agreed not to?' Her voice shook slightly. She still held on to him, unable to quite let go, and Finn smiled down at her.

'We did. But maybe we were too hasty in our decision-making. After all, here we are in this beautiful place, enjoying each other's company. I'm happy to bend the rules a little if you are.'

Was she? Should she? The sensible answer was no, of course not. But she'd bypassed sense when it came to Finn Hawkin a long time ago.

'I'm all in favour of a little rule-bending now and then.'

His smile widened. 'In that case, let me thank you again. I don't think I got it quite right last time.'

The village was full of restaurants and cafés to fit every inclination and budget. Finn found them a table at a small intimate restaurant overlooking the lake, where the atmosphere wasn't too loud or glitzy and there were no groups of weekenders enjoying shots at the bar, nor tables of bankers ordering bottles of champagne as they lived out their rock star dreams.

The food was simple but good, everything was cooked perfectly, and the décor was a little traditional but not too touristy. It was perfect.

Alex was perfect too. Dangerously so. She was relaxed, seemingly happy. She had no edge tonight, no wariness. She asked and answered questions, chatted inconsequentially about frivolous things like TV programmes they both enjoyed, music and books.

She listened, too, as Finn opened up about how complicated his feelings were about taking his nieces to live with him, about the feeling of guilt that he had deprived his sister of her children and the girls of their mother, the worry that he had acted too soon, the even bigger regret that he hadn't acted sooner. He touched on his father's death, and shared some of the stories from the first year of Hawk, when money had been so tight he'd lived in a student house, only for the brand to soar when a celebrity snowboarder had been photographed in one of their jackets.

'It's been a surreal journey,' he said at last. 'Hard work, but worth it.'

'It's been really interesting today. I filmed you a little, but I was also doing vox pops with some skiers and snowboarders who were in Hawk ski-wear. They all feel a real connection to the brand and to your values. They're making a definite statement when they buy your clothes. It's inspiring, and there's a lot you can do with that. I know Penelope already works with some influencers and successful surfers and climbers, but I'd suggest aligning yourself with people who share your values too. Eco-warriors and environmentalists… people who want to make a difference, to change the world. Have you found someone to cover the rest of Penelope's time off?'

'Not yet. I don't suppose you would stay on?'

He was only half joking and her smile was full of regret.

'I don't think that would be a good idea. Things are already complicated. Besides, I'm needed back in Chelsea. With Harriet's wedding this year, and Emilia's engagement surely on the horizon, there will be a lot to do. And over the last two weeks I've looked at what you've achieved, and I have to say I am a little envious. My goals were smaller, safer. I knew I wanted to work in PR, but I hadn't thought too far beyond being good at my job and where that might take me.'

'You *are* good at your job,' he interjected, and she smiled at him.

'Thank you. It's always good to have happy clients. I wanted to be head of and own my own agency. To have control, to be safe. And the last few months have been more successful than we could have imagined. Emilia is working on huge international events. I was in New York just before I came to you, working with a lifestyle brand who want to expand into the UK. Harriet's been placing PAs all over the world, and the demand for British trained nannies is so huge Amber is seriously considering setting up a section to focus on that area. We could be properly international. A household name.'

'You could.' It was brilliant to see her like this, inspired by the future, lit up with ambition, just as she had used to be. 'What do your partners think?'

'I haven't discussed it with them yet. To be honest, Finn, I don't think they'll be so actively involved in the future. Deangelo travels so much and Harriet likes to go with him. When Laurent proposes, Emilia's life will change completely. And as for Amber… Amber definitely wants marriage and a family of her own. It's just a matter of time.'

Finn desperately wanted to ask about *her* plans beyond work. Did she want marriage too? A family? But he knew what the answer would be. Why would a girl whose life had been destroyed by her family, who had never known unconditional love, aspire to love and marriage? If he'd been free, then maybe he could have tried to help her. To give her the time and love she didn't know she needed.

But he wasn't free.

How he wished he was.

'Tell me about them…your friends.'

He should have been there to help her when everyone had failed her. He couldn't help but be curious about the women who had stepped in where he had faltered. The women Alex clearly thought of as her family.

Alex took a sip of her wine. 'What do you want to know?'

'When did you meet?'

'One Christmas Eve. Not a good day for me, as you know. We all worked together, for Deangelo Santos, but we didn't know each other well—it's a huge company. I was head of PR, Harriet was Deangelo's PA, Emilia managed events and Amber was in charge of looking after visiting clients and their families. We might have been in the same meetings, but we didn't know each other. But on Christmas Eve four years ago we all had reasons not to leave early and bumped into each other on the way out of the office. It was clear none of us had anywhere to be, so we spent the evening together—and met up the next day for a walk. It was the best Christmas I'd had for a long time.'

'Why were the others alone?'

It almost physically hurt Finn to hear her loneliness laid out so starkly. He looked over at her, soft and warm in the candlelight, but with that glittering edge she'd always had, and knew with a shattering certainty that now Alex was back in his life he would never allow her to be lonely again.

He'd thought he was too busy to fall in love before. Too invested in his work, choosing Hawk before relationships time and time again, and only faintly regretful when that choice led to break-ups. But maybe he had never fallen out of love with Alex, the determined girl he'd grown up alongside. The only person he had ever really counted on. No wonder it had wounded him so badly when she'd turned on him.

Their reasons for parting this Christmas Eve were valid. Alex wanted to return to London, and his life was at Blakeley. He'd promised himself no relationships. Not while the girls lived with him, and not unless he was pretty damn sure the relationship would be a for ever one—and who could make that guarantee? But he had known and loved Alex his whole life. There had to be a way to make them work if she wanted to as well. And he was as sure as he could be that she did. He just didn't think she knew it yet.

Alex poured them both some water and sat back. 'Harriet's dad has dementia. She'd been looking after him since school and was really isolated. Emilia didn't get on with her dad and stepfamily, and Amber was estranged from hers. I don't know the details; we don't pry and we don't have to tell. There's an unspoken pact, I guess, not to ask. We've spent the last three Christmases together. It will be weird this year without Harriet and Emilia…' Her voice trailed off.

'Stay with us,' Finn offered. 'Your friend is very welcome too. The girls would love it.'

It was a spontaneous response, but the more he thought about it, the more sense it made.

'We're having a small Christmas too. There's plenty of space. Show your friend where you were brought up.'

'She doesn't know. About before. None of them do. Only you.' She stared down at her empty plate. 'They're the people I am closest to in the world and they know nothing about me. I let no one in, Finn.'

'You've let me in. I'm here. I'm not going anywhere. Whenever you want me you just have to ask. No, don't even ask. Tell me.'

'Finn…'

He laid his hand over hers, their fingers slotting together as if they were made to fit. 'I mean it, Alex. We've wasted so much time through misunderstandings and fear and hurt.'

He took a deep breath, trying to figure out the next step, not wanting to scare her off, but needing her to know exactly how he felt. That this time he was in— all in.

But at that moment the glamorous woman at the table next to them, whom Finn had noticed eying him several times over the last hour, leaned over and tapped his arm.

'Finn Hawkin? Is that you? How lovely to see you.'

Damn. Finn smiled automatically, his brain trying to compute who the woman might be. As he did so he noticed Alex stiffen and shrink back in her seat.

'It's been too long, but you are looking amazing,' he said.

It must have been the right response because the woman beamed. 'The Hawk campaign feels like a life-time ago.'

He was on solid ground here. 'You look younger than ever.'

'I wish! Five years is a long time, especially in this game.'

'Not at all,' he said. 'We're just lucky to have people like you representing Hawk. Are you enjoying the season?' He turned to the mystery model's companion, hoping for some clues, and was rewarded when she beamed at him.

'Antoinette. Lady Antoinette Anstruther. I was at school with Spiffy here.'

Right. Spiffy.

That narrowed it down. It was like one of those hideous parties Alex used to have, when every girl he met had been called Flopsy or Bunny or Popsy, as if they were characters in a children's book. He'd never understood the upper class penchant for saddling children with a string of long and unpronounceable names and then shortening them to something infantile.

He thought hard and recognition finally dawned. 'So how are you, Sofia? Are you still modelling?'

'Oh, no. I gave it all up when I got engaged to Jimsy. In fact, that's why I'm here—joint hen and stag dos skiing over Christmas. Toni and I are the advance party. I can't believe I ran into you. Everyone is talking about how you bought Blakeley. No one believes me when I tell them that I met you there before, with Lolz.' Her laugh was as high as it was false. 'It's amazing to think I knew you back then. You always did have that brooding Mellors thing going on, even as a teenager. We all had quite the crush, but Lola made it very clear we could look but not touch.'

Alex had become so self-effacing during the conversation she might have turned invisible, and neither woman gave her as much as a glance. Finn couldn't look at her as he replied. 'That was a long time ago.'

'Not that long…'

Sofia stopped speaking, waiting as the waiter came over to remove their plates, and as Alex murmured a quick thank-you her attention shifted. Finn could see the moment recognition hit her, blue eyes widening and mouth opening.

'Lolz? Is it you? Oh, my God, Lola Beaumont. Where have you been?'

CHAPTER TWELVE

'THE SITUATION IS completely manageable.' Finn strode down the path, mouth set.

Alex understood his reaction, even though she didn't agree. He assumed that every situation could be controlled. After all, he was used to calling the shots. Thought a simple 'no comment' would suffice. But he must know this wasn't going to happen this time.

He'd been there when the story broke last time. Had driven through the crowds of photographers, seen the headlines. Did he really think that the sighting of a missing It Girl and the realisation that she'd been working back at her scandalous old home wouldn't create a media storm? That the whole saga wouldn't be raked over again and again? That those photos wouldn't find their way back onto front pages?

Her stomach tightened, nausea writhing around inside her.

It was all going to happen again.

Maybe exposure had been inevitable from the moment she'd found herself at Blakeley. Or from the minute Emilia had been catapulted into the public eye. She should have known that she couldn't hide for ever. But to be discovered at Blakeley on the anniversary of the tragedy was nothing short of a disaster. She was a mistress of spin, but she had no idea how to handle this.

She looked at her hands and realised they were shaking, but she couldn't feel them. She didn't even feel sick any more. She was numb.

'Plausible deniability.'

It was amazing, under the circumstances, how she could sound so calm. As if her carefully put-together life *wasn't* about to be blown into smithereens.

'If Sofia goes to the press, or her friend does, you go with plausible deniability. You employed Alexandra Davenport to work on the reopening of Blakeley Castle. You haven't seen Lola Beaumont in years, and you have no idea if Lola and your temporary employee are the same person, but you doubt it. Meanwhile I'll prepare a statement saying that we provided you with PR support and have no prior acquaintance. Hopefully no one will dig any deeper. Even better, maybe Sofia will forget about seeing me. Either way, we need a plan, and I think it's definitely for the best if I head straight back to London tonight. I can handle the rest of the work from there. You don't actually need me on site. We'll monitor the situation. At least we didn't confirm anything to Sofia. She might just decide she was wrong.'

But she knew that hope was futile. Even when Finn had introduced Alex and explained that she was just a colleague she'd seen the disbelief in her old friend's eyes. The chances of her not telling anyone about her suspicions were slim to none.

Sofia might not go to the press herself, but she wouldn't be able to help gossiping. And, maybe not today, maybe not tomorrow, but at some point a journalist was going to start looking into the co-founder of the

Happy Ever After Agency. The links to her godmother and the address in Chelsea were there for anyone who knew what they were looking for.

'So what if they do dig?'

Alex blinked. Surely she must have misunderstood. 'Sorry?'

'So what if they realise who you are? What difference does it make?'

What difference did it make? How could he even ask that?

'I thought you wanted your nieces kept safe? Any suggestion that Lola Beaumont has been back at Blakeley and they can wave goodbye to a normal life for weeks. There will be cameras at every gate, journalists at every event. Your life, Nicky's, your father's will be exhumed and picked over. Our prior acquaintance—everything. You escaped the scrutiny last time, Finn. Believe me, you don't want to be the target this time.'

'It will be uncomfortable for a few days, but it will die down. Alex, the girls love you. *I* love you. I always have. If the truth is out there, then what does it matter? You could make your home at Blakeley. Figure out who you are and what you want with us by your side. No one will bother you; you'll be safe.' He stopped and turned her to face him, dark eyes burning. 'I love you, Alex.'

Alex couldn't meet his intense gaze. His words echoed around and around her head, and her hands were shaking harder. She clasped them together, trying to still them. He'd said he loved her. Finn Hawkin, her one constant, the boy who had made her childhood happy, the man who had saved her, woken her from a decade's half-life, loved her.

For one moment she felt his heat coursing through

her, warming her, and the tantalising possibility of a future with him flashed through her mind like the end credits of a movie. All she had to do was say the words trembling on her lips, words she had said only to him, and that future could be hers. A life of laughter and companionship and love. A life in which she would fall asleep and wake up next to this man. A life back home at Blakeley. A life with two girls who needed to be shown that happiness was possible.

The words withered and died. How could she, of all people, give them stability? How could she trust that what they shared now would last? How could she even trust in this? Finn said he loved her, but she was a lie. She always had been.

'I can't.'

'Why not?'

She couldn't look at him. Instead she started walking again, almost at a trot. The hotel gates were within view, and that meant the lodge was less than five minutes away. She could be packed and out through the door within an hour. On the first plane back to London by dawn. Home by morning. The thought of the Chelsea townhouse, her own bedroom, safety, was almost overwhelming.

'I've enjoyed this walk down memory lane, Finn, but that's all it was.'

'Nonsense. Don't lie to me, Alex. I know you. What happened earlier this week, this evening, wasn't just nostalgia.'

'You love Lola, Finn. You want me to be her. Well, I'm not. She's gone and she won't be coming back. I'm sorry but you have to move on. I have.'

There was a long silence before he spoke, and when

he did his voice was hoarse with emotion—with passion, with sincerity and with sorrow. Sorrow she had caused. The pain of it ripped through her.

'The boy I was loved Lola, yes. But even then I knew that Lola wore a mask, even with me. And when I met you again you wore a mask too, but I saw through it. I see through it now. You know what I think? I think the real you is somewhere in between. Not as reckless as Lola, not as guarded as Alex. I think the real you sent those photos to me that night and that's why you were so very hurt when they were leaked. Lola would have turned their existence into a PR campaign. I think it was the real you a week ago, in the cottage, and it's the real you tonight. I think that the real you loves my girls and understands them, and they love her. I think I have a chance at a really happy future with you. But I get that you're scared. I get that letting people in is hard. But trust me, Alex. Trust in love.'

'This summer I told Emilia the same thing. I told her to trust in love, and she did. But she's different to me.' She had difficulty speaking, her voice so small she wasn't sure he'd even heard her.

'How?'

She winced at the catch in his voice.

'Why is she different?'

'It's not just us, Finn. It's my past and your girls and Blakeley itself. I can't be there. I just can't. Even if Sofia miraculously tells nobody someone will recognise me eventually, in the local shop or in the village. I can't hide in the cottage and the office for ever. And I can't be recognised.'

'Alex, you did nothing wrong. Your parents' sins are not yours.'

'But I ended up paying. Finn, I've worked so hard to protect myself. Please don't ask me to undo all that work. Please don't ask me to be vulnerable. Please don't ask to be let in.'

'I don't want to ask. I want you to welcome me in. You don't have to do this alone, Alex.'

If only she could believe him. 'I do. I have always had to. It's the only way I'm safe. Don't you see that, Finn?'

'So tonight, last week, all we've shared, all we've been, all we are, means nothing? You are just going to walk away?'

'We could be friends,' she suggested, aware of what a poor offer 'friends' was compared to the love he had so openly offered. 'You and I could see each other some-times…if we were careful.'

It wasn't much, but it was all she had.

It was Finn's turn to shake his head, his eyes darker than ever with sorrow. 'I've said all along that I can't embark on any relationship that puts the girls' security at risk. Sneaking around to see you sometimes isn't something that works for them or me. We deserve more.'

Alex swallowed. 'It's all or nothing? Is that it?'

'I never said any differently,' Finn said gently.

He stopped again, tugging gently at her hand to get her to stop too. Reluctantly she stilled, allowed him to turn her to face him, allowed his hand to tilt her chin so she met his eyes.

'What we have, Alex, it's pretty special. Not many people get to be with someone who knows them so com-pletely. Not everyone gets to right the past. We can do both. Sure, it's scary. I get that. I'm scared too. There's so much at stake. But I believe in us. I believe in you. I always did. Believe in me, Alex.'

How she wanted to. How she wanted to lean against his broad shoulder and allow Finn to carry her through life.

He hadn't sold those photos, had never betrayed her. He hadn't destroyed them. She had. She was as reckless with people's lives and hearts as her parents. How could a person who had never known stability and unconditional love offer it? She wouldn't just be screwing up her life or Finn's life if she got it wrong, there were Scarlett and Saffron to consider. She recognised a kindred spirit in Saffron, seeing a girl scared that she wasn't good enough, ready for rejection. What if she messed her up even more?

'Damn you, Finn,' she whispered, and his grip tightened.

'Believe in me,' he said again.

She reached to cover his hand with hers. 'I do. I always did. But I don't believe in *me*. I don't know how to and I need to figure that out. Being back with you, loving you, has shown me the way. Shown me that maybe I can reach for more than security, that I can have ambitions and hope. Thank you for that. But I'm not safe, Finn. Not just because I could find myself back on the front pages at any time, or because my very presence could disrupt your home and your business, but because I don't know how to be part of a family. I can't take the risk that one day you'll realise I'm not enough. I don't trust myself to be what the girls need...'

'Alex, we all feel like that. I feel like that every day. There's no rule book—not for parenting or for love. All we can do is our best. That's the secret.'

'Finn. When I'm with you I feel anchored. I always

did. But it's just another act. Nothing about me is real—
not even my name. My whole life is about spin, from
my job to the way I want people to see me. I want you
to love me. I always did. But how do you know I'm not
spinning you? Being the person you want me to be?
How do I know that?'

'Because I have always known you, and I have always
seen you. Doubt yourself, Alex, but don't doubt me.'

'You're my one constant and I can't risk losing that.
Not again.' She reached up with her other hand, cupping his cheek, drinking him in. 'I do love you, Finn. I
have loved you my whole life. I love your heart and your
soul, your courage and your kindness. I love watching
you with the girls and seeing how safe they are with you
looking out for them. I love your vision for Hawk and
the company you've built. I love what you are doing at
Blakeley and knowing that my ancestors are respected
by you. I love you. If I loved you less I might take a
risk. But you deserve more. Your girls deserve more.
Let me do the right thing, Finn. Let me go.'

Standing on her toes, she pressed a soft kiss to his
mouth, trying to imprint every sensation on her memory: his scent, his taste, the way his mouth felt, firm
and yet so tender. She tasted salt and didn't know who
was crying, him or her.

'Be happy,' she whispered against his mouth, then
turned and walked away.

CHAPTER THIRTEEN

'EMILIA, WHAT ARE you doing here?' Alex jumped up from her office chair to embrace her friend. 'It's so good to see you. But I thought you were in Armaria?'

Alex had been home for a day and a half, but the townhouse wasn't quite the sanctuary it usually was. Amber was busy with a series of corporate Christmas parties, Harriet was auditing another company's administrative procedures before heading straight to Rio de Janeiro, and Emilia had gone to Armaria at the weekend to spend a few days with her father and his family, who had recently relocated there, before her stay at the palace.

This meant Alex had been home alone most of the time, as the receptionist they'd employed a couple of months ago, when they'd realised they needed someone full-time in the office had taken annual leave. The townhouse had never felt so empty. It felt a little like purgatory.

They'd worked so hard to make it a home as well as an office space, knocking down the wall between the sitting and dining room to create a welcoming office and reception area, where the wooden floorboards shone with a warm, golden glow, and the original tiled fireplaces had been renovated to shining glory. Two comfortable-looking sofas sat opposite each other at the front of the room, an inviting space for potential clients or staff to relax in, and the receptionist's desk was on the wall behind.

Their own desks, an eclectic mixture of vintage and modern classic, faced the reception area in two rows, with paperwork neatly filed in the shelves built into the alcoves by the back fireplace. Flowers and plants softened the space, and there was a warm floral print on the blinds and curtains, the same theme picked up in the pictures hanging on the walls.

The door at the back led to a narrow kitchen and a sunny conservatory extension that they used as a sitting-cum-dining room, and they each had a bedroom on the first or second floor—two to a floor, sharing a bathroom. Cosy for four, it was too big a house for one person.

Alex gave Emilia a quick hug. Neither was a demonstrative woman, but they had grown closer during the summer, when Alex had helped Emilia organise the Armarian Midsummer Ball and encouraged her to tell Laurent how she felt about him.

'You do know it's Christmas Eve, right? You *are* supposed to be in Armaria.'

'I came back because we always spend Christmas Eve together,' said Emilia. 'So put the "out of office" on, switch the phones to "off". No one is going to need anyone at midday on Christmas Eve. Let's go. The car is coming to whisk me back to the airport at four, so we have all afternoon.'

'It's so good to see you.'

Alex swallowed the lump in her throat, blinking back

threatening tears. She was the calm and collected one. She never cried, never had emotional crises. She didn't intend to start now, but she hadn't realised how much she needed to see her friends.

Pulling on her coat and grabbing her bag, Alex followed Emilia out of the house into the cold, crisp day. The snow was gone from the London streets, but the temperature was still below zero, the railings and bare tree branches glistening with frost despite the winter sun.

They didn't walk far. Emilia stopped at the small wine bar and restaurant at the top of their street, where they often went for an after-work drink or weekend brunch.

'After you,' she said.

Alex pushed the door and walked into the dimly lit restaurant. Only to stop in surprise, feeling something as close to happiness as she had felt over the last few days rushing through her.

'Harry! Aren't you in Rio? What's going on? Amber—lovely to see you.'

'It's like I said,' Emilia said, squeezing her hand. 'It's Christmas Eve and we spend it together. Harry and I are going to the airport together at four. I'll be in Armaria by six—'

'And I'll land in Rio tomorrow morning, so I'll be with Deangelo and his family for Christmas.' Harriet enfolded Alex in a hug. 'How could I miss our Christmas Eve?'

'And you and I will go for our usual walk tomorrow.' Amber smiled at Emilia as the waiter brought a bottle of champagne over to their table and expertly opened it. 'But first we deserve a Christmas party of our own. We've all worked so hard this year.'

Alex had never told them that Christmas Eve was her birthday, nor how much she appreciated their tradition of meeting up and spending the day together. And yet somehow they knew she needed them. She wasn't as alone as she thought; even with all the changes on the horizon they were still a team.

It had been far too long since all four of them had been together, and the next couple of hours passed quickly as they sipped their champagne and ate a delicious assortment of tapas.

By common assent they decided against talking about work for a while, which meant Alex didn't have to talk about Finn or Blakeley. Instead she listened as the other three discussed their Christmas plans.

Emilia immediately invited Amber and Alex to Armaria when she heard they were planning to book a last-minute deal for the week.

'I should have thought before,' she said remorsefully. 'Of course I'm a guest, both at Dad's and at the palace, so it's not really my place to invite people, but it's not fair for Harry and I to be away and leave you two alone. Laurent won't mind. I'll text him. There's great skiing; you ski, don't you, Alex?'

This would be the perfect time to mention that she'd been in Austria at the weekend, but Alex had no words to touch upon what had happened there. Instead she just nodded and applied herself to her barely touched plate.

The discussion quietened and when she looked up all three of her friends were staring at her.

'What is it?'

'You've been quiet, even for you.'

'And you came back early from your last job and didn't say why.'

'Alex, you look so sad. Please let us help.' Amber spoke last as she covered Alex's hand with hers.

Alex inhaled breath, long and painful, thoughts tumbling around her head. If she told them who she was—what she really was—those words could never be taken back. But she was so tired of carrying secrets.

She stared at her still full plate, her barely touched glass, and felt her resistance shatter into tiny pieces. She couldn't be this alone any more. She just couldn't. And if she didn't let in these girls, these amazing resilient women, then she was doomed for sure.

She looked up at the three concerned faces and tried to summon a smile. 'My name isn't Alex,' she said slowly. 'At least it is now, but I was born Lola Beaumont and I grew up at Blakeley Castle.'

'But isn't that where you've just been?' Emilia asked.

Alex nodded.

Amber's hand tightened on hers. 'It must have been very difficult,' she said softly.

And the sympathy in her voice and in the faces of all three of her friends undid Alex. She couldn't stop the tears gathering in her eyes and falling down her face as she finally told them it all. Every detail of who she was, what had happened—and about Finn.

'Here's your tea.'

Amber handed Alex a steaming mug and Alex accepted it gratefully. They were all back at the house, with Alex placed firmly on the sofa with a blanket and told not to get up.

'Your Finn sounds like a hottie!' Harriet had her

phone in front of her and now she squealed, holding it up so they could all see the picture she'd found of Finn, looking rugged, surfboard in hand. 'Oh, he *is*! Tall, dark and handsome—just the way I like them.'

'And you an engaged woman,' Amber scolded her.

Harriet laughed. 'Deangelo knows I love him completely, but that doesn't mean I can't appreciate a good-looking man when I see one. But, more importantly, he sounds kind. Looking after his nieces the way he does is a wonderful thing, and Hawk has a great reputation as an employer and for its ethos.'

'He is kind,' Alex said. 'He's a very good man.'

And hot too, she silently agreed.

'In fact...' Harriet smiled at her. 'He sounds like a keeper. Alex, why are you here with us and not with him?'

It was a very good question.

'I told you. He needs a stable person for the girls. Not someone who has no idea who she really is.'

'A very wise person once said something to me and I've never forgotten it,' Emilia said, perching on the sofa next to Alex. 'She said: "If the worst comes to the worst we're here for you. We're your family. We'll pick you up and heal you. But going through life too scared to put yourself out there isn't living, it's existing, and you deserve more. We all do." *You* told me that this summer, and you were right. Living fully is scary, Alex. It's much easier to sleepwalk through life. But it sounds to me like Finn woke you up. It's up to you what you do with your life now, but do you really want any more regrets?'

'It's easy to be wise for other people,' Alex said, but her own words, repeated back to her, resonated through her. 'It's not just me. It's the girls, it's being found out again, it's being Lola once more, and the press…' She shivered. 'If they're going to find me I can't bring that to their door.'

'So you're going to hole up here and withstand the siege?' Harriet asked.

'I'm hoping there won't be a siege, but, yes. What else can I do?'

'What would you tell me to do if I was in your position?' Amber asked, pulling up a chair to sit opposite, her large green eyes fixed firmly on Alex. 'I've a secret and there's a good chance it might be discovered. I don't know if the press will descend tonight, or tomorrow, or next week. All I know is that I am going to spend the next few weeks, months, years in fear. What would you tell me to do?'

'I'd tell you to own it,' Alex said reluctantly.

'How?'

'I… I would tell you to get your side out first. To find a friendly journalist and offer an exclusive. And to pick a time of year when the news cycles are busy to minimise the exposure.'

'Like Christmas?'

'Like Christmas…'

Amber didn't say anything else. She just waited. Harriet and Emilia sat still and silent as Alex stared at her tea. Amber was absolutely right. Her advice was always to own the story, to control as much of the narrative as possible. And yet here she was, allowing the narrative of her life to be controlled by fear, by what might happen. Finn was right too. Lola would have laughed at the headlines, turned them to her advantage. Alex was hiding from them.

What if there were a middle way? And, more importantly, if there was, was she brave enough to take it?

A phone beeped, breaking the silence, and Emilia got to her feet, pressing a light kiss to Alex's head. 'The car is here and Harry and I need to go. It would be lovely to see you and Amber in Armaria, so let me know if you're coming. But if I were you I'd be on my way to another castle. Think about it, Alex. Merry Christmas, Amber.'

'I'll see you both soon. Have a wonderful Christmas.' Harriet threw her arms around first Amber and then Alex.

The two women left in a flurry of hugs, kisses and 'Merry Christmases', leaving Amber and Alex alone in the darkening kitchen, looking at each other.

'You know what I really want for Christmas?' Amber said. 'A nativity scene. Any idea where we can see one?'

Alex stared at her. Could she do it? Go to Blakeley and know she would certainly be unmasked, sooner or later. Risk finding happiness knowing it could end at any time, that there were no guarantees? But, more importantly, could she *not*? She'd thought there were no second chances. Not for her. But fate—and Finn—had shown her the possibility of a different life. All that was stopping her from taking it was fear. And she was so tired of being afraid.

'It's a good thing I know where there is one. Pack your bag, Amber, we have an invitation to a castle this Christmas. But first,' she said, resolution filling her, 'I have a phone call to make.'

CHAPTER FOURTEEN

'ALEX PROMISED SHE'D be here.' Scarlett's lower lip wobbled dangerously.

Finn knew how she felt. He still couldn't believe Alex had packed her bags and left that very night in Austria. No backward look. Uncaring of who she left behind. Again.

Heaving a sigh, Finn pulled at one of the woolly ears adorning Scarlett's head. 'She'd be here if she could, Scar. It's not her fault she has to work.'

'No one has to work on Christmas Eve apart from Father Christmas and his elves. Oh, and vicars.'

'Lots of people work over Christmas. Come on, let's get you backstage. Can you imagine the disaster if we didn't hear your "baa" at the right moment? The whole play would be ruined.'

Finn watched Scarlett prance ahead. She was never down for too long. She looked adorable in her white fleecy costume with its little woolly tail and pointy ears—and he had no one to share the moment with.

His sister should be here—he'd sent her an invitation and offered to pay her plane fare from wherever she was, but Nicky hadn't replied. He didn't know if it was a good or bad sign that the girls never asked about their mother, and nor did they expect to see her. But they did want to see Alex. The thing he had promised himself never to let them do had happened: they had got attached to someone temporary.

And they weren't the only ones. It wasn't Nicky he wanted next to him, much as he hoped she'd make an appearance for the girls' sake, he wanted to share this moment with Alex.

The real question, the question which had been nagging at him for the past two days, was what he was going to do about it. Should he respect Alex's wish to live a quiet, safe life or do what he wished he'd done ten years ago and go after her? Show her he was hers, always?

So far he hadn't had any enquiries about the identity of his temporary PR manager. Maybe Sofia had believed Alex when she'd denied any prior acquaintance, but the truth was bound to come out one day. Wouldn't it be better for her to be with people who loved her when that happened? Wouldn't it be better for her to be with people who loved her whatever the future held? Shouldn't that be how everyone lived?

He looked around the ballroom, filled with laughing, chattering people. It was as unlike the Beaumonts' famously decadent Christmas Eve parties as a party could be. Instead of the great and the good, the famous and curious, he'd invited the whole village, owners of local businesses and neighbours, plus all his staff, with coaches laid on to take them back to London and Reading and a shuttle bus prepared to do several station runs for those wanting to catch trains back to family. Some people had come dressed up, others were in jeans. There was no dress code, no expectation., All he wanted was to see the ballroom full of seasonal cheer.

At one end of the ballroom a buffet table groaned under the weight of food, while waiters and waitresses circulated with canapés and trays of drinks. A kids' bar and buffet were in the attached dining hall, along with paid entertainers, to give the adults a chance to relax and their over-excited offspring an opportunity to work off their Christmas Eve energy.

Finn had also arranged for a TV to be set up, with rows of comfortable chairs and beanbags, and a selection of kids Christmas films ready to go. After the nativity play and some carols, the children would have their own party while a band entertained the adults, and the whole thing would finish at eleven to give those who wanted to attend Midnight Mass time to get there.

He'd been planning the event for months. It was his statement as the new owner of the castle, ushering in a new era. He should feel pride at its success, but instead he was just desperately tired. He felt as if he'd let Alex down all over again, that he should have found the right words to make her trust in him, in them.

But if telling her he loved her weren't the right words then he wasn't sure what they were. Would she ever be ready to accept love? Would it ever be their time?

With a start he realised that the small stage set at one end of the ballroom was filling with children and that people were beginning to sit in the rows of chairs placed in front. The school choir stood to one side, self-important in their smart cassocks, and the orchestra was nervously tuning up next to them. Right at the front of the stage, standing to one side, was Saffy, white with nerves, biting her lip.

Finn held a hand up to attract her attention, giving her a grin and a thumbs-up when he had it.

He wanted his nieces to be the best they could be, not to be afraid to love or to go after what they wanted. Didn't he owe it to them to set a good example? Didn't he owe it to himself?

He still had Alex's Christmas tree ornament in his pocket, like a talisman. He should go and give it to her. Tell her he was here for her whenever she needed him. That this time he wasn't going to just watch her walk away. It was up to her what she did with the information, but at least she would know.

Mind made up, Finn strode to a seat at the back, phone out, ready to record Scarlett's big moment, having promised Saffy not to embarrass her with as much as a photo.

As he sat down the orchestra began to play the first strains of 'Once in Royal David's City', and a boy with a cheeky smile and tousled hair sang the first verse with a voice of such sweet power Finn could hardly credit someone so small could manage it. The rest of the choir joined in and then, blushing furiously, Saffy spoke.

'Once upon a time there was a woman named Mary, and she lived in a place called Nazareth…'

Her voice shook at first, but grew steadier as she went on. He could see the relief on her face when the girl playing Mary delivered her first line and attention switched to the actors.

It was the most traditional of traditional nativities. No whales or dinosaurs at this manger. But it had a simplicity that appealed to Finn, with the old carols threading through the narrative, the whole audience joining in with a gusto that clearly amazed the vicar.

Finn sat still, proudly blinking back tears as Saffy, her confidence growing with every word, narrated beautifully.

And then his absorption was broken by low voices and a clatter by the door next to him.

He looked round, annoyed, as the door opened and the sound of high heels announced the entrance of newcomers, their attempts to walk quietly almost comical, before switching his attention back to the stage, vaguely aware that two figures had stopped behind him.

At that moment a spotlight highlighted the back of the hall, in readiness for the shepherds to walk down the aisle, and he heard Saffy let out a peculiar little cry, half-sob, half-unintelligible word, her face shining with shock and happiness as she gazed at the spotlight.

Finn twisted round to see what she was looking at and it was all he could do not to repeat his niece's cry.

It was Alex.

Happiness burst through his body, through his very soul at the sight. He didn't need to go and find her. She had returned to him.

To them.

'Hey…' he whispered.

'Hey.'

At that moment the shepherds ushered their small flock into the back of the hall, ready to be dazzled by an angel on the stage, only for one lamb to utter a loud cry and break away from the herd to fling itself at Alex.

Finn looked at Alex as she bent down and enfolded the lamb in her arms, meeting his gaze with her own steady one. And he knew for certain. She'd come back for them all. For good.

* * *

'Okay, girls. Go and get some food and let Alex and her friend get a drink and some food of their own. It's lovely to meet you,' Finn said to Amber. 'I'm so pleased you are joining us for Christmas.'

'You're really staying for Christmas?' Scarlett asked, still in her lamb costume.

Alex nodded. 'If that's okay with you two?'

'Yes!' Scarlett nodded so enthusiastically her ears were in danger of coming off.

Saffron's smile was more sedate, but her dark eyes shone and Alex gave her a gentle hug.

'You were brilliant. I'm sorry we were so late; it was hard getting a taxi at Reading station.'

'That's okay,' Saffy said. 'I'm glad you're here. Come on, Scar. Otherwise only the yucky sandwiches will be left.'

Alex watched the two girls run off to the dining room, taking in the ballroom as she did so. Christmas Eve at Blakeley, a party. Just like old times. A band up on stage, people milling and talking and laughing. But this was a family occasion—a community event. If people were drinking to excess or taking drugs or engaging in affairs and dares then she couldn't see it. Everyone looked festive, many in party clothes, but no one was in haute couture, costing enough to feed a family for a year, or dripping in diamonds. Her ancestors would probably think it a tame affair, but she liked the simplicity of it.

She knew people were watching her, trying to figure out who she was. Some had noticed her in the last two weeks, but many of the villagers hadn't seen her at all while she'd been working there; she'd done her best to stay out of sight of the village.

With her hair down, and wearing a severely cut black cocktail dress, she knew she looked more like Lola than she had done during her whole stay at Blakeley. It was likely someone would recognise her sooner rather than later. But that was okay.

Alex inhaled, nerves fluttering. With Finn by her side she could handle it.

'I'm going to get some food,' Amber said, touching her arm reassuringly. 'And Saffy tells me that the first film scheduled is *The Muppets Christmas Carol*. So, much as I'm looking forward to the band, I might join the kids for a bit. I can't resist that film.'

Dear Amber. Subtly telling Alex that she was okay and would be fine by herself. 'Have fun.'

Amber's green eyes sparkled. 'You too.'

'Would you like a drink?' Finn smiled down at her and Alex's stomach flipped with nerves mingled with desire.

'You're in a suit again? This is becoming a habit.'

'You look beautiful,' he said softly, and her desire ramped up, painful in its intensity.

'Thank you. Can we go for a walk? I need some air.'

And to talk without everyone surreptitiously watching them.

'Sure.'

Finn guided her out of the ballroom and back through to the west wing, so they could slip out through the side door, avoiding all the other people getting some cool air after the heat of the ballroom, stopping only to collect their coats to guard against the winter chill.

Alex took a deep breath, feeling the shock of what

she had just done enfolding her. 'I called a journalist. A feature writer I've known a while. She's fair. I trust her to be fair. I am going to meet her back in London on Boxing Day and give her the story—all of it.'

Finn took her hand, his fingers warm and strong and comforting. 'Tell her to come here.'

'Finn…'

'Blakeley is embedded in you, in your story. You should tell it here. I want to be with you this time.'

Relief flooded her, and the tension she'd held since making the call melted away. 'I'd like that.'

'You're very brave. I'm proud of you.'

'It was Amber. She made me see that I was ignoring my own best advice, letting the story rule me, not me it. I'm not brave—I am quite frankly terrified—but it's time. How can I have a future if I'm hiding from the past?' She looked out across the moonlit landscape. 'Would you mind if we walked to the lake?'

He raised an eyebrow in surprise. He must have noticed how she had avoided the lake over the last few weeks, but if she was going to do this, be here, there were a few more ghosts to lay to rest first.

The path was lit by lanterns, the same lanterns as those hanging in trees around the castle, and the moon was hidden by low clouds. It smelt like snow.

Finn took her hand as they neared the lake and Alex entwined her fingers with his, glad of his strength. Finally they reached the low platform bordering the lake. The same platform she had fished from, launched boats from and swum from summer after summer. She stepped onto it, looking out into the dark, inky depths, thinking of the young woman who had died there exactly ten years ago and in doing so had set in chain a series of events which had totally changed Alex's life.

'She was high,' she said after a while. 'So out of it that she thought it was a good idea to swim in the lake on Christmas Eve night. The inquest said that if she hadn't drowned she would probably have died of hypothermia. Dad realised she was missing and came to find her. He pulled her body out of the lake. She was only twenty-three, did you know that? Meanwhile my mother was sleeping with that girl's husband back at the castle. We thought normal rules didn't apply to us, that we were somehow above it all. But we were so wrong. And that poor young woman paid the price. Kate paid the price.'

She hadn't spoken the name for years, and doing so now lifted a weight from her heart she had been carrying for so long she'd forgotten it was there.

'And my dad. I never knew whether he was taking the coward's way out or whether he truly thought he was doing the right thing. I've always wondered if he thought about me at all...'

Finn held her close, his clasp firm and reassuring. 'You are not your parents. What happened here was tragic, and it was desperately sad, but it shouldn't define you. You can't let it define you any more. I told you. I don't care if you call yourself Alex or Lola or anything else. Names are just words. What matters is what is in here.' Finn touched his chest. 'You have a good heart. That's what matters. And you have *my* heart, whatever you want to do with it. It's yours.'

He reached into his pocket and brought out a small paper bag.

'I didn't get a chance to wrap it…sorry. Happy Birthday, Alex.'

She recognised the logo on the bag. It was from the glass shop in Austria, where she'd bought the girls' necklaces, now both wrapped and in her bag ready for the morning. Opening it, she saw a tissue-wrapped object. She slowly pulled it from the bag, unwrapping the tissue to reveal an exquisite crystal Christmas tree ornament—a heart.

She held it up to the lantern light, watching the light sparkle off it. 'It's beautiful.'

'Will you take it, Alex? Will you take my heart? I come with a lot of baggage, I know. Memories you want to forget and two pre-teen girls and a castle full of your ancestors. But I love you. I always have. I want to be by your side no matter what life throws at you. You think you need to be alone. You don't. I'm here. I'll always be here.'

Alex looked at the crystal heart a little longer, her own heart too full for her to find words. Then, slipping it into her pocket, she reached out and took Finn's hand, drawing him away from the lake. She looked back at the lake for one long moment and felt the last ghost slip into its depths.

She waited to speak until they were halfway along the path, drawing him close to her under a tree, looking at the castle lit up against the snow-heavy sky.

'I'm scared,' she said honestly. 'Scared that I'll let you down, that I'll let the girls down. Scared that one day you'll wake up and realise I'm not enough. It's almost overwhelming. It's as if I pushed all that fear deep down and hid it, along with every other emotion. That I survived by not feeling and not living, by being asleep in my own life. And then you fought your way back into my life and woke me up, and it's been more painful and harder than I could ever have imagined. But also more wonderful. You, the girls, being back here at Blakeley... It's like all the wishes I never dared to dream have come true. And it's all thanks to you. My knight, the only person who has always seen me. I can't believe you love me. I can't believe I get to be that lucky. I have always loved you, Finn. Always.'

'I know you have your business, and your life in London, and I know you have huge ambition and that's part of what I love about you,' Finn said hoarsely. 'But we can make it work. You can have your own offices here or commute. Whatever you need. All I know is that if you agree to give this a go then I won't be stupid enough to let you walk away a third time.'

'I can't believe that I can be this lucky. That I get to have my agency and my friends, you and the girls and Blakeley. There were so many times when I never thought I'd be happy again. But you do know, don't you, that Hawk and Blakeley don't change anything? I'd want to be with you and the girls no matter where you lived or what you did. Being able to come home is just the cherry on the cake, but you're the cake.'

Finn gave a sudden shout of laughter at her words, his expression turning serious as he gazed down at her. 'Welcome home, Alex.'

He bent to kiss her and she reached for him, entwining her arms around his neck, pressing so close to him she could feel every sinew and muscle, feel the beat of his heart in time with hers.

As his mouth found hers the snow began to fall, settling in her hair, on her arms and shoulders, but she was warm within his arms, warmed by his embrace.

'Merry Christmas,' she whispered against his mouth, and felt him smile.

'Merry Christmas, my love.'

* * * * *

THE RANCHER'S
BEST GIFT

STELLA BAGWELL

To my family and the treasured memories
of our Christmases together.

Chapter One

"Two weeks! Hell, Blake, that's a long time for me to stay down at Red Bluff."

Saddle leather creaked as Matthew Waggoner twisted around to look at Blake Hollister, his boss and manager of Three Rivers Ranch.

With a grunt of amusement, Blake leaned forward and fondly stroked the neck of the bay horse he was riding. "What's the matter? Afraid this place will fall apart without you?"

Matthew stared out at the herd of cattle grazing on tuffs of grass hidden among the thorny cacti and chaparral. The Arizona landscape was rough and rugged, especially in this area of the seventy-thousand-acre ranch. And with each day taking them nearer the end of October, the grass was getting as scarce as hens' teeth.

"Three Rivers would never miss me."

A moment passed in silence, and in the distance a coyote let out a lonesome howl, signaling that twilight was falling on the jagged peaks and deep arroyos cut by centuries of flash floods.

"No. After having you around for fourteen years, we'd never realize you were gone." He muttered a curse. "Don't give me that bull, Matthew. You know why I'm sending you to Red Bluff. I can't trust anyone with the job but you."

The Hollisters' second ranch was located in the southern part of the state, near the tiny town of Dragoon. Although at thirty-five-thousand acres, Red Bluff was only half the size of Three Rivers, it was blessed with sheltered green valleys where mama cows and calves could graze during the deepest part of winter. Each October, they shipped a large herd of cattle to Red Bluff, so this was nothing new for Matthew. Except that normally, he finished the job in two days. Not two weeks.

Lifting his hat a few inches from his head, Matthew raked fingers through the blond curls flattened to his scalp. "Are you sending the same five men with me that went last year?" he asked.

"Yes, plus one more. Scott is going along, too."

Matthew jammed the hat back down on his head and drew in a deep breath. "Guess that means we'd better take another cot for the bunk house. There's hardly enough room for five beds, but we'll jam another one in there somehow."

"Forget about an extra cot," Blake said. "I've already told Camille that you'll be staying in the big house with her."

Stunned, Matthew swung his head toward the other man. "You did what?"

"You heard me. You'll be staying in the ranch house. There's plenty of room and my sister won't bother you."

Bother him! Camille Hollister had bothered him ever since she'd grown into a woman more than ten years ago. But Blake hardly needed to know that bit of private information.

"I've always stayed in the bunkhouse with the men," Matthew reasoned. "I don't want to set myself apart from them."

Blake said, "You're the foreman and their boss. And they see you as such. Besides, you're the only man I'd trust in the house with Camille."

Careful to hide his reluctance, he said, "I don't expect your sister is going to appreciate this setup."

"Camille doesn't own or run Red Bluff Ranch. She's simply staying there until—" He broke off, a sour grimace on his face. "She gets that damned head of hers on straight," he said sourly.

Camille had left for Red Bluff more than two years ago, and since that time she'd not been back once to Three Rivers. The whole family believed she was still pining for the no-account bastard who'd broken their engagement. As for Matthew, he refrained from expressing any sort of opinion as to why the youngest member of the Hollister family had chosen to stay away. He only knew it was going to be worse than awkward sharing the ranch house with her.

"She's been down there a long time," Matthew said. "I expect by now she's thinking straight."

"Then why the hell doesn't she come home?" Blake asked, directing the question as much to himself as to

Matthew. "It's no wonder that Mom is in such a dark state of mind. And Camille could do plenty to make it better for her, but no, she's too busy thinking about herself."

Matthew inwardly winced. It wasn't often that Blake voiced such strong opinions about his siblings. Usually, he was very easygoing and especially forgiving. This ire directed at Camille was unlike him. But the weight the man carried on his shoulders as manager of Three Rivers was far more than Matthew could begin to bear.

"You think that's what your sister is doing?" Matthew asked.

"I don't know. I'm tired of trying to figure her out." He reined his horse in the direction of the ranch house. "Let's go. It's going to be dark before we get back to the ranch yard."

Matthew guided the buckskin he was riding alongside Blake's mare, and the two men urged the horses into a long trot.

Twenty minutes later, they arrived at the horse barn. As Blake had predicted, it was dark, and the ranch hands had already finished the evening chores and lit out for the bunkhouse. Except for T.J., the barn manager, and the rows of stalled horses, the cavernous building was empty.

As the two men unsaddled their mounts and put the tack away, Matthew asked, "When did you want the cows rounded up? I figure that's going to take three days, maybe more."

"Better start tomorrow," Blake told him. "The new herd should be here by then."

This was the first Matthew had heard about a new herd. "You've bought more cattle?"

Grunting, Blake shoved his saddle onto a pipe rack. "Yeah. I've been meaning to discuss the matter with you. But I've just been so damned busy, Matthew. Sorry."

"It's okay."

"No. It's not okay. You're the man who has to keep the hands going and the cattle tended to. You need to know what you're dealing with."

"So how many new cows are you talking about?"

"Five hundred more head. And I want them all to go to Red Bluff with the rest. They'll need shots and ear tags after you get them there. So figure that in with everything else you'll need to get done. Two weeks might not be enough time."

Matthew was going to make damn sure everything was wrapped up in two weeks. He wanted to get back to his own house and own bed and away from Camille Hollister as quickly as possible.

Later that same night, Camille Hollister walked across the courtyard at the back of the hacienda-style ranch house and let herself into the kitchen. After switching on a light that swung over a long table made of hand-hewn pine, she hung her jean jacket on a hook by the door, then crossed to a short row of cabinets and put a pot of coffee on to brew.

Funny, she thought, how she worked for long hours each day at a diner in Dragoon and the waitresses were constantly filling coffee cups for the customers, but Camille rarely had the chance to enjoy a cup for herself. She was too busy cooking short orders and baking pies in between. But she wasn't about to complain.

She loved her job. Even if it wasn't the sort of career her family expected of her.

While she waited for the coffee to drip into the carafe, she plucked bobby pins from the bun on top of her head and allowed her long, light brown hair shaded with a mixture of red highlights to fall down to her waist.

Massaging her scalp with one hand, she pulled a cell phone from her handbag and quickly scanned for any calls or messages she might have missed.

She found one message from Blake and punched the screen of the phone to open it.

Matthew and the crew should be there Friday. I'd appreciate it if you'd make him feel welcome.

Camille rolled her blue eyes toward the low ceiling of the kitchen. *Make Matthew feel welcome.* What the heck did her brother think she was going to do? Give the Three Rivers foreman the cold shoulder? Just because she hadn't been home in a couple of years, Blake must think she'd turned into a hateful hag or something.

Well, haven't you, Camille? For a long time after Graham asked for his engagement ring back, you didn't want to communicate with any human being. You buried yourself here on Red Bluff and rarely got off the property. And you're not exactly Miss Sociable now.

Smirking at the sardonic voice in her head, Camille walked back to the cabinet and poured herself a large mug of the coffee. As far as Matthew Waggoner went, she didn't need to be Miss Sociable. Over the past ten years, the man had probably spoken twenty words to her, and that would probably be stretching things. And the way he looked at her—she'd never been able to decide if he liked her or if she grated on his nerves.

Either way, she'd not given the man much thought these past couple of years. But then her family would say she'd not given anyone much thought, except for herself.

And maybe they were right, she pondered as she sat down at the table and propped her feet on the chair next to her. She had gone a little crazy when Graham had jilted her. But she'd gotten over him ages ago. She was getting on with her life now and she was doing it without a man. And without her family breathing down her neck. It felt good. And that's the way she intended for things to stay.

Picking up the phone, she typed in a reply to her brother: Don't worry. I'll roll out the red carpet for Matthew.

Friday evening when Camille arrived home from work, the ranch yard was buzzing with activity. Pickup trucks, along with several semi-truck cattle haulers, were parked at different angles near the barn area. Portable pens had been erected next to the permanent wooden corrals to hold the extra cattle that were being unloaded.

Working dogs were barking and nipping at the heels of the lagging cattle, while misplaced calves bawled for their mamas to find them. Dust boiled high in the air, men shouted to communicate above the din of noise, and horses neighed to each other.

For a couple of minutes, Camille stood watching the activity, and then an odd thing happened. A hard lump lodged in her throat and tears filled her eyes to the point where the ranch yard became nothing but a watery blur.

Cursing to herself, she entered the house and wiped her eyes. Darn it, she'd been done with tears a long time ago. And she sure as heck wasn't homesick. No, she'd spent twenty-six years of her life on Three Rivers and that was enough. She loved it here on Red Bluff. But seeing the men on horseback, the cattle and dogs had all reminded her of her late father, Joel. Next to his wife and children, ranching had been his deepest joy and if he'd still been alive, he'd be out there right now with the rest of the men, doing the job he'd loved.

Nearly nine years had passed since her father had died, yet Camille still endured unbearable moments when she longed to see his grinning face and feel his comforting arms around her. She'd been a daddy's girl and once he'd died nothing had been the same.

Giving herself a hard mental shake, Camille walked straight to her bedroom and stripped off her slacks and blouse that were permeated with the odors of fried food and burnt cooking oil. It being Friday, the diner had been extra busy all day. She'd lost count of the burgers and chicken strips she'd cooked today. Now, instead of relaxing with a cup of coffee and the book she'd been reading, she had to shower and get ready for Matthew Waggoner.

Oh well, it would only be for a couple of weeks, she reminded herself. Surely she could put up with the man's company for that long.

The Red Bluff ranch house was built in a square with a low sandstone wall and a slatted iron gate serving as an entryway at the back of the structure. On the bottom floor, a covered porch ran the whole length of the house, while the second floor was structured with a roofed balcony. The thick walls were covered with stucco and painted a dark beige, while the flat-style roof consisted of board shingles weathered to a pale gray. The windows and doors were framed with wood that had once been black, but had long ago faded to a charcoal color.

It was a gorgeous example of a traditional hacienda ranch house and made even more charming by the inner courtyard landscaped with succulents, a tall saguaro and three large Joshua trees. Years ago, the Hollisters would often drive down in the dead of winter and enjoy a few days of the warmer climate. But plenty had changed since then. Joel was gone and all of the Hollister siblings, except for Camille, were married with children. And she would've been a wife by now, too, if Graham Danby hadn't changed his mind about marrying her.

That last thought was going through Matthew Waggoner's mind as he let himself through the wrought-iron gate that connected the sandstone wall and walked around the edge of the courtyard to the back door of the house.

Although he had keys to both front and back doors, Matthew was loath to use either one. Even though the house didn't belong solely to Camille, it was currently her residence, and he didn't want to barge in as though he had a right to the place.

After knocking on the back door, he glanced over his shoulder to a view of the ranch yard. From where Matthew stood, he could see a corner of the bunkhouse. Smoke was coming from the chimney and though it was well after ten, lights blazed in the windows. Barely fifteen minutes had passed since Matthew and the other men had called it a night. Now he figured they were all pestering Curly, who'd reluctantly taken on the job of cook, to fix them something to eat. As for Matthew, he didn't care if he ate a bite of anything. After the exhausting day he'd put in, all he wanted was a mattress and pillow.

The sound of the door creaking open caused his head to turn back to the house, and he suddenly found himself staring straight into Camille Hollister's face.

"Hello, Matthew."

"Hello, Camille."

A long stretch of silence passed, and all the while Matthew could hear a pack of coyotes yipping in the far distance, while closer to the house the penned cattle continued to bawl in protest.

Red Bluff was wild, rugged land and far from town or any kind of civilization, yet Camille lived here alone. What kind of twenty-eight-year-old woman made such a choice? The kind that was still nursing a broken heart?

He was trying to answer that question as she pushed the door wide and gestured for him to enter.

"Please, come in," she said. "I hope you haven't been knocking long. I dozed off on the couch. And the walls of the house are so thick it's hard to hear outside noises."

"I've only been here a minute." He stepped into the kitchen and blinked as she switched on a light hanging over the table. The room basically looked the same as it had the last time he'd been in the house, and that had been at least five or six years ago when Blake and Maureen had come down to stay a few days during fall roundup. For the past couple of years since Camille had moved in, Matthew and the men had steered wide of the ranch house.

"Sorry it's so late," he apologized. "I hope you didn't wait up just to let me in. I have a key."

She shut and locked the door, then walked over to where he stood. Matthew desperately tried not to notice the soft scent of flowers emanating from her hair and skin. It swirled around him and pulled his gaze to the gentle features of her face. She'd always been beautiful, but tonight she seemed to be even lovelier. Or was that because he'd not seen her in two long years?

"I didn't know whether you had a key or not. But it's no big deal," she said. "I usually don't get into bed until eleven anyway. Uh, would you like something to eat, or drink?"

"Don't worry about feeding me," he said. "I can fend for myself."

Her lips pursed together as though his answer offended her. "I didn't ask whether you could fend for yourself. It's a simple question. Are you hungry?"

She sounded so much like her mother, Maureen, he very nearly smiled. "Put like that, then yes, I'm hungry. But it's late and I'm tired. I'll grab something in the morning."

To his complete surprise, she clamped a hand around his arm. "Come with me," she said in a tone that warned him not to argue.

With her hand still burning a ring around his forearm, she guided him out of the kitchen. Before they reached the living room, she turned to the left and down a long hallway. Soft nightlights glowed from the baseboards and illuminated the rich tile on the floor. The walls were decorated with huge framed prints of the

Hollisters and the ranch hands doing various jobs here on Red Bluff.

She came to a sudden stop and pointed to one of the photos. "Just in case you're wondering if you're in any of these, here's one of you and Daddy. Remember that day?"

Shoving the brim of his hat back off his forehead, he stepped forward and peered at the picture. The image struck him hard.

"I've never seen this before," he said, his voice thick. "That horse is Dough Boy. He always bucked when you first got on him, so you had to be ready. Your father was riding him that day. We'd been gathering cattle in Lizard Canyon. Dough Boy was a real gentleman that day and Joel joked that he was the only cowboy on the ranch who could ride him."

"Yeah," she murmured thoughtfully. "Isn't it ironic that Daddy was on Major Bob the day he was killed instead of Dough Boy?"

Ironic? No. Matthew's views on Joel Hollister's death were no different than those of the family. No matter the horse he'd been riding, Joel would've died that day because someone had meant to kill him.

"I'd rather remember other days. Not that one," Matthew told her.

He heard her long sigh, and then the hand on his arm was urging him toward the nearest door to their right.

"This will be your room while you're here. I could've given you one overlooking the courtyard, but I figured you'd rather have the best mattress than the best view."

She pushed the door open and gestured for him to enter. Matthew felt like he was stepping into the room of a Mexican villa. The dark wooden furniture was heavy, the bed fashioned with four posts that nearly touched the ceiling. The tall headboard was intricately carved with the images of blazing suns, fighting bulls and trailing moonflowers. At the windows, thick burgundy-colored drapes were pulled to show a moonlit view of the desert mountains.

"Is that one bag all you have?" she asked.

"No. I have another case in the truck, but I don't need to unpack it tonight."

She nodded. "Well, just put your things wherever you like. There's a private bath through the door over by the closet. Make yourself at home."

He moved into the room while thinking with each step that he didn't belong in this house with this woman. They were both too rich for his blood. But being here was Blake's order and Matthew would bend over backwards to make the man happy. Not because he was his boss, but because Blake and his three brothers were like his blood brothers and always would be.

"Thanks. This is nice." He placed his duffel bag on the green-and-burgundy-patterned spread, then glanced over to her. "I—uh—think I ought to tell you that it wasn't my idea for me to stay here in the house."

"I never imagined it was."

Although he didn't know why, he felt the need to further explain. "Blake sent an extra man this time. There wasn't enough room for another bed in the bunkhouse."

She shrugged. "No problem. You won't bother me. And I'm gone most of the time so I shouldn't bother you."

Maybe not, but she sure as hell was bothering him right now. Strange how he'd not remembered her looking exactly like this. Her hair had grown and now reached the back of her waist. She was wearing some sort of loose flowing pants made of flower-printed material. The top that matched had a low V-neck, and when she turned a certain way he could see a hint of cleavage. Before she'd left Three Rivers she'd been extremely slender. Now she was voluptuous and it sure looked good on her, he thought.

"Don't worry. The men and I have so much work to do while we're down here that I doubt our paths will cross much."

Her plush lips curved into something close to a smile. "Go wash up and come back to the kitchen. I'll have something for you to eat."

He wanted to argue with her, but he knew it would be a losing battle. And why bother? After tonight, he expected she'd leave him to see after himself.

"All right. Thanks."

Chapter Two

Back in the kitchen, Camille opened the fridge and pulled out a ribeye steak she'd been marinating. As she heated an iron skillet and tossed in several hunks of butter, her mind spun with thoughts of Matthew Waggoner.

When had he turned into such a hunk of a man? She'd not exactly remembered him being so broad through the shoulders, his waist so trim, or his legs being that long and corded with muscles. And that blond, blond hair. He used to wear it buzzed up the sides. Now it was long and curled against the back of his neck and around his ears. But it wasn't just the hair or the breadth and strength of his body that had caught Camille's attention. There was something different about his rugged features. Perhaps it was the hardened glint in his gray eyes or the unyielding thrust of his jaw. Whatever it was, he looked too damned sexy for her peace of mind.

A mocking laugh trilled inside her head. *Just what I thought, Camille. You weren't really serious when you swore off men for the next ten years. You take one look at the Three Rivers foreman and you start swooning like a silly schoolgirl. Snap out of it, girl! You have nowhere else to run to!*

Run? No, Camille thought as she shoved the voice right out of her head. She wasn't going anywhere. And she wasn't afraid of her heart or anything else getting tangled up with Matthew. She'd known the man since she was a teenager and they'd hardly been anything more than acquaintances. Nothing was different now. Nothing at all.

She was still frying the steak when Matthew returned to the kitchen. He'd not changed out of the clothes he'd been working in, but he'd knocked off most of the dust. The long sleeves were rolled up to expose thick forearms burnt to the same nut-brown color of his face. He'd left his hat behind and Camille decided he must have run wet hands through his hair. Damp tendrils fell across his forehead and tickled the tops of his ears.

Just looking at him caused a flutter in her stomach.

"Go ahead and have a seat at the table, Matthew. Would you like a glass of wine or a beer?"

He pulled out a chair at the end of the table and sank into it. "A beer would be nice."

She carried a tall bottle and a glass mug over to the table and set both in front of him. "If you're wondering if I've turned into a drinker, don't worry. I mostly keep beer and wine to cook with."

"I wasn't thinking anything like that," he said.

She went back over to the gas range and switched off the blaze under the steak. By now the French fries were done and she loaded a pile of them along with the steak onto a large plate, then gathered a small bowl of tossed salad from the fridge.

When she set the whole thing in front of him, he cut his gray eyes up to her. "This is overdoing it, Camille."

Her heart was beating fast and it had nothing to do with his words and everything to do with the way he was looking at her, the way he smelled, the way his masculine presence filled up the small kitchen.

"What's wrong? I cooked the steak too long?"

He shook his head. "This is not a part of the deal."

"What deal? I didn't know we had a deal?"

He made a flustered sound as he reached for the knife and fork she'd placed next to his plate. "I'm not your guest. I'm here to work cattle."

"You don't have to tell me why you're here, Matthew." She left the table and walked over to the cabinets. "You've been doing this for years."

Yes, fourteen years to be exact. When Matthew had first gone to work for Three Rivers Ranch, Joel had brought him and four other hands down here to Red Bluff. The work had been exhausting, but the special time working closely with Joel had changed Matthew's life. He'd found the father he'd always needed and the home he'd never had.

She plunked a bottle of salad dressing along with a pair of salt and pepper shakers in front of him. "You want any ketchup or steak sauce?"

Her question pulled him out of his memories and with a tired sigh, he pulled the plate toward him. "No, thanks. This is good."

Once he started to eat, he thought she might leave

the kitchen and go on about her business. Instead, she pulled out the chair angled to his right elbow.

"Looks like Blake sent plenty of cattle this time. I saw the extra pens."

He glanced at her. "He's been on a buying spree. When prices drop, your brother takes advantage."

She smiled wanly. "Blake always did know how to turn a profit."

The steak melted in his mouth, a fact that surprised Matthew. He would've never guessed Camille could do much in the kitchen. Reeva had ruled as the Three Rivers house cook for long before Camille had been born and the woman wasn't the sort who wanted to share the domain.

"I guess you've taken to living here on Red Bluff," he said. "You've been gone from Three Rivers for a long time."

She slanted him a shrewd look. "Did my family send you on a fishing expedition?"

He chewed another bite of steak before he answered. "That's funny. But I'm too tired to laugh."

"What's funny about it? You're a part of the family. You know as well as I do that they're trying to figure me out—or come up with a way to get me back to Three Rivers."

He glanced over to see a smirk on her face, but whether her ire was directed at him or her family he couldn't guess.

"I didn't ask you anything," he said. "I only made an observation. Guess the subject of you living here on Red Bluff is a prickly one."

"You know it is."

Deciding it took too much energy to talk to this woman, he focused on finishing the food on his plate.

Quietness settled around them until she spoke again. "Sorry, Matthew. I didn't mean to sound so—defensive. It's just that I'm beyond weary of answering my family's questions. They can't accept that I want to live here and leave it at that."

"They think you're still pining over that Danby guy and that makes them worry about you."

Her lips pressed to a thin line. "For your information and theirs, Graham Danby is a thing of the past," she said firmly. "I'm perfectly happy living single and I have no interest in the male population in Yavapai County, or here in Cochise County, or anywhere else for that matter."

"Okay."

His simple response didn't ease the frown on her face.

She said, "Since my personal life seems to be fair game, maybe it's time I asked you a few questions. Like have you ever gotten over your failed marriage with Renee?"

Although he was stunned that she'd brought up the subject of his divorce, he realized he couldn't tell her to mind her own business. Not without looking like an ass.

"Renee who?"

She snorted. "You can't fool me, Matthew. That was what—at least ten years ago and you've never remarried. You're either still crazy in love with the woman or too scared to try marriage again."

He stabbed his fork into the fries. "Your first assumption is dead wrong. Your second one is not exactly right, either."

Her vivid blue eyes continued to peruse his face, and Matthew wondered what she was looking for. A sign of weakness? A crack in his armor? Well, if anyone could find it, she could.

He said, "I'll admit that when Renee and I divorced it knocked me off my feet."

"It shouldn't have," she said bluntly. "I could've told you before you ever married her that she was all fluff."

He scowled at her. "How would you know that? You were only a teenager back then."

"A girl doesn't have to reach the age of twenty before she learns how to spot a female piranha."

He grunted. "Men are slow learners."

A faint smile touched her face. "The last I heard you were dating a redhead from Yarnell. Are you getting serious about her?"

"No. I haven't seen her in more than a year. And I'm not planning on getting serious about anyone. I'm going to leave marriage up to you and Vivian, and your brothers."

Her face went void. "Leave me off that list, Matthew. The chance of me ever marrying is as about as good as snow falling here on Red Bluff. And that'll be a cold day in hell."

The bitterness in Camille's voice matched the feelings he'd carried around inside him for all these years. He understood the humiliation she'd gone through when Danby had chosen another woman over her. He'd felt that same sting when Renee had left him high and dry.

"So what do you with yourself now?" he asked. "I imagine it's awfully quiet around here when the ranch hands aren't around."

Faint surprise arched one of her delicate brows. "You

mean none of the family has mentioned my job to you? That's a shocker."

He shook his head. "No. You found an office job over in Benson or Tucson?"

Rolling her eyes, she got up from the table and walked over to the cabinets located directly behind him.

"Lord no! I'd have to be starving to death before I ever work in an office again."

He glanced over his shoulder to see she was filling a coffeemaker with grounds and water.

"Why? That is the reason you went to college," he stated the obvious. "What are you going to do? Let all that education go to waste?"

He didn't know why he'd let himself be sucked into such a personal conversation with this woman. Maybe because in the quieter moments of his life, he'd often thought of her and hoped she was happy.

With the coffee dripping, she walked back over to the table and took her seat. "No. That isn't why I went to college. I worked to get my degree in business management because that's what Daddy wanted for me and I promised him I would."

"He died shortly after you graduated high school. He would've never known if you'd chosen to take a different path."

"Maybe not. But I would have known it. I made a promise to him and I wasn't about to break it."

Her loyalty to her father didn't surprise Matthew. Even though Camille had never been the cowgirl that her mother and sister were, she'd been very close to Joel, and he to her. Perhaps because she was the baby of the family, or perhaps it was the fact that she was so different from Vivian that Joel had been extra protective of his youngest.

"So if you don't have an office job, what are you doing?" he asked.

"I'm a cook in a diner over by Dragoon."

Hearing she'd been hired on as a cook was almost too much for his tired brain to register. "The population can't be three hundred there. I wasn't aware it had an eating place. I only remember it having a few houses and old buildings."

"It's there. Not far from the interstate. Lots of folks from Wilcox traveling through to Benson and Tucson stop to eat. The building isn't much to look at and we mostly just have short orders, but the customers seem to enjoy it and I love working there."

The moment she'd started to talk about her job, the taut expression on her face had relaxed.

"To tell you the truth, Camille, I didn't even know you could cook until tonight." He gestured to his empty plate. "By the way, it was delicious."

"Thanks. That's what I like to hear." She leaned back in the chair and crossed her arms across her breasts. "I think Mom regrets that Reeva allowed me to help her in the kitchen. I probably don't have to tell you that she expects more out of me than being a cook."

"Why? Because you're a Hollister?"

She wrinkled her nose. "Isn't that enough?"

"Yeah," he said after a moment of thought. "It's a lot to live up to."

She smiled and the expression on her face was suddenly sunny and sweet and exactly the way he remembered her when he'd first come to Three Rivers. The sight sent a poignant pang rifling through him and he hated himself for being so sentimental. Especially with Camille. Of all the Hollister siblings, she'd often been more of a rebel than Holt.

She said, "I actually think you understand."

"Why wouldn't I? I'm not a Hollister, but Joel always expected a lot from me. More than I thought I was capable of. It was never easy trying to live up to the expectations he had of me. I tried. But I honestly don't know if it was ever enough."

"It was more than enough. You were like a son to him."

Hearing those words from Camille twisted something deep inside him, and he wondered why seeing her again was bringing up thoughts he'd tried so hard to keep in the past.

She picked up his empty plate and carried it over to the sink. While she was gone, Matthew rubbed both hands over his face. These next two weeks were going to be even longer than he'd first imagined, he thought. And he was wondering just how early he'd need to get up in the morning to avoid running into her before he left the house. Or how late he would need to stay out at night until she went to bed.

Her fragrance drifted to him and he dropped his hands to see she'd returned to the table with a small plate of chocolate pie and a cup of coffee.

"I realize you're tired, but I thought you might like dessert."

"Did you make this?" he asked.

She gave him a half smile. "Yes. I bake pies for the diner, too. They're a big hit with the customers, so the owner pays me extra for doing it."

She's simply staying on Red Bluff until she gets her head on straight.

Blake couldn't be more wrong, Matthew thought as the man's remark came back to him. Camille didn't look or sound like she was suffering a broken heart. In fact, she appeared to be content. If the Hollisters were expecting her to return to Three Rivers to cry on their shoulders, they were all in for a rude surprise.

"This is very good," he said after he'd taken the first bite. "It tastes like Reeva's."

"Thanks. That's the best compliment you could've given me."

"Are you not having any?"

"No. I've already eaten my quota of sweets for today."

She propped her elbows on the table and rested folded hands beneath her chin. "So, what's been happening at Three Rivers lately? Mom mostly keeps me informed, but I think she purposely avoids talking about certain things."

"Like what?"

"Like my brothers' and sister's babies. She thinks hearing about them makes me sad because I don't have any." She moved her head back and forth. "And I guess in a way, it does. But if I'm meant to have children I'll have them in due time."

She had the frankness of her mother and the practicality of her father, Matthew thought. Together, she was unlike any of her siblings.

"All the children are fine and it won't be long until Holt's baby arrives. It's going to be strange to hear him called Daddy."

"I'm very happy for him. And Isabelle is wonderful.

She's the perfect match for him," she said, then gave him a long, pointed look. "So, what about my brothers and their search into Dad's death?"

Matthew shook his head. "You know about that?"

"Mom and my brothers don't talk to me about it, but Vivian does. She says Mom clams up if she asks her anything about it and our brothers are obsessed with the subject."

"What do you think?" he asked curiously. "That they should continue to search for answers or leave the whole thing be?"

Sighing, she closed her eyes, and Matthew used the moment to study her face. She'd always had beautiful features but now they held a maturity that made her even more attractive. All he could think was how stupid Graham Danby had been to ask for his engagement ring back and how lucky Camille was that he had.

"Answers would be good, I suppose," she finally said. "But in the end it won't bring Daddy back. That's harder for me to live with than the not knowing."

"Your brothers want justice."

"Don't you mean vengeance?"

"Maybe. I'd definitely like to serve up a little vengeance of my own."

He rose from the chair and picked up the dirty dessert plate along with his cup. "Thanks for the meal, Camille. I really need to get to bed. The men are going to be saddled up by five thirty. That's going to come pretty early."

Nodding, she rose along with him and reached for the dishes in his hands. "I'll take care of those. You go on."

He started out of the room, then paused at the doorway to look back at her. "Camille, from now on you really need to let me fend for myself."

The faint smile on her face said it didn't matter what he said. Ultimately she'd do whatever she wanted to do.

"Good night, Matthew."

"Good night, Camille."

The next morning at the diner in Dragoon, Camille slid a stack of pancakes and a pair of over-easy eggs onto a warm plate, placed it on a tall counter and slapped a bell to alert Peggy that the order was ready.

The waitress immediately snatched up the plate and hurried away. Camille reached for the next order and recognized with a sigh of relief there wasn't a next order. For the moment she was caught up.

"Wow! What a run. I haven't had time to draw in a good breath!" Peggy exclaimed as she pushed through the swinging door and into the small kitchen. "Where are all of these people coming from?"

Camille sank onto a wooden stool and looked over at the tall woman with a messy black bun pinned to the top of her head. In her early thirties, with big brown eyes and a wide smile that hid all kinds of disappointments in her life, Peggy had become a dear friend to Camille.

"The few times I glanced out to the dining area, I didn't spot one familiar face. They must all be travelers."

"Hmm, good thing, I guess. If we had to depend on customers from Dragoon, we might as well close up the doors." She looked over at Camille and shook her head. "Honey, I'll never understand why you're wasting yourself in this lonely little spot in the desert."

She smiled wanly at her friend. "Because I like this

little lonely spot in the desert. I've tried the big city thing. The traffic and hustle and bustle. The business suits and high heels. Yes, I made a nice salary, but it wasn't worth it to me."

Peggy tightened the bobby pins holding her bun. "Hmm. I wouldn't mind trying it someday. Just to see what it was like to live in a house that wasn't filled with dust and to smell like a woman instead of burnt coffee and cooking grease."

"Who cares about dust?" Camille retorted. "And if men were honest, most of them would say they'd rather have a woman who smelled like food instead of flowers."

"And who around here wants a man?" Peggy asked with a cynical laugh. "I certainly don't! And even if I did, the single male population around here is darned scarce."

Camille thoughtfully regarded her friend. If Peggy took more pains with her appearance, she'd be a knockout. But makeup or a hairdo wouldn't take the jaded shadows from her eyes. Only deep-down happiness could do that.

"So it is, but that doesn't mean you should stop looking. You've told me before how much you'd like a child of your own," Camille reasoned. "You can't very well make one without a man."

Peggy slanted her a tired look. "There's always a fertility clinic."

Camille couldn't believe her friend would actually go to that length to have a baby on her own. "Are you saying you're ready to do that?"

Peggy shrugged. "Wouldn't that be better than putting up with a creep who spouts words of love, then cheats every chance he gets?"

From what Peggy had told her, she'd been engaged once, but the guy had turned out to be a verbal abuser and she'd dumped him before the wedding plans could get started. After that misjudgment, she'd married a car salesman from Tucson, but a week after they'd gotten back from their honeymoon, he'd cheated on her. Given the briefness of the marriage, she'd gotten an annulment. Now she looked at men as though they all had horns and a forked tongue.

"Peggy, there's a good man out there just waiting for you to find him."

Peggy's short laugh was mocking. "Coming from you, Camille, that's very funny. A beauty like you, hiding yourself away." She pushed away from the work counter and started out of the kitchen, only to pause at the swinging doors. "By the way, what are you doing tonight? I thought I'd drive over to Benson and try to find something to wear to Gideon's Halloween party. Wanta come?"

"Gideon is having a party?"

Gideon was a seventy-five year old war veteran and widower who bussed the tables here at the diner. He was a happy-go-lucky guy, but Camille couldn't picture him throwing a Halloween party.

"His grandchildren are coming to visit and he wants to do something special for them, so I've offered to lend him a hand."

Any other time, Camille would have given her friend a quick yes. But she hated to think of Matthew dragging himself in tonight, exhausted and hungry, and her not being there to take care of him.

What the heck are you thinking, Camille? Matthew isn't your man. He's a grown man who's lived alone for years. He doesn't need you or anyone to take care of him!

The sardonic voice going off in her head couldn't have been more right, Camille thought. She'd be more than stupid to start planning her life around Matthew. In two weeks he'd be gone back to Three Rivers and she wouldn't see him again until next year. On the other hand, if she did want to spend any time with the foreman, she needed to make the most of the next fourteen days while he and the roundup crew were at Red Bluff.

Rising from the stool, she picked up a spatula. As she scraped grease and meat particles from the flat grill, she said, "Thanks for asking, Peggy, but the crew from Three Rivers is at Red Bluff now and I feel like I need to be there."

Peggy frowned. "Be there for what? I've never known of you doing ranch work."

Normally, the woman's remark would have rolled off Camille's back, but for some reason it stung today. "Well, I have been known to ride a horse and herd cows. I just haven't done that sort of thing in a long time. Anyway, I just meant they might need me to run errands or something."

The waitress shrugged. "Okay, you go ahead and play cowgirl. I've got to find something spooky to wear."

Peggy disappeared through the swinging doors, and Camille dropped the spatula and swiped a hand across her forehead. She honestly didn't know what was coming over her.

Ever since Matthew had shown up at her door last

night, she'd been thrown into a strange state of mind. All of a sudden she'd forgotten about keeping a cool distance from the man. Seeing him had evoked all sorts of poignant memories. Seeing him had been like a sweet homecoming, and his company had filled her with a sense of belonging. Which didn't make any sense. She'd never been close to the Three Rivers foreman before. So why did she want to be close to him now?

The cowbell over the door to the diner clanged, breaking into Camille's thoughts, and moments later, Peggy was pinning up two orders for chicken-fried steak.

Glad for the distraction, Camille went to work. But it wasn't enough to make her forget about seeing Matthew again.

Chapter Three

The five ranch hands working with Matthew on Red Bluff were a good, dependable crew ranging in ages from twenty to sixty. Curly, the designated cook for the bunch, was the oldest, and Pate, a tall lanky cowboy with a shock of black hair and a lazy grin, was the youngest. In between, there was Scott, in his midthirties and a wizard with a lariat. Abel, a redhead with a face full of freckles and a boisterous personality to match, was 25, but already experienced in ranch work. TooTall was a Native American from the Yavapai tribe and a skilled horseman, who often worked alongside Holt. A quiet loner, TooTall had never told anyone his age. Just by looking, Matthew guessed him to be thirty, but he wouldn't be surprised to learn he was much older.

This morning Matthew had ordered Curly and Abel to remain behind at the ranch yard to tend to the penned cattle, while the others rode with him to hunt for steers. The sky was cloudless, and by midday the Arizona sun was blazing down on the jagged hills and piers of red rock that made up the southern range of the ranch.

For the past few hours, Matthew and the men had been rounding up steers from the thick patches of chaparral and prickly pear. So far they'd gathered twenty head and penned them in a wooden corral built next to a tall rock bluff. It had been a productive morning, but Matthew knew for certain there were at least ten more steers somewhere on this section of range. It wouldn't necessarily hurt to turn the cows and calves in with those last ten, but Blake wanted them back at Three Rivers and Matthew wasn't the kind of man to leave anything undone.

"My arms feel like a pair of pincushions," Pate said. "I'll bet I've been stuck fifty times with thorns and pear spines."

Matthew looked over at the young cowhand sitting next to him beneath the meager shade of a Joshua tree. A half hour ago, the group had stopped for lunch, and now the horses stood dozing and resting in the shade while the men finished the food they'd pulled from their saddlebags.

"Make sure you get all those thorns out tonight," Matthew told him. "They'll fester if you don't."

"I should've worn my jacket, but it's too damned hot." Pate turned his head and squinted at the western horizon. "If you ask me, it's going to take another day or two to find the other steers. There's too many arroyos and rock bluffs where they can hide. And we've not spotted hide nor hair of them."

Pate was a good worker, but he still had lots to learn.

The same way Matthew had all those years ago when Joel had taken him under his wing. "Whether it takes a week or ten days, we'll get them," he told the young cowboy.

Pate whistled under his breath. "At that rate it'll be Thanksgiving before we get back to Three Rivers!"

Matthew's grunt was full of humor. "What's the matter? You don't like sleeping on a cot, or eating Curly's pork 'n' beans?"

"I'm not particularly fond of either one." The young man grimaced, then slanted Matthew a sly glance. "Guess you were comfy in the big hacienda. What's that place like inside?"

"Nice."

Pate frowned. "That's all you can say? Nice?"

Matthew shrugged. "I didn't take that much notice to the house."

"No. Don't guess you would when you got Camille Hollister to look at."

Matthew stabbed him with a steely glare. "I'm going to forget that you said that, Pate. But if I ever hear it again, I'll knock your damned head off."

The young cowboy looked stunned and just a little scared. "What the hell is wrong with you?"

"You heard me."

Matthew stuffed the leftovers of his lunch into a set of saddlebags, then carried them over to the dun he was riding. After tying them onto the back of the saddle, he made a circling motion with his arm.

"Let's go. We'll search this draw until we reach the southern fence. If we don't find anything there, we'll haul the ones we have into the ranch yard and start again tomorrow."

Nearly an hour later, Matthew was riding along the edge of a rocky wash when Pate reined his horse alongside him.

"You find anything?" Matthew asked him.

"No. None of us have seen a sign of a steer." He lifted his hat and swiped a hand through his thick black hair. "I—uh—I just wanted to tell you I'm sorry if I offended you earlier. I wasn't meaning to be disrespectful about Miss Hollister. I just meant—well, I've never met her, but some of the men say she's really pretty."

Matthew let out a long sigh. Pate couldn't possibly know that he'd spent all night and most of today trying to get Camille out of his head, but everywhere he looked he was seeing her face and thinking about all the things she'd said to him. She wasn't the same woman who'd left Three Rivers more than two years ago and this new Camille was eating at his common sense.

"Forget it, Pate. My fuse is running short and—staying in the ranch house is a prickly subject with me."

"Why? I mean, this is hard work. You deserve the extra comfort."

"I don't like being away from you men."

"But you're the boss."

"Yeah. And sometimes that means doing things you don't want to do."

Pate shook his head. "No need to worry about us men, Matthew. We won't let you down. When we get back to Three Rivers, Blake will be proud of the job we've done down here."

Proud. Pate's word drifted through Matthew's mind later that night as he let himself in the back door of the ranch house. Would Blake be proud if he knew his foreman had carnal thoughts toward his sister? Like hell. He'd probably be hopping mad. Or would he?

The Hollisters were far from snobs. Even though they owned two of the biggest ranches in the state of Arizona, they treated everyone as equals. Unless a person crossed them, which didn't happen often.

"Matthew, is that you?"

He was about to turn down the hallway to his room when he heard Camille's voice and looked over his shoulder to see her standing in the arched doorway that led to the living room. Tonight she was wearing a long flowing skirt with swirls of green and purple and turquoise. Her blouse was green velvet and cinched in at the waist with a belt of silver conchas. If possible she looked even lovelier than she had last night, and the sight of her caused his stomach to clench in a nervous knot.

"Yes. I used my key so I wouldn't disturb you."

She walked down the hallway to where he stood, and for one wild second he wondered how she would react if he pulled her into his arms and kissed her. It was something he'd often thought about over the years. Kissing Camille. Making love to Camille. It was a crazy fantasy and one that he definitely couldn't act upon.

"Trying to sneak past me?" she asked.

Her smile was shrewd, but held just enough warmth to let him know it didn't matter if he had been trying to avoid her. One way or the other, she was going to catch him.

He shrugged. "It didn't work, did it?"

She shook her head. "When you get washed up I have something for you in the kitchen."

"Camille, I told you—"

"I know what you told me," she interrupted. "But

as long as you're here, you're going to eat what I give you. No arguments."

His nostrils flared at the sweet fragrance drifting from her body. "It's Saturday night. Why aren't you out doing whatever it is you do for entertainment?"

She smiled. "I've already had plenty of entertainment at the diner today. Why? Are you planning on going out tonight? They've opened a nice club on the edge of Benson. I hear they have a great live band. You might want to check it out and kick up your heels."

It was already past ten. Did she think he was up to that sort of nightlife after sitting in the saddle all day, popping brush?

"I'm thirty-three, not twenty-three, Camille."

Laughing, she turned and left him standing there staring after her.

When Matthew appeared in the kitchen some fifteen minutes later, Camille set a plate of enchiladas, Spanish rice and refried beans in front of him, along with several warm flour tortillas.

"I suppose you just happened to whip this up in your spare time," he said as he took his seat at the table.

"Listen Matthew, don't go getting the idea that my cooking is something special I'm doing just for you. I'm not a sandwich person. Nor do I like things out of a box. I cook for myself. You get what's left over. Does that make you feel any better?"

"Okay. I won't say another word about it."

She clapped her hands together. "Yay! We're finally getting somewhere."

She placed a beer in front of him, then opened one for herself and took the same seat she'd sat in last night.

Apparently she had no plans to leave him alone while he ate.

"You could eat in the dining room if you like," she offered. "But it's much nicer in here."

"This is fine with me."

"So, how did things go today?" she asked. "I noticed there were lots of cattle still penned out by the barns."

Her long hair was loose and it slid over her shoulder as she rested a forearm against the table. When he'd first gone to work at Three Rivers, Camille had been in high school. She'd worn her hair bobbed to chin-length and it had matched her perky personality. The years since had transformed her into a very sensual female. One who was impossible for Matthew to ignore.

He said, "We've not moved any yet. We've been rounding up steers. Blake wants all of them shipped back to Three Rivers. So that has to be done before we turn the cows out on the range."

"And after that?"

He finished chewing a bite of tortilla before he spoke. "We'll move certain herds to different areas of the ranch. It all depends on the available grazing." He glanced at her. "We're doing the same job this year that we did last year. You didn't come around or ask questions then."

Shaking her head, she said, "You men have enough to do without a woman showing up and getting in the way. Unless you're talking about Mom, or Vivian, or Isabelle. They all know what they're doing on the back of a horse or in a cow lot. I was never good at any of that."

Her admission surprised him. "You never wanted to learn?"

"I tried, but I usually ended up getting in trouble more than being helpful. Once I dropped my rein, and when I leaned forward to pick it up, my spur hit the flank of the horse. I ended up being bucked off into the fence and got two black eyes from the wild ride. Another time I was helping at the branding fire and somehow got my arm caught between the rope and the calf. I wore a cast for two months after that incident."

"Those things happen all the time in ranch work."

"Yes, but they never happen to Mom or Viv. They're smart enough to avoid trouble."

He leveled a challenging look at her. "So you're afraid to get out among the cows and horses."

Her spine stiffened to a straight line. "I'm not afraid of anything!"

"Hmm. Maureen will be glad to hear that. She thinks you're afraid to come home."

Her chin thrust forward. "I am home. Red Bluff is Hollister range, too, you know."

Yeah, he knew. Just like he knew that she was like a piece of dynamite. Jostle her too much and she might just explode in his face.

"So, what are you afraid of, Matthew?" she tossed the question at him. "Getting burned again by another piece of fluff like Renee?"

Compared to the heat of the day, the kitchen was cool. So why did he feel a sheen of sweat collecting beneath the collar of his shirt?

"I've learned about women since Renee," he said, his gaze fixed firmly on the food in front of him.

He heard her let out a long sigh.

"I've learned about men since Graham, too," she said, then reached over and gave his forearm a gentle squeeze.

"Ouch! Damn!"

She jerked her hand back and stared at him in comical confusion. "Oh! I guess I don't know my own strength. Sorry if I hurt you."

He shook his head. "It's not you—I was in a lot of thorns and cacti today. I think some are still stuck in my arms."

Concern wiped the humor from her face and she quickly rose to her feet. "Finish eating," she instructed. "And don't get up until I get back."

She was bossier than Blake ever thought about being, Matthew thought. But what the hell, giving in was easier than trying to argue with her.

A few minutes later, as he shoveled in the last bite of food from his plate, Camille returned carrying a large straw basket.

She placed it on the table and then, pushing his dirty plate aside, ordered him to roll up his sleeves.

Seeing the basket was full of first aid items, he let out a loud groan.

"No! I don't need doctoring! Forget it!"

Her pretty lips formed a tight line as she stared at him. "I'm not forgetting anything. And I'm not going to hurt you! So quit being a big baby."

"The guys that rode with me today also got thorns and stickers. Are you going to go out to the bunkhouse and treat them, too?" he demanded.

"No. The men in the bunkhouse can help each other. You only have me."

She began to lay out an assortment of cotton swabs, ointment, peroxide and a pair of tweezers. Matthew bit back a groan, and rolled up the sleeves of his denim shirt past his elbows.

"Hell, Camille, you act like I've never been stuck with a thorn before," he muttered. "This happens all the time."

"Maybe it does. But I happen to know that mesquite thorns are poisonous to humans. If you don't get them out and disinfect the spot, it will become infected."

"I know all that. I told the men to be careful."

"Humph. Guess you think your hide is so tough you're immune," she said.

She sat down and reached for the arm nearest to her. Matthew tried to ignore the feel of her hands on his bare flesh, but it was impossible to do, and after a moment, he decided to quit fighting the sensation and simply enjoy it.

Bending her head, she carefully studied the back of his forearm. "This is awful. It's no wonder you yelled when I squeezed your arm. I see three, maybe four thorns still stuck in the flesh."

"We rode through thick brush today."

"Guess you were wearing your chaps." She picked up the tweezers and, after disinfecting them, attempted to pull out one of the longer thorns.

He said, "I don't leave home without them."

"Good thing. Otherwise your legs would be full of these things."

And Matthew couldn't imagine her hands touching his legs. No. That would be more than he could handle.

"This is probably going to hurt," she warned. "I'm going to have to probe with a needle."

"Go ahead. You're a long distance from my heart."

She lifted her head and their gazes locked.

"Really?" she asked. "I never believed you had one of those things."

He had one, all right, Matthew thought. And at the

moment it was banging against his ribs with the desperation of a trapped bird.

"You think I'm a rock—or something?"

Her gaze fell to his lips and for a crazy second he thought she was going to lean forward and kiss him. But his thinking must have been dead wrong because all of a sudden she dropped her gaze back to his arm.

"Or something," she murmured. "Except for Daddy, I always thought you never felt much about anyone or thing."

A hollow sensation spread through his chest and made his voice stilted when he spoke. "Joel was the first man who ever treated me like I was more than a doormat. He taught me that I was just as worthy as the next man and just as capable if I wanted to be. He changed my life."

She stopped the probing and, clasping her hands warmly over his arm, she lifted her gaze to his. "Daddy was special like that. But I— I'm missing something, Matthew. What about the uncle who raised you?"

He grimaced. "I'm surprised you knew about him."

"I don't. I mean, I remember Daddy saying you came from Gila Bend and that an uncle had raised you. That's all I ever knew."

"Odin Waggoner was a bastard and his brother, my father, was no better."

Her eyes were full of questions as she studied his face, and Matthew wanted to tell her that he didn't talk to anyone about his growing-up years. But that wasn't entirely right. He used to talk to Joel about them. Because he knew the big-hearted rancher had understood and never looked down on him for being raised in a dysfunctional family.

"Well, guess you couldn't put your feelings about them any plainer than that."

The questions in her eyes were now shadowed with something like sorrow. That wasn't what Matthew wanted or needed from her.

"No use trying to make something ugly sound pretty. When I was just a little boy, my father would leave for months at a time, to work in the copper mines, or so my mother would say. He supposedly would send money to her to keep me and my older sister fed and clothed and a roof over our heads. But if he did, it was very little. My mother worked cleaning houses for the more well-to-do families around Gila Bend. That's how we actually survived."

Shaking her head, she asked, "How did you end up with your uncle?"

He let out a long sigh. "Well, Mom eventually saw the writing on the wall and divorced Aaron, and not long afterwards, we got word that he'd been killed in a mining accident down in Bisbee. The news hardly caused a ripple through our house. My sister and I could only think that our mother was finally and truly free of the man. But a couple of years later, she developed a blood disease and died. And because my sister and I were still minors, we had to go live with Uncle Odin or be dealt out to foster homes."

"I take it that your uncle wasn't father material," she said quietly.

Matthew snorted. "He had about as much business trying to take care of two young kids as a rattlesnake with a nest full of bird eggs. As soon as Claire and I were old enough, we lit out of there. I wound up in Gila

Bend, and my sister didn't stop until she reached California. She lives in Bishop now."

"Is she married?"

"She was. But it didn't work out. I guess us Waggoners aren't built for marriage."

Something flickered in her eyes, but before he could figure out what she was thinking, her gaze returned to the thorns in his arm.

"So, how did you find your way up to Three Rivers Ranch?"

"It was branding time and Joel had put an ad in the Phoenix newspaper for dayworkers. I took a chance and drove up there. I knew it was a huge, respected ranch and I figured if I could get hired to work for a few days, the reference would help me get hired at a ranch that needed to fill full-time positions."

She continued to probe for the thorn. "After you came to Three Rivers I don't ever remember you leaving."

"No. To this day I'll never know what Joel saw in me. I was young and green with so much to learn."

She glanced up long enough to give him a faint smile. "Guess you did learn. Mom and Blake say they couldn't run the ranch without you."

"They won't have to try. I'd never leave Three Rivers." Renee had tried to pull him away, to drag him to California, where she thought there would be bigger and brighter things for both of them. But even his infatuation for his pretty young wife hadn't been enough to lure him away from the only real home he'd ever known.

"No," she said. "I don't expect you would."

Matthew didn't make any sort of reply, and for the next few minutes Camille concentrated on removing the thorns from his arms. After disinfecting the areas, she began to smooth ointment over the torn skin.

Her fingers were velvety soft, like a butterfly's wings, and he found himself mesmerized by the gentle touch. So much so that he hardly noticed when she rolled down his sleeves and snapped the cuffs back around his wrists.

"There," she said softly. "That should help, but you need to keep an eye on them."

"Thank you, Camille. You're a good nurse."

The smile on her face was a little mysterious and definitely tempting. "I'd rather be called a good cook."

As she started to gather up the medical supplies, Matthew rose to his feet. "All right. You're a good cook, too. Thanks for supper."

"Why don't you go on into the living room and make yourself comfortable. I'll bring you some dessert and coffee."

He didn't need dessert and coffee. Nor did he need to lounge around in her living room like he belonged there. What he needed was to get as much distance as he could from the woman. If he didn't, he was going to end up doing something very stupid. Like kiss her.

"It's getting late. I really should go to bed," he said.

"Tomorrow is Sunday."

"That doesn't change anything for me and the men. We're heading out again at five thirty."

Disappointment caused her features to droop. "Oh. I thought I might talk you into going to church with me. It's a simple nondenominational church over by Dragoon."

Matthew truly would've liked going with her. Attending church with the Hollisters was a routine he'd never broken since he'd gone to work for the family. It gave him a feeling of togetherness and a sense of belonging.

"I'll try to go while I'm here. Maybe next Sunday. Okay?"

He didn't deserve the wide smile she gave him. "Okay. So you go sit. I'll be there in a minute."

She practically shooed him out of the kitchen, and Matthew found his way through a wide arched doorway and into the living room. The long room was mostly dark, with only two small table lamps lighting the area around a red leather couch and matching armchair. Across from the leather furniture, another couch and two armchairs were covered in a brown, nubby-type fabric. At the far end of the room, a TV was playing without the sound. Currently, there was an old Western on the screen. A group of cowboys were riding frantically to turn a stampeding herd of cattle.

As Matthew took a seat on the leather couch, he felt like he'd been run over by a stampeding herd just like the one on the TV screen. The thorn wounds on his arms stung, his shoulders ached from hours of riding, and his eyes burned from lack of sleep and squinting for hours in the fierce sun.

Leaning his head against the back of the couch, he closed his eyes and allowed his body to relax against the soft cushions. Outside he could hear the faint sound of the wind rattling the bougainvillea growing near the window, and farther away, the cattle continued to bawl. Not as loudly as last night, but they were still impatient to be on the open range.

The hypnotic sounds lulled him closer to the edge of sleep. He didn't know Camille was anywhere in the room until he felt her hand cupping the side of his face.

Chapter Four

The contact of Camille's hand against his cheek caused Matthew's eyes to fly open, and he looked around to see she was sitting close to his side, studying him with a mixture of concern and indulgence.

"Uh—sorry—I guess I must've dozed off."

"Yes. I could tell," she said softly. "I should've let you sleep. But I was afraid you'd stay here on the couch all night. And you need to be in bed."

He needed to be in bed, all right, Matthew thought. With her soft body beneath his. The erotic thought was a hopeless one, but he couldn't stop it from entering his mind and lingering there like a haunting dream.

"No need to worry," he said a little gruffly. "I'm awake now."

She dropped her hand and leaned forward toward the long coffee table in front of the couch. Matthew's head had cleared enough for him to see she'd brought a tray with two cups and two bowls. Apparently she was planning to have dessert with him.

"I brought coffee and bread pudding," she said. "I made it at the diner today and the customers seemed to enjoy it. You might like it, too."

She handed him the bowl and cup, and Matthew expected her to take hers to a different chair, or at least scoot a cushion or two down the couch from him. But she didn't. Instead, she remained by his side, so close that her shoulder and thigh were touching his.

Trying to ignore the tempting contact, he asked, "Are you the only cook at the diner?"

"Yes. It's not big enough to need more than one. Although the owner does have a backup in case I'm sick or need to take off for some reason. But that only happens rarely."

He spooned a bite of the pudding into his mouth and very nearly groaned at the delicious taste of cinnamon, raisins and custard-soaked bread. "This is delicious," he said, then shook his head with disbelief. "I'll be honest, Camille, I never thought of you as liking to cook. But apparently you do. I can see you take pride in your work."

"Thank you, Matthew. I do. It makes me happy to create something that gives people joy." She turned an eager look on him. "I'd like for you to come by and see the place before you leave. If you get a chance, that is."

"I'll try."

His half-hearted promise was enough to put a bright smile on her face, and Matthew was suddenly thinking about Blake's remark about Camille needing to get her head on straight. As far as Matthew could see, she had her head on perfectly straight. She wasn't crying, or pining, or miserable, and though the whole family believed she was hiding from life, she seemed to be doing just the opposite.

"I'll tell you a secret, Matthew. I've been having some serious talks with the man who owns the diner. The place is getting busier every day. And I want to expand the menu and start having daily specials. You know, the old-fashioned blue-plate thing—like meat loaf and pinto beans and that sort of home-style food. He's not sure he'd profit over the expense, but I'm sure he would. Since he's been hedging, I decided to offer to buy him out."

That sounded like she'd already made up her mind to stay here in Cochise County permanently, Matthew thought.

"And how did the owner react to your offer?"

"He's thinking on it. Which I understand. He's owned the place for twenty years. But he's talked a lot about retiring so that he and his wife can travel. I'm keeping my fingers crossed that he'll decide to sell."

Matthew scraped the last of the pudding from the bowl, then placed it on the coffee table. "That would be a huge responsibility," he said. "Not to mention the money involved."

"I have enough and more."

She wasn't bragging, simply stating a fact. But then, none of the Hollisters ever bragged about their bank accounts. Maybe about their babies, or a horse or a cow, but never about money.

"I've heard that cafés and restaurants are very risky businesses."

Nodding, she returned her bowl and cup to the tray

on the coffee table. "That's true. But this one is an old establishment. And if the blue plate thing didn't work out, I could always go back to just short orders—like it's always been."

Questions rolled through his mind. "What do you think your family would say about all this? Or have you already mentioned it to them?"

Surprise crossed her face. "Are you kidding? You're the only one I've told. And I hope you'll not say anything—for a while, at least."

Using his thumb and forefinger, he pulled an imaginary zipper in front of his lips. "My lips are sealed."

She grinned. "Thanks," she said. "It's not like I want to keep the idea from them completely. But I'd rather wait—until I see if Norman will decide to sell."

"I'll be honest, Camille, I don't think they'll be happy about your plans."

Shrugging, she glanced away. "No. They won't be happy at all. But that's okay." Turning her gaze back to him, she reached for his hands, and as her fingers curled tightly around his, she said, "Matthew, I need to do what makes me happy. I think you can understand that, don't you?"

"Sure." But did she really know what would make her happy? That's what her mother and siblings would be asking. As for Matthew, he understood that as the baby of the family, she'd had to contend with lots of pampering and sheltering. Too much of it, in fact. "But I'm not the one you need to convince."

Her lips twisted to a wry slant. "I suppose not. But it would make me feel better to hear you say I'm not going around with my head in the clouds."

She wanted his approval. He'd never expected that

from Camille. Maybe because Renee, and the few women he'd dated afterwards, had never seemed to care what he thought about their ideas or plans. All that mattered was their own opinions.

Before he knew what he was doing, his thumbs began to stroke the backs of her hands. "Your head is very much attached to the rest of your body, Camille. And the way I see it, you have a right to dream and hope and plan."

To his dismay, her eyes began to glisten with moisture, and then she leaned forward and pressed her lips against his cheek. "Thank you, Matthew. For being so sweet."

His resistance didn't crumble, it snapped like a dry twig beneath the heel of his boot. And suddenly his hands were in her hair, tugging her face away from his.

"I'm not sweet, Camille," he muttered roughly. "And I don't want to see tears in your eyes. I'd rather see fire! And need!"

She gasped, and then her eyes took on a look of wonder as they searched his face. Matthew's fingers began to move in her hair and in the back of his mind, he could only think how she felt like silk and satin and smelled like a meadow of sweet grass and sunshine.

"Oh, Matthew," she whispered. "Please, kiss me. Please."

Her plea struck something deep inside him, but he didn't take the time to ask himself what the feeling meant. Instead, he jerked her into his arms and wrapped his lips over hers.

There wasn't anything soft, or sweet, or tender about the union of their lips. It was like two winds colliding and merging to create one wild storm. He was so caught up in the hungry search of her lips, he barely heard the tiny moans in her throat or felt her arms curl tightly around his neck.

It wasn't until the two of them had fallen over onto the couch and his upper body was draped over hers that he finally came to his senses. But even then he was slow to pull his lips from hers.

"I—uh—think that turned out to be more than a kiss." His voice sounded like he'd been eating roofing tacks, but she didn't seem to notice. Instead, her hands tightened on the back of his neck and tugged until his mouth was hovering above hers.

"I'm glad that it turned out to be more," she whispered. "Because I want much more than a kiss from you, Matthew."

Just hearing her say such a thing caused a battle of wills to erupt inside him. "You don't know what you're saying."

He started to pull away from her, but she held on tight, until giving in to the tempting call of her lips became a far easier choice than forsaking the warmth of her arms.

This time when he kissed her, he tempered his need and made a slow but thorough exploration of her lips. He'd thought the calm connection would cool the fire racing along his veins, but instead, it was like pouring a slow, steady stream of gas on a simmering blaze.

By the time he managed to straighten himself away from her, a hot ache was gripping his loins and he was sure he'd never be able to get enough oxygen back into his lungs.

"I'm sorry, Camille. But that isn't going to happen." He still sounded hoarse and a hank of hair was stabbing his right eye. He shoved the curl back off his forehead and attempted to clear his throat. "This—whatever this was—should've never happened."

He was expecting her reaction to be angry or, at the very least, offended. But it was neither. Instead, she sat up, and with a soft little smile on her face, she touched fingers to his cheek.

"You don't believe that any more than I do."

He was trying to come up with some sort of response when she suddenly turned away and began gathering the dirty dishes on the coffee table.

Jarred by the sudden switch of her attention, he asked, "What are you doing?"

"Isn't it clear? I'm picking up our mess."

He stared at her in disbelief. Moments ago they'd been on their way to having sex. Now she was cleaning up their dessert dishes as though nothing had happened!

"And that's all you have to say?"

She stood and picked up the tray from the coffee table. "No. I say you're very tired. Go to bed."

Go to bed? For one damned minute he thought about grabbing her hand and leading her straight to the bedroom. The trouble with that notion was that Matthew knew she wouldn't resist. And later, after the fire in his body had cooled, he'd hate himself.

Not bothering to say more, she left the living room.

Matthew watched her go and then, cursing under his breath, he pushed himself off the couch and went straight to his bedroom. But even after he climbed into the queen-sized bed and shut off the lights, he knew it would be hours before he'd be able to sleep.

Sunday was the only day the diner was closed, and Camille usually used the off time to catch up on errands that she couldn't normally do during the week.

After church, she made the twenty-minute drive to Benson and purchased a large supply of groceries before she drove home to Red Bluff. She'd carried everything into the house and was putting the last of the canned goods away when her phone rang.

Seeing it was her mother, Camille carried the phone out to the courtyard and made herself comfortable on a chaise lounge.

"Hi, Mom. What's up?"

"Hello, honey! We just finished Sunday dinner and I thought I'd call to check on you."

The last of October meant winter was coming for most people, but the sun was still exceptionally warm in southern Arizona, and Camille loved the feel of it sinking into her skin and warming her face.

"I'm doing great. What about you?"

Camille could hear her mother's sigh. It was full of weariness or sadness. She wasn't exactly sure which, but she did know they were sounds that weren't normally made by her mother.

"I'm okay. We've been very busy up here—moving all the cattle down from the Prescott range. Snow has already hit Flagstaff. We don't want to take any chances with the cow/calf pairs being caught in a snowstorm."

Camille could've reminded her mother that there was no need for her to spend hours of the day in the saddle, doing a job that was tiring, even for a man. But she'd be wasting her breath. Maureen loved to be outside, riding and working with the cattle. It was something she'd done all her life and it had especially bonded her with Joel during the years of their long marriage.

"Do you have them all moved?" Camille asked.

"No. We're heading back up there in the morning. Tomorrow should wrap it up, though."

"It's hot down here," Camille said. "I don't look for it to cool much until Christmas."

There was a long pause, and then Maureen said, "I don't suppose you've thought much about coming home for the holidays."

"No. I wouldn't dream of leaving Norman at such a busy time at the diner."

"But it doesn't bother you to neglect your family during Thanksgiving and Christmas." She let out another long sigh. "Camille, there are times I just don't understand you. If you're worried that people around here are still talking about Graham Danby jilting you, then you're wrong."

Camille let out an unladylike curse. "Mom, I've told you a hundred times or more. The guy means nothing to me. He did me a giant favor when he asked for his ring back. I'm happier now than I ever have been. And if I saw Graham today, I'd thank him for having more sense than I did. He knew we didn't belong together—it just took me a while to see that."

Maureen snorted. "That would be easy to believe if I hadn't seen all those tears you shed when you were packing your bags and leaving Three Rivers. You were crushed."

"No, Mom. *I* wasn't crushed. Only my pride," Camille assured her, then said, "You know, you and my brothers and sisters are all welcome to come down here and spend the holidays at Red Bluff. I think there would be plenty of room, even with all the babies."

"Ha! It would take a caravan to move us all down there. But I might take you up on the invitation—at least for a few days. The boys have really been getting on my nerves."

Camille frowned. It wasn't like her mother to complain about her sons for any reason. Especially now that all of them had settled down with their own families. "What are my brothers doing to get on your nerves?"

"Hovering over me like they expect me to fall apart any minute. I may not look like I did ten years ago, but I'm hardly ready to sit in a rocker!"

"Give them a break, Mom. Now that they all have wives, I think they're just more aware of how hard you work."

"Maybe. But I don't believe that's the cause of their behavior. Especially Joe. He thinks I'm having some sort of PTSD over Joel's death. And none of them appreciate the fact that I've told them to let the whole incident go. They're all like terriers digging beneath a chain link fence. They refuse to give up until they've reached some sort of conclusion." She heaved out a heavy breath. Then, after a brief pause, she said, "Sorry, Camille. You don't want to hear this. And I don't want to talk about it. So tell me, how's it going with Matthew?"

Camille sat straight up. "Matthew?"

"Yes. Our foreman," she answered drolly. "Blake tells me he's staying there in the house with you. But I don't guess you see him that much. I know how busy the men stay when they're moving cattle down there."

"Oh, well—I see him when he comes in at night. I've been feeding him and uh—making sure he has everything he needs."

"That's good. I was hoping you'd be nice to him."

Camille frowned. "Mom, did you honestly believe I wouldn't be nice?"

"Oh, I don't know. I always got the impression that he rubbed you the wrong way."

Except for those hot kisses last night, he'd never

rubbed her in any way. That was the problem. Funny how it had taken Camille years to figure that out.

In the most innocent tone she could manage, she said, "I can't imagine where you got that idea."

"Well, you practically laughed with glee when he and Renee divorced."

"That's because she was horrible for him," Camille reasoned. "And Matthew should have realized she was a horrible fit for him."

"Uh-huh. You mean like you should've seen how Graham was all wrong for you?" Maureen asked smugly.

"Exactly," Camille retorted, then sighed as images of last night whirled through her mind. "Actually, Mom, I'm—enjoying Matthew. He's a lot different than the way I remembered."

"Different? In what way?"

Instead of a spindly young guy, who'd been totally unsure of himself, Matthew had turned into a sexy hunk of confident man, she thought. To her mother, she said, "Well, he was always sort of quiet. That hasn't changed much. But I'm learning he has a bit of a sense of humor and he's a good listener." Pausing, she chuckled. "Or he might just be letting me talk so he won't have to."

Several seconds of silence passed and just when Camille was wondering what her mother was thinking, Maureen said, "I'm glad you're enjoying him, honey. I don't have to tell you how much Matthew means to the family. And he's—well, I'm not sure he's ever gotten over his difficult childhood."

The things Matthew had told her about his family, or lack of one, were still haunting Camille, and she wondered how he'd grown up to be such a responsible man. If asked, he'd probably give all the credit to Joel, but that wouldn't be entirely right. He'd been a hardworking, trustworthy man when he'd first come to Three Rivers. Joel had simply nourished the goodness in him.

Camille said, "Last night he mentioned having a sister. I wasn't aware that he had a sibling. I've never heard any of you mention her. Does he ever see her?"

"Not often. The last time was right after you left for Red Bluff. Blake purchased a bull over in California and he sent Matthew to haul him home. The trip gave Matthew a chance to stop by Claire's place."

"I see." Deciding she'd better change the subject before her mother started to think her interest in Matthew was a bit excessive, she said, "I guess you're going to have a Halloween party. Do all the kids have their costumes yet?"

Maureen chuckled. "Abagail and Andrew are going to be cats with tails and whiskers. That's the most important thing, of course."

"How cute," Camille said with a laugh. "What about Nick and Hannah? They probably think they're too old to party with the babies."

"Not in the least. Nick and Hannah love being big bosses of their little siblings. And anyway, Viv has promised to take those two to a party on the res that's just for teens and tweens."

Missing out on spending time with her nieces and nephews was the one regret Camille often had about making her home here on Red Bluff. On the other hand, it would be difficult living back on Three Rivers and her being the only Hollister sibling without a spouse or a child. It was hard enough to deal with living two hundred fifty miles away.

Single and childless at the age of twenty-eight was not the way Camille had envisioned or hoped her life would be. But it had turned out that way and now she was determined not to lament the situation, but embrace her independence. As far as she was concerned that was far better than nursing a broken heart.

"Have you seen Emily-Ann lately?" Camille asked.

"No. But Katherine sees her regularly. She misses you. I know that much."

Emily-Ann had been Camille's best friend since their days in grade school. She ran Conchita's, a tiny coffee shop in Wickenburg that served bakery treats and specialty coffees. "I miss her, too. I'm hoping she can come down for a visit soon."

"Emily-Ann isn't exactly flush with money," Maureen pointed out. "I doubt she can afford to stay away from her job for more than a day or two."

Camille's friend was dependable and hard working. She'd be great as a waitress for the diner. But in spite of the struggles and stigma she'd suffered through, Emily-Ann would never move away from Wickenburg. It was her home.

"I'd make sure she wouldn't have to spend a dime, Mom."

"I expected you to say that. So why don't you invite her down for Thanksgiving?" Maureen suggested. "You could take her to Tucson and do some Christmas shopping."

"That's a nice idea."

"Good. I—"

Her mother's words were suddenly interrupted by the sound of distant voices.

Camille asked, "Mom, do you need to get off the phone?"

"Uh—yes, I'm afraid I do. Blake needs me for something. Love you. And be sure and take extra good care of Matthew."

"Yes—I will. And I love you, too."

Camille punched the phone to disconnect the call, then rose from the lounge chair. As she walked back to the house, her mother's words played over in her mind. *Take extra good care of Matthew.*

What would Maureen think if she knew just how much Camille wanted to care for Matthew? Would she think her daughter was reaching for something she could never have? Last night, when he'd kissed her, she'd thought he was finally going to lower the barriers he'd erected between them. For those few brief moments he'd held nothing back and she'd met the reckless desperation of his lips with the same hungry need.

She'd never wanted any man to make love to her as much as she'd wanted Matthew at that moment. But he'd pulled away and implied that their kisses had been a mistake. Could he be right?

As Camille went to her bedroom and changed out of her church clothes, the question continued to circle through her thoughts. For the past two years she'd done a lot of growing, and now it was easy to see where and why she'd made the mistake in getting engaged to Graham. Yes, she'd learned her lesson. But what about now? What about Matthew?

Oh Lord, never in her wildest dreams had she thought his time here at Red Bluff would mean anything more than having a visitor in the house. She'd honestly expected him to be sullen and curt and she'd planned to ignore him as best she could.

How laughable was that? she asked herself as she pulled on jeans and a thin pink shirt. The moment she'd looked across the threshold at Matthew's tired face, something had smacked her right between the breasts. And try as she might, she couldn't get rid of the feeling.

But he wasn't down here for romance, she reasoned with herself. Besides, he'd been divorced and single for nearly ten years. The man clearly had no desire to marry again. So what good would it do her to have a brief affair with him? No good. Matthew was right and she knew it. But for some reason her heart wasn't listening to reason.

Chapter Five

After searching the southernmost range of the ranch for the entire day, Matthew and the small crew of cowhands helping him came up with six of the missing ten steers. Although the men were disappointed that they'd not found the last four, Matthew was pleased with the effort. They could've just as easily ended up with zilch for the day.

"When are we going to vaccinate and tag the new cattle, Matthew?" Pate asked, as he steered the double-seated work truck coupled to a long stock trailer over the rough ground.

Slumped in the passenger seat, Matthew was attempting to grab a bit of shut-eye during the drive back to the ranch yard, but with Pate hitting every rock in the old roadbed, his head was banging around like a punching bag.

Biting back a tired groan, he straightened on the worn leather seat and gazed out the window at the desert hills covered with purple twilight. Red Bluff was an enchanting place and not just because Camille was here, he decided. There were parts of the ranch that were incredibly green to be located in such a desert area. Then there were other parts that were full of high rocky bluffs and hundreds of tall saguaros with their arms reaching toward the wide, endless sky.

He wondered how much, if any, of this land Camille ever seen. Did any of it truly matter to her? Or did she only care about the house and having her privacy? Last night, when she'd talked about trying to help out with the ranching chores at Three Rivers, he'd gotten the impression that she'd wanted to be as much of a cowgirl as her mother and sister, but she lacked the confidence to keep trying.

Last night. Oh Lord, he wished he could quit thinking about last night. He wished he could block out every scent, every taste and touch his brain cells had gathered when he and Camille had kissed so passionately. If he lived to be a hundred, the memory would still be enough to curl his toes.

"Don't you think we ought to be letting some of the other cattle loose?" Pate continued to throw questions at him. "Curly and Abel have already poured out tons of feed and hay."

Since Pate had the least experience of all the men here and was constantly peppering him with questions, Matthew tried to hold on to his patience and remember how it was to be green and uncertain.

"And they'll keep pouring out more tons until we

have everything ready," Matthew explained. "That includes finding the last four steers."

"Pate, why are you concerned about the feed and hay?" Scott asked from the back seat. "You're not paying for it out of your paycheck."

Looking over his shoulder, Pate smirked at the other ranch hand. "No. But I'm riding for the brand. I don't want Three Rivers to spend money unnecessarily."

TooTall grunted. "No need to worry. We'll find the four steers tomorrow. Right, Matthew?"

TooTall was always positive and a man of few words. More often than not, he called Matthew Yellow Hair. But tonight he'd used his given name, and the sound of it put a wry smile on Matthew's lips.

"You're always right, TooTall. And I don't know what I'd do without your level head around."

Scooting to the edge of the seat, TooTall poked his face between the bucket seats. "Does that mean you're gonna let me stay down here on Red Bluff and work with you?"

Completely bewildered by TooTall's question, Matthew twisted around to look at him. "What are you talking about? We'll be going back to Three Rivers in a couple of weeks, or less."

"Yes. But you'll be coming back."

"Not until next winter."

TooTall shook his head. "No. You'll be coming back sooner. And then you'll stay."

TooTall had always been the mystical sort. But even for him, this prediction was far out in left field.

Tired as he was, Matthew had to laugh. "You're way off base, TooTall. I won't have any reason to come back here to Red Bluff, unless Blake wants me to come with him just for a look around."

His expression completely serious, TooTall shook his head. "You're wrong, Matthew. So do I get to come with you and be your right-hand man? Your ramrod?"

Matthew couldn't think of any other man he'd rather have as his right-hand man. So, not to hurt his feelings, he said, "Okay, TooTall, if your prediction comes true, you'll be my ramrod."

"You promise?"

"I'll put it down in writing," Matthew assured him.

"No. You cross your heart, Yellow Hair. That's better."

Seeing that the cowboy was truly serious, Matthew complied by making an X mark across his heart. "Okay. Does that make you happy?"

"I'm happy," TooTall told him.

Behind the steering wheel, Pate guffawed. "What a crock of crap. He's been chewing agave!"

Matthew cut the young man a steely glare. "What the hell are you laughing at? No one has been chewing agave—unless it's you! And if I ever catch you doing it, I'll kick your ass all the way back to the ranch yard. Got that?"

Pate's expression sobered instantly. "Yes. I got it."

A half hour later, Pate parked the truck and trailer near the big red barn, and the four men climbed out and went to work unloading the steers and the horses. Once they had all the livestock settled for the night and their tack and gear stored away, Matthew started to the house, only to have his phone start ringing.

Seeing it was Blake, he answered, but the signal was too weak for the man's voice to come through clearly.

Matthew hung up and walked on to the house. When he reached the inner courtyard, he sat down on a padded lounge chair and tried to return Blake's call.

"Blake, can you hear me?"

"Clear as a bell now," Blake answered. "I was just calling to see how things are going down there."

"We're making progress," he told him. "No problems. I figure we can ship the steers up day after tomorrow. TooTall predicts we'll find the last four tomorrow."

Blake grunted with amusement. "And TooTall's predictions always come true."

Matthew wasn't about to bring up the man's other prediction. It was far too strange and frankly unnerving to repeat out loud.

"I'll have a man ready to come after the steers," Blake assured him. "Is there anything else you need? Is the feed and hay holding steady?"

"We're okay there."

"And the water? I don't suppose you've had a chance to check the wells yet?"

Matthew wiped a weary hand over his face. "No. But we'll get to it."

Blake cursed under his breath. "I should've sent at least two more men with you, Matthew. There's too much to do down there and you don't have near enough help. I don't want you collapsing on me."

"Hell, Blake, I'm not going to collapse. Everything will come together. Don't worry about any of it."

The other man let out a long breath. "Both ranches are growing and Holt keeps telling me that more cattle means more men. I think my brother is right."

Matthew massaged his closed eyelids. His mouth felt like he'd been eating dirt and his eyes had been scraped with sandpaper. "Are you thinking about running cattle down here all year round? I'm talking about more than just a few steers?"

"Funny you should ask that. Mom and I have been tossing the idea around. It would mean investing a lot of money. But we think it would pay off. Why are you asking?"

Because TooTall was making strange prophecies, Matthew could've told him. Aloud, he said, "With you buying the five hundred extra head, it crossed my mind."

"Hmm. What do you think about the idea? And don't be afraid to speak frankly, Matthew. I always value your opinion, whether I agree with it or not."

"Well, I don't think I've ever covered this whole ranch. Not on horseback or in a vehicle. At least, not for several years—since Joel was still with us. I couldn't say how many cattle this land is capable of supporting until I had a good look at all of it."

Blake went silent for a moment and then he said, "You know, you've given me an idea. And before you start cursing a blue streak, just hear me out. Once you get the cattle settled, I'd like for you to take a few extra days to really look the place over. I hate to admit that it's been years since I've seen much of it myself. And since you're already down there, it would be the perfect opportunity."

Hell, no! He wasn't going to stay down here any longer than he had to. Even though the thought was racing through his head, Matthew didn't say it to Blake. He'd wait a few days, after things were smoothing out here, before he began to curse that blue streak at his boss.

"You don't need for me to do it," Matthew hedged.

"Any of the men can have a look around and give you a report."

Blake let out a loud laugh. "Sure, Matthew. Like I could trust just anyone's judgment. Why do you think you're the foreman of Three Rivers? Because of your good looks?"

Matthew snorted. "Not hardly."

"Damn right, not hardly. It's because you have an eagle eye and a rancher's mind. But we'll talk about this later. Right now Kat is helping the twins try on their cat suits and they want me to come watch."

"Cat suits?"

Blake laughed and Matthew realized that in spite of the heavy load the eldest Hollister brother carried, he was a happy man now that he had Katherine and the children in his life.

"Yes. You know. Meow! Thursday night is Halloween and Mom's throwing one of her big parties. The kids can't wait. Sorry you can't be here, buddy. I'll eat some candy just for you."

"Thanks, Blake. But I really think I'd rather have Holt drink a bourbon and Coke for me."

Blake laughed loudly. "I'll tell him. I'm sure he'll be more than happy to do that little thing for you. Talk to you later, Matthew."

Blake cut the connection, and Matthew dropped the phone back into his shirt pocket, but he didn't immediately leave his seat on the lounge. His head was whirling and he needed a minute in the quiet before he walked into the house and faced Camille again.

Who are you kidding, Matthew? You're not worried about facing Camille again. Your insides are tied into knots with worry about how you're going to keep your

*hands off her, when every cell in your body is aching
to make love to her.*

Cursing at the damning voice in his head, he lifted
his hat from his head and raked a hand through his
hair. He was hot and dirty and sweat had dried to salty
patches on the front and back of his shirt. Thank goodness he and the men had gotten in early enough tonight
that he had time for a shower before he ate.

"There you are. I thought I heard someone out here
talking."

Camille's voice startled him, and he jerked his head
around to see her walking up the stone pathway to
where he was sitting. She was wearing jeans and cowboy boots, and the front tails of her shirt were knotted
at her waist. The clothes suited her, but it was the smile
on her face that transformed her into an enchantress.

"I had a call from Blake," he explained.

"Oh. I hope you told him hello for me."

"No. I didn't. I will next time."

She sat down next to him on the lounge and he was
suddenly assaulted with her sunny scent and the feel of
her soft, warm shoulder pressing against his.

"Blake is annoyed with me because I'm down here
instead of up there," she said. "He blames me for Mom's
state of mind."

"Not completely."

"Humph. You don't have to handle me with kid
gloves, Matthew. Anyway, I've got news for Blake.
Mom might like for me to move back to Three Rivers,
but what's really aggravating her is that her sons are
ignoring her wishes."

He studied her from the corner of his eye. "You're
talking about the investigation into Joel's death now."

"Right."

Matthew wasn't sure how much Blake, Holt, Chandler, or Joseph had told Camille about the information they'd discovered a few months back. Initially, when Joseph had learned that Joel had been spotted with a woman at the Phoenix livestock sale barn before his death, the brothers had decided to keep the information to themselves, their reason being that none of them wanted their sisters hurt by the idea that Joel might have been cheating on Maureen. But they could've changed their minds and let their sisters in on the development. Either way, Matthew wasn't going to repeat something to Camille that might ultimately hurt her and anger her brothers.

"I wouldn't dwell on it, Camille. Your mother is hardly falling apart. She's too strong for that."

"I wish my brothers viewed everything as sensibly as you do."

He shook his head. "It's always easier to see the whole picture when you're standing on the outside looking in. It's when a guy gets too close to something that he has trouble seeing everything."

Even though he wasn't looking at her directly, he could feel her gaze drop to his lips. He was trying to decide whether he should jump to his feet and leave the lounge, or jerk her into his arms, when she suddenly reached over and wrapped a thumb and forefinger around his chin.

"I'm close," she murmured as she steered his face toward hers. "So what are you seeing?"

He needed to draw in a deep, cleansing breath, but his brain wasn't communicating with his lungs. It was too busy thinking about having her lips next to his.

"I'm seeing a little vixen that's asking for more trouble than she could possibly know."

Her fingers moved to his cheek. "Yes," she whispered. "But it's worth the risk. Don't you think?"

Even though it was dark, the footlights edging the stone floor of the porch were enough to reveal the inviting look in her eyes, and Matthew decided he was tired of fighting her and this unbearable need to have her in his arms.

"Worth the risk and more," he muttered. Then, clamping his hands at the back of her head, he drew her face up to his. "And right now I don't care if this makes the roof fall in on us."

"Mmm. We don't have a roof over us. Just the open sky—and the stars and—"

"This," he murmured against her lips.

Instantly, she deepened the contact by opening her mouth and wrapping her arms around his neck.

Matthew had never been shot out of a cannon, but he figured this was darned close to it. Like a lighted match landing on a dry tumbleweed, fire exploded inside of him, catapulting him into a dark, dreamy space. Unable to stop the flight, he mindlessly pushed her upper body down on the lounge chair and draped himself over her.

The exotic taste of her kiss intoxicated what was left of his senses, and when he felt her tongue probing for an entryway into his mouth, he gladly gave it to her, all the while knowing he wouldn't be satisfied until he had more and more.

His hands cupped her breasts and as he kneaded their fullness, he imagined his mouth on the softness, his teeth sinking into the budded centers. Above the roaring blood in his ears, he heard her moan, and then he felt her hands working their way to the snaps of his shirt. The moment her hands found enough space to slip inside the fabric and flatten against his skin, he tore his mouth from hers and sucked in a fierce breath.

"I—uh, think we'd better stop this—and go inside."

Her eyes half-closed, she smiled like a contented cat. "Why? The night air feels like cool velvet and you feel even better."

Groaning, he brought his face back to hers and nuzzled his lips against her cheek. "I'm dirty and smell like—"

"Like a real man," she finished before he could. Her fingertips rubbed against the stubble on his jaw. "I like the whiskers and the dust and the sweat. I like—everything about you, Matthew."

"You're crazy. But I'm beginning not to care."

As soon as he said the words, his lips moved back to hers, and as their kiss deepened, Matthew had one thing on his mind. Getting her off the chair and into his bed.

And then the quietness in the courtyard was suddenly interrupted by the distant sound of men's voices shouting back and forth.

Matthew desperately wanted to ignore the commotion, but the responsibilities attached to his job were deeply ingrained in him and he slowly lifted his head and pushed himself to his feet.

"Something is happening at the barn. I hear the men yelling."

Frowning, she sat up and listened along with him.

"Damn it, don't push her leg that way!" Curly shouted loud enough for the sound to carry all the way to the courtyard. "Abel, go get a lariat! We'll pull her out!"

Snapping his shirt back together, Matthew cast Camille a rueful glance. "I have to go."

She jumped to her feet. "Of course you do. I'll see you when you get back."

Matthew hurried out of the courtyard and as his long strides carried him to the barn, he decided he'd either made a great escape, or lost the chance of a lifetime.

Chapter Six

More than an hour later, after Matthew had left to go to the ranch yard, Camille was upstairs in her bedroom when she heard him return to the house. The sound of his movements below was enough to cause her heart to trip all over itself, and with trembling fingers she hurriedly finished pinning her hair into a messy bun.

She didn't know why she'd bothered to change into a long dress and sandals or pin up her hair. If Matthew really wanted to make love to her, it wouldn't matter what she was wearing or how she looked, she thought.

But it mattered to her. Ever since Graham had thrown her over for Crystal Thompson, she'd harbored all kinds of doubts about herself. If she'd not been pretty enough, or woman enough, to keep her fiancé from falling for another woman, then how did she expect to hold on to any man? Especially one like Matthew, who was sexy enough to have women throwing themselves at him.

Isn't that what you're doing, Camille? You know good and darn well that you've been throwing yourself at Matthew from the moment he arrived on the ranch. What has come over you anyway? You've never behaved this way in your entire life. And to make matters worse, you've been vowing to stay celibate and unattached. Now you're trying your best to veer way off course! You're going to get your heart broken, you little ninny, and when you do, you'll have nowhere else to run. No place to hide your wounds.

The sardonic voice going off in her head caused her lips to compress into a thin line. So what if she was the one doing all the pursuing? What was wrong with that? Her father had always taught her to be strong and go after the things she wanted in life. And Lord help her, she wanted Matthew with every fiber of her being.

With that thought in mind, she fastened a pair of golden hoops to her ears and hurried downstairs to the kitchen.

"What was happening down at the barn?" Camille asked as she carried a platter filled with pot roast and vegetables over to the table. "I hope nothing serious."

"Everything is okay now," he assured her. "A cow managed to get her leg stuck through one of the fencing panels. If Curly hadn't happened to go outside and find her in the predicament, she would've probably broken her leg trying to get herself loose. And you know what that would've meant."

"Yes," she said ruefully. "You would've had to put her down. Does she have a calf?"

"Yes. Probably no more than two weeks old. It would've had to be bottle-fed. Which is quite a time-consuming job. But thank God, the mama is okay and so is her calf."

She went back to the cabinet counter to collect a bowl of brown gravy and a basket of hot rolls. As she placed them next to the roast, she said, "I've heard people make stupid comments about ranching life. Like all you have to do is put a few cows on some grass and let them multiply. They couldn't be more wrong. It's a very hard job and many times, heartbreaking."

"You say that like you know firsthand."

"I wasn't just a klutz around the horses and cows, but I was a big softie. I couldn't bear seeing any of the animals sick or injured. Once a cow had twins and I was so excited over them. Daddy gave me the job of giving them bottle milk to help supplement what the mother was able to provide her two babies." She paused and shook her head. "But the weaker of the two calves eventually died and I was totally devastated. I cried for a month over it and after that I refused to go to the barn. I know that was childish of me. But it hurt too much."

"There are a lot of things about ranching that can be brutal," he said. "But the rewarding parts balance it all out."

She gestured to the table. "That's everything," she said. "Let's eat."

He pulled out a chair for her and she thanked him as she took a seat and he pushed forward.

As he sat in the chair angled to her left, he said, "I wasn't expecting you to be eating with me this evening. You didn't have to wait, you know."

She smiled at him. "It's nice not to have to eat alone. And I didn't mind the wait."

They filled their plates and as they began to eat, she

glanced at his arms, which were covered with a long-sleeved white shirt.

"Did you get back into the mesquite and chaparral today?"

"Yes. The area of the ranch where we've been riding is rough and full of brush. But I tried to get them out when I took a shower."

"I'll have a look after we eat."

He didn't say anything, but the look he slanted her spoke volumes. Like if she touched him he wouldn't be responsible for his actions. The idea caused Camille to tremble inside.

After a few moments passed, she asked, "Are you still living in the old foreman's house up on the ridge?"

"Yes. Why?"

She shrugged. "I just wondered, that's all. It's been a while since I left Three Rivers. Some things have changed since then." She laughed lightly, then shook her head. "Let me rephrase that. Many things have changed since then. The house is full of babies and wives. Blake married Katherine and together they have Nick, Abagail and Andrew. Then Chandler married Roslyn and they have little Evelyn."

"You've left out your other siblings," Matthew said. "Joseph married Tessa and they have Little Joe and baby daughter, Spring. Vivian married Sawyer and now, along with Hannah, they have twins, Jacob and Johnny. And Holt and Isabelle will be having their first baby soon. It's been a very productive few years for your family."

Her lips twisted to a wry slant. "My siblings have always been high achievers. Blake manages Three Rivers, Chandler is a veterinarian and owns a very successful clinic. Joseph is deputy sheriff for Yavapai County, Holt is a prestigious horse trainer, and Vivian is an experienced park ranger. And what is little Camille? She's a short order cook in a desert diner. I take everything back I said about my brothers. I'm the reason Mom is depressed."

"Stop it," he ordered. "The poor, pitiful me act doesn't suit you."

She straightened her shoulders. "No. You're right. It doesn't. But sometimes I think—"

"You think too much," he interrupted. "About the wrong things. You've already said that being a cook makes you happy. If that's the case, then you should be proud of yourself and proud of your job."

She nodded glumly. Then, after a moment's thought, she nodded with more enthusiasm. "You're right. I could go dig out my college degree and hang it on the wall. I could even go to Tucson and get an office job with an impressive title attached to it. But I'd hate every minute of it. Just like you'd hate it if you had to take over Blake's job and sit behind a desk for most of the day. You'd be a big shot, but would it be worth it?"

"Not to me. I don't want to be a big shot. I'd rather be a saddle bum."

He grinned as he said the last word and Camille laughed. Then, unable to stop herself, she reached over and squeezed his hand.

"I'm so glad that you're here, Matthew. You make me feel good."

His expression suddenly sobered and the regret she saw in his gray eyes was worse than being cut with a knife.

"Camille, I—about what happened out there in the courtyard—I—"

She quickly interrupted, "I don't want to talk about that now, Matthew. Let's just enjoy our food. And—talk about other things. Tell me about Blue Stallion Ranch and this dream ranch that Holt and Isabelle are building together."

For a moment she thought he was going to ignore her plea and begin a long tirade about how they should keep some sensible distance between them. But to her relief he relented and said, "It's on the old Landry Ranch. Just north of Three Rivers. Remember it?"

"Yes. Vaguely. I went over there with Daddy once. It was very pretty over there. Do you think Holt likes being away from Three Rivers?"

"Well, it's not like he's away entirely. He works at Three Rivers on weekdays. His nights and weekends are spent at Blue Stallion. And yes, he's very happy."

Camille thoughtfully shook her head. "Amazing, really. Wild Holt finally under a bit and bridle and with a baby on the way, too. I would've never dreamed it. But I guess the old saying that nothing stays the same is true."

"Yes," he said softly. "Look at you."

"Yeah," she said with a twinge of cynicism. "Look at me."

Another span of silence passed before Matthew spoke again. Even though she'd cut him off when he'd brought up their encounter in the courtyard, Camille couldn't help but wonder what he'd been about to say. That he didn't want to get involved with her? That no matter how much she tempted or taunted, he wasn't going to make love to her?

Just as she let out a long sigh, he asked, "Has Maureen mentioned anything to you about Sam?"

She arched her brows at him. "You mean Sam Leman? Tessa and Joseph's ranch foreman?"

Sam was a crusty cowboy somewhere in his seventies. For years he'd worked for the late Sheriff Ray Maddox until Ray had passed away and Tessa had inherited the Bar X.

He nodded. "Yes, that Sam."

"No. Why? I hope nothing is wrong with him. I always thought he was a charming old guy."

Matthew slanted her a wry look. "All the women do. Especially Isabelle's mother, Gabby. Seems as though a romance has sparked between the two."

Camille's mouth fell open. "Isabelle's mother? I saw her in a few of the photos of Holt and Isabelle's wedding that Mom sent to me. Gabby is a very attractive blonde and quite a bit younger than Sam, isn't she?"

He sipped from his glass of iced tea before he spoke. "I have no idea what Holt's mother-in-law's age actually is, but I'd say she's at least twenty years younger than Sam."

"Wow! Sam is an old desert cowboy who loves horses and goats and bourbon, but he obviously still has what it takes! Wonder how those two got together?"

"Gabby's an artist and it seems she was so taken with the character in Sam's face that she wanted to do a portrait of him. You can imagine how shocked everyone was when Sam agreed to sit for her. The way things have turned out, Sam must've been doing more than just sitting. And Gabby more than painting."

Camille cast him a suggestive smile. "So Gabby is still living back here in Arizona?"

He nodded. "On Blue Stallion Ranch with Isabelle and Holt. But your brother says Sam and Gabby are planning to marry soon. They want to be together while he's still young. That's the way Gabby puts it."

A bittersweet pain squeezed her heart. Would any man ever feel that way about her? To love her so much he didn't want to miss a day, an hour, or a minute without her in his life? Maureen had been blessed with that kind of love. Now Vivian had it with Sawyer. But Camille was beginning to doubt she would ever be the recipient of that kind of devoted emotion.

"That's so romantic," she said huskily.

He leveled a meaningful, knowing look at her. "I expected that kind of response from you. Maureen says the same thing. She gets all teary-eyed whenever she talks about the two of them."

Camille's throat was so tight that she forced herself to swallow a few bites of food before she replied. "Well, Sam has been a friend of the family for as long as I can remember. I'm sure she's happy for him. And—maybe a little sad for herself. You know—losing Daddy like she did."

"Maureen deserves some happiness."

From the corner of her eye, Camille thoughtfully watched him slice into the roast beef on his plate. She said, "Viv tells me that Holt and Chandler have the idea that Mom has fallen in love with someone. Do you believe that?"

"Joel has been gone for a long time. And your mother is human." He glanced at her. "You wouldn't oppose her having a man in her life, would you?"

"No. I want her to be happy. That's all I want."

He fell silent after that, and Camille decided all their

STELLA BAGWELL
87

talk about family and romance had left him uncomfortable. Well, she could tell him that just sitting across the table from him unnerved her. But he probably already knew that, she thought. She'd made her desire for him clear enough.

Camille had never pursued a man in her life. Even Graham had been the one to seek her out, and she'd been unable to resist his sweet talk and promises of the kind of future she'd always wanted. It hadn't even mattered that he'd liked the fact that she was an office manager and had wanted her to continue the job after they were married. And when he'd insisted they would make their home in Phoenix, she'd gone along like a helpless calf being dragged to the branding fire.

She'd been so foolish and weak-willed back then, she thought. She'd let Graham define who she was and what she was. But never again. She'd emerged from their broken engagement a different and stronger woman. And this time around she wasn't going to give up, or give in.

Every bite of food was gone from Matthew's plate when he finally rose from the table and carried it and his glass over to the sink. Behind him, he could hear Camille leave the table, and he turned just as she came to stand next to him.

"Thanks for supper, Camille. It was delicious."

"I have apple pie," she told him. "I'll get the coffee going."

"No," he blurted. Then, seeing the confused frown on her face, he added, "I—uh—the pie can wait. I want to talk with you first."

Her expression stoic, she stacked her plate on top of

his. "If you're going to start in about us kissing in the courtyard—"

"That was more than kissing, Camille, and you know it," he stated flatly.

As her blue gaze probed his face, her chin tilted upward. "What if it was more? Don't try to tell me you weren't enjoying it."

Frustration pushed a groan past his throat. "Hell, Camille, what do you think I am? Made of steel?"

"I'm not sure," she said quietly. "Just when I start to think you're human, you want to put a cold wall between us."

Cold? Everything was about her was burning him up, even the part of his brain that was supposed to be holding on to his common sense.

"I'm trying to stop a shipwreck, Camille. We can't just—"

"What? Make love?" As she asked the questions, she moved close enough to slide her palms up the middle of his chest. "Why can't we? We're both adults and unattached."

His nostrils flared at the simple image she was painting. She made it sound so easy and right. And maybe that was the way it should be, he pondered. Maybe he was making too damned much of everything. Maybe he needed to forget about her last name and start thinking of her as the woman he wanted. "You think that's all there is to it?"

Sliding her arms up and around his neck, she arched the front of her body into his. The warm curves pressing into his flesh were impossible to ignore, and with a will of their own, his arms wrapped around her waist and anchored her tightly against him.

"I think you're afraid to admit that you want me," she said softly. "And I don't understand why."

"I'll be gone from here in a few days." Strange how that fact was beginning to weigh on him. Any other time he'd be looking forward to heading home to Three Rivers.

"That's more good reason why we shouldn't waste this time, Matthew."

Like Gabby and Sam, he thought. The couple wanted to make the most of the years they had left. But they were different, he mentally argued. They were in love.

Love. Like hell, Matthew thought cynically. If he waited on love to find him, he'd be living the rest of his life like a monk. This thing he felt for Camille was pure, hot lust and that's all it ever would be.

He looked down at her and as their eyes met, he felt the tight grip he had on his self-control snap. Relief flooded through him, followed by a rampant wave of desire.

"Time. No," he murmured. "We don't have enough."

Deliberately pushing any more thought from his mind, he lowered his mouth to hers.

His sign of surrender must have pleased her because her lips were suddenly moving against his in a way that was both tender and enticing. No woman had ever kissed him like this. Like he was precious and something to cherish. Matthew realized he didn't want it to end. He didn't want this connection with her to end.

When the need for air finally parted their lips, Camille buried her cheek against his chest. "Oh, Matthew, this isn't wrong."

He groaned as his hands roamed her back. "Even if it's wrong I can't fight you anymore."

Lifting her head, she touched her fingertips to his cheek, and in that instant, fear slashed through him. This wasn't the way she was supposed to be looking at him, or touching him. And the middle of his chest wasn't supposed to feel like warm mush.

"I don't want you to fight anything," she whispered. Then, taking his hand, she led him out of the kitchen.

With her hand wrapped firmly around his, Camille didn't let go until they'd climbed the stairs and entered her bedroom. Except for the moonlight filtering through the sheer curtains on the window, the room was dark.

"If you promise not to run off, I'll let go of your hand and switch on the lamp."

"I don't need a lamp. I have cat eyes," he said. "And you don't need to worry about me running off. Not tonight."

Not tonight. But maybe tomorrow? The question flashed through her mind, but she purposely pushed it to a dark, out-of-the-way place.

"Tonight is all that matters," she whispered. Then, rising on the tips of her toes, she pressed her lips to his.

With his arms wrapped tightly around her shoulders, he kissed her so deeply that her head began to swirl, and with the slow, drunken whirl, a kaleidoscope of colors flashed behind her closed eyelids.

When he finally lifted his head, they were both dazed and panting.

"I hope you have some sort of birth control," he said gruffly. "Because I came down here to herd cattle. Not this."

She very nearly laughed. "No worries. I take oral contraceptives. So we're good."

A long breath rushed out of him. "That's a relief. Because right now I don't think I could drive all the way to Benson for a box of condoms. And I sure as heck couldn't walk out of this room without making you mine."

Loving the sound of that, she reached for the snaps on his shirt. "And I sure as heck don't intend to let you out of this room for a long, long time."

She pulled the fabric apart and then promptly pressed a row of kisses across his chest, down the center of his abdomen, then back up to one flat nipple. He allowed her tongue to circle it once, twice, and then he was pulling her head back.

"That has to wait." His raspy voice sounded like a man in agony. "Until we get out of these clothes."

"Then let's do something about them," she said in a low, seductive voice.

Reaching up, she pushed the shirt off his shoulders and down over his wrists. As it dropped to the floor, her hands came together on his belt buckle.

"Let me," he said. "It'll go faster."

Deciding faster was better, Camille turned the job over to him and began shedding her own clothing. Once she'd stripped down to a set of lacy black lingerie, she momentarily considered leaving the last two garments on, then just as quickly decided against it. She didn't want anything, not even two strips of tiny fabric, coming between them.

Once she was finished, she looked over to see he'd sunk onto the edge of the bed to pull off his boots.

She quickly swept his hands aside. "Let me do that chore for you, cowboy."

Leaning back on the mattress, he lifted both legs, and

Camille went to work removing his boots. They slipped off easily and after setting them aside, she tugged his jeans and boxers down over his feet.

The last of his clothing had hardly had time to hit the floor before he leaned up and snaked an arm around her waist. He pulled her down beside him and Camille couldn't get her arms around him fast enough.

He turned on his side and, with a hand at the back of her waist, pressed the length of her body close to his.

"Camille," he whispered against the side of her hair. "I can't believe I have you next to me—like this."

The awe in his voice matched the same wondrous feeling rushing through her. It was euphoric to the point of being scary, she thought. Having Matthew's naked body next to hers wasn't supposed to feel this good. But it did, and she couldn't wipe the smile from her lips or stop her hands from racing over the hard muscles of his arms and back.

"And I can't believe how incredible it feels to touch you. To have you close." She thrust her hand into his hair and allowed the blond curls to slip slowly through her fingers. "I've been dreaming about this—about us. If this is a dream, Matthew, then don't let me wake up."

In the moonlight, she could see his eyes sweeping over her face, and for a moment she thought she saw something real and tender in the gray depths.

"You're not dreaming, sweetheart. Let me prove it to you."

With that, he covered her lips with his in a kiss that was so all-consuming she could only grip his shoulders and hang on for dear life. But he didn't stop with just one kiss. He planted several more of them on her eager lips before he finally departed her moist mouth and started a downward trail to her breasts.

By the time he reached one nipple, Camille's breaths were coming in short, shallow sips. Her limbs felt heavy and lifeless, while the rest of her body felt as though it had been torched by a thousand sunbursts.

He suckled the center of her breast until the needy ache inside her became so unbearable, she lifted his head from the throbbing nipple.

"Matthew—I can't keep waiting!"

"Yes—you can," he said thickly. "Just a little longer."

Before she could protest, his head dropped back to the other breast, and for long moments he gave it the same erotic treatment as he had the other. And then, seemingly satisfied that he'd branded that part of her body, his mouth moved away from her breasts and began a downward trail, along her rib cage and onto her stomach.

When he reached her belly button, he paused long enough to circle it with the tip of his tongue before he moved lower still. The pulsating ache between Camille's thighs had reached the point of agony, and she was about to push his head completely away when his tongue suddenly touched the intimate folds of her womanhood.

"Oooh, Matthew! I—this is—too good—too much!"

As she spoke the last words, his tongue slipped inside and the erotic sensation caused the last thread of her self-control to unravel. Undulating waves of pleasure rippled through her body until she was nothing more than a feather in the wind, floating, twisting helplessly back and forth until consciousness finally returned.

Through a foggy daze, she recognized her hands were clenching fists full of his hair and her legs were wrapped around his waist. She allowed both to fall away from him and he immediately moved up and positioned himself over her.

Breathing hard, she lifted her gaze to his. "If you're trying to kill me, you're coming awfully close."

Smiling, he bent his head and rubbed his cheek against hers. "I'm only trying to please you, sweet Camille. That's all."

She framed his face with both hands and lifted it just enough for her to look into his eyes. "Everything about you pleases me, Matthew."

He smiled down at her. "Even my stubbornness?"

"Even that," she said with a sigh, then pulled his mouth down to hers.

He was quick to take control, and as he kissed her, Camille tasted hot desire, but something else, too. Something very sweet and very tender and so strong it brought a rush of tears to her eyes.

Not wanting him to feel the salty moisture on her cheeks, she furiously blinked it back and slipped her arms around him.

The kiss stoked the fire that was already burning between them, and the familiar ache to her body connected to his started all over again.

To her relief, he didn't make her wait. He entered her with one smooth thrust and then they were both moving together as one, giving and taking with a need so fierce it robbed the breath from her lungs and set her mind free of every single thought but him.

After a long time, or maybe only a few short minutes—Camille couldn't know because she'd lost all sense of time—she felt Matthew urging her faster and faster to the edge of a deep abyss. She didn't want to go there. Because she knew that once she fell, the incredible pleasure he was giving her would all end.

Yet no matter how much she stubbornly tried to hold back, his kisses and the driving thrust of his hips kept tugging and pulling forward, until she had no choice but to follow him.

She heard the harsh intake of his breaths above her, and then he was repeating her name over and over as he clutched her hips and poured himself into her.

Camille clung to him tightly and as she buried her face against his damp chest, she knew her life had been forever changed.

Chapter Seven

Matthew turned his head on the mattress and looked
at Camille's tangled hair and sweat-sheened face. Her
eyes were closed, but not in sleep. Her breasts were still
rising and falling at a rapid pace, and beneath his hand,
he could feel the wild thump of her heart.

The past few minutes had stunned him, and as his
gaze slipped over her smooth little nose and perfectly
bowed lips, he wondered if this was how it felt to actually make love.

Matthew didn't know. He only knew that it hadn't
been anything like the sex he'd had with his ex-wife, or
any other woman for that matter. This union with Camille had been mind-bending, and he still wasn't sure
his senses had returned to full working order.

Her hand moved gently against the middle of his
chest. "Mmm. I think we should get under the covers.
Don't you?"

No, he thought. He should get out of her bedroom as fast as he could. But that idea was totally ludicrous. He could no more leave her side than he could cut off his arm.

"Are you cold?" he asked.

"A little."

"Then we'll get under the covers," he told her.

They both shifted around on the bed until their heads were resting on the pillows and a comforter was covering their bodies.

She snuggled her face into the curve of his neck, and Matthew lifted a long strand of her hair and tested the silky texture between his fingers. Touching her was a precious gift, and he decided that until his time here at Red Bluff was over, he was going to take all the gifts she offered him. Because once he went back to Three Rivers, he knew this thing with her would be over.

"You smell like lily of the valley," he said as he nuzzled his nose in the side of her hair.

A wan smile touched her lips. "How do you know about lilies of the valley?"

"My mother used to wear that scent. That is, whenever she had the money to buy a small bottle."

"It's a simple, old-fashioned fragrance. I suppose that's why I like it. That, and my Great-Grandmother Hollister used to wear it. When I was a little girl she would let me brush her hair and if I did a good job, she'd treat me by dabbing lily of the valley on my neck and wrist. It made me feel like a princess."

"Does it make you feel like a princess now?"

Her fingers slid up and down his arm. "No. But it fills me with warm memories of her and that's even more special."

As he absently stroked his fingers through her hair, he thought about her family and how, in many ways, she was a frontier princess. From the day she was born, Camille's roots were already set deep and solid, whereas Matthew's were so shallow and weak it was a miracle he'd managed to grow into any kind of decent man. The differences between them were staggering, yet here in her bed, with her hands touching him so tenderly, it felt like he belonged in her life and she in his.

"Three Rivers Ranch has been around so long it's a part of Arizona history. I've often wondered what it feels like to come from that sort of legacy. God knows, I'll never experience the feeling."

Her arm settled across his chest and she hugged him close. "You've been at Three Rivers for fourteen years. You've become a part of the family."

In many ways that was true, Matthew thought. Joel and Maureen had taken him in and treated him like a son. He would always love them for giving him a home.

"In a way," he agreed. "But that doesn't change the fact that I'm a Waggoner. Ask anyone around Gila Bend what that name means. My father and uncle left their own kind of legacy."

"You're not in Gila Bend anymore," she gently reminded him. "And you're making your name into something to be proud of."

"Hmm. Right now you're feeling soft and generous. In the daylight you'll see me differently."

She pressed a tiny kiss to the side of his neck. "I've studied you close up in the daylight and I like what I see."

"That's because you're wearing rose-colored sunglasses."

Smiling, she gently pinched his arm and then she

let out a wistful sigh. "Sometimes, Matthew, being a Hollister isn't easy. Did you know the ranch has been going since 1847?"

"Yes."

"Most all of the Hollisters have devoted their lives to the ranch. Some of them even lost their lives in a range war. And then there are the ones like me and Viv, and Joe. And Uncle Gil. He left Three Rivers and became a lawman. He's the reason Joe got the itch to be a deputy."

"And where did you get the itch to be a cook? From your great-grandmother who wore lily of the valley?"

She laughed softly and he momentarily closed his eyes and enjoyed the light, tinkling sound. Until he'd gone to work for the Hollisters he'd never heard much laughter. Oh, Renee had laughed, he thought. But most of the time it had been a cynical sound directed at him. She'd rarely laughed with him. But why would she? Nothing about living with him had made her happy.

As though Camille had been reading his mind, she suddenly asked, "Why did you ever marry Renee?"

He grimaced. "Don't you think this is an awkward time to be asking me that question?"

Propping up her head with her hand, she gazed down at him. "No. I happen to think it's the perfect time. Because I've wondered if you ever wanted her back in your life. In your bed."

He moved his head back and forth against the pillow. "I married Renee because I was very young and didn't know any better. I thought we would be partners. And at that time in my life I really needed one. Someone at my side to support me and encourage me." He paused and let out a cynical snort. "Hellfire, I've never been so wrong about anyone as I was about her. She had no intentions of ever being a cowboy's wife. As soon as the ink dried on the marriage license, she tried to change me. When I refused, she lit out. It was that simple. And no, once she was gone, all I felt was relief. And stupidity."

Her blue eyes traveled softly over his face. "That's the way I felt about Graham," she admitted. "Stupid."

"So why did you ever get engaged to him? I knew right off that he was a jerk."

She let out a low, self-deprecating groan. "I thought being engaged to a rich banker's son would show everybody that I wasn't just the spoiled baby Hollister. I had the crazy idea that being married to Graham would make everyone say, 'Look at Camille. She's really made something of herself.'"

He gave her a reproachful look. "You hardly needed him to be something."

A wry smile slanted her lips. "Dear God, do you know how glad I am that he fell in love with Crystal Thompson and asked for his ring back? I want to laugh until my sides hurt—that's how glad I am."

He smiled back at her and then, as his hand began to roam over the soft curve of her naked hip, he began to chuckle. "You know, I kinda want to laugh about it, too. Now. Now that I have you here with me. Like this."

She laughed with him and then lowered her lips to his ear. "Have you forgotten that we haven't had dessert yet? Want to go down to the kitchen and have some?"

"Mmm. I had forgotten. What did you say you made?"

"Does it matter?"

"Doesn't matter at all," he murmured. "Because my dessert is right here in my arms."

She gently sank her teeth into his earlobe. "That line is so corny it's sweet."

He flipped her over onto her back and as he gazed down at her, he trailed the tips of his fingers along her smooth cheek. "You have it wrong, Camille. This is sweet."

Lowering his head to hers, he placed soft little kisses upon her lips, until one of her hands curled around the back of his neck and anchored his mouth to deepen the kiss.

Her reaction was all it took to ignite a fire low in his belly, and the need to have her all over again caused his lips to turn hungry and urgent.

It was the need for air that finally forced their lips apart, and as her gaze locked with his, her blue eyes glittered with something Matthew had never seen before. Whether it was lust or love or something in between, he couldn't guess. Nor was he going to waste this moment wondering about it. Not when she was melting in his arms.

"Oh, Matthew, I want you—so much."

Maybe for tonight, he'd be enough for her. And maybe for the next two weeks, she'd be satisfied with just having him in her bed. But the future was a different matter.

Pushing the thought out of his head, he pressed a kiss on her forehead. "And I want you, Camille—more—than—you know."

She wrapped her legs around him and as he entered her again, he wondered how he was going to go back to Three Rivers and live without her.

Two days later, Camille locked the front door of the diner and went to work helping Peggy stack chairs as they prepared to shut down for the evening. Gideon had left a half hour ago to hurry home and get ready for his grandchildren's Halloween party, while Edie, the diner's other waitress, had left the diner before him in order to drive her sick sister to see a doctor at Benson.

The day had been busy, but Camille was too happy to be feeling tired. "When are you supposed to be at Gideon's this evening?" she asked Peggy as the women continued to place chairs atop the small square tables.

"I told him I'd be there at six thirty. I have my costume with me so I'll change after I get there."

"What are you going to be, Superwoman?" Camille asked impishly.

Peggy laughed. "I couldn't pull off a bodysuit! No. I'm going as myself—a nasty witch."

"Oh, Peg, you're hardly a witch. Maybe a witch's helper," Camille teased. "But never a nasty one."

"Ha! You've never seen me when I get out of bed at five in the morning," she said, then asked, "What are you going to do for Halloween tonight? Anything special?"

Camille's thoughts went straight to Matthew. She couldn't wait to get home to see him, to have him back in her arms. It was insane how much she wanted the man.

"No, I'll be staying home. In fact, I don't even know what I'm going to cook for supper."

Peggy groaned. "Cook again? After all the cooking you've done today? Uh—no way. Fix yourself a sandwich and have a bowl of ice cream for dessert."

Camille was about to tell her that a sandwich was out of the question when footsteps sounded behind them. She glanced over her shoulder to see Norman standing just inside the swinging doors to the kitchen. What

STELLA BAGWELL   103

was he doing back here? He'd left for home more than two hours ago.

"Camille, let Peggy finish the chairs. I'd like to speak with you in my office."

The short, pudgy man with thinning brown hair turned and disappeared through the swinging back doors to the kitchen. Peggy cast Camille a speculative glance.

"Wonder what he wants? Lord, I hope he's not planning on cutting our wages. I'm barely making ends meet as it is."

Shaking her head, Camille plopped the chair she was holding onto the top of a table, then started out of the room. "I don't think it's anything like that. I'm hoping he's decided to hop on the idea of the blue plate special!"

Norman's office was a little cubbyhole of a room directly behind the kitchen. The space was windowless and always hot, and since she'd gone to work for the man, she'd never once seen the top of his desk. There were too many stacks of papers, coffee cups and manila folders to actually see the wood beneath.

"You wanted to talk with me, Norman?" she asked as she stepped into the cluttered space.

He gestured to the folding chair in front of his desk. "Yes, sit down, Camille."

She moved a nylon jacket and a box of table napkins from the chair, then took a seat. "We had a whale of a lunch run today," she told him. "We're going to have to put bread, steak fingers and gravy mix on the food order list."

He waved his hand in a dismissive way. "That's not what I wanted to talk to you about. In fact, you're going

to have to start taking care of all the orders and ship-
ments."

She stared blankly at him. "Me? Why? Are you taking some time off or something?"

"Permanent time off." He turned his palms up in a
gesture of resignation. "I've decided I'm going to sell
the diner to you. That is, if you still want it."

Camille's heart was suddenly thumping loudly in
her ears. Two months had passed since she'd made an
offer to Norman for the diner, and in between then and
now, he'd not given her any sort of hint as to his feelings on the matter.

Incredulous, she scooted to the edge of the chair.
"Are you serious?"

He nodded. "Jan and I talked it over. I don't have to
tell you I was reluctant about the idea. This place has
been my baby for many years and it's been good to
us." His shrug was a sign of surrender. "But we both
decided that time is ticking by. We want to do some of
that traveling we've always talked about."

Seeing he was actually sincere about his decision,
excitement bubbled inside her. "You've stunned me,
Norm. Are you sure you really want to do this?"

The smile he gave her was a bit melancholy. "Yes.
With the understanding that you're still willing to give
what you offered. We think it's a fair price."

"Oh, yes! The price is fine with me!" She jumped up
from the chair and clapped her hands with glee. "Thank
you, Norm. Thank you! This is wonderful!"

Her happy reaction caused him to shake his head
with dismay. "A few months from now I hope you still
feel the same way. Running this place isn't easy, Camille. I don't have to tell you that it's more than just

cooking. There's finding the right food distributors, keeping deliveries on schedule, the utilities and licenses and insurance. I could go on and on, you know."

"I'm not blind, Norm. I've seen how hard you work and everything it involves, but I believe I can handle the job."

"Good. I'm glad you feel confident about it. Now I can go home and give Jan the news. I promised to take her to Tucson tonight. It's our wedding anniversary and she wants to go shopping."

"Congratulations! You've sold the diner, so tell Jan she can buy as much as she wants," Camille joked.

He let out a mocking laugh. "Ha! Technically I've just become unemployed. She'll have to cut back on her spending."

Camille laughed. "Norm, you can't fool me. I'll bet you have the first penny you ever made."

He smiled knowingly. "Not exactly. But I will say the diner has been good to me. And I hope it will be just as successful with you at the helm, Camille."

"Thank you, Norm." She reached across the desk and shook his hand. "So, when do you want to officially do the deal? I'll need to make some banking arrangements."

"I'll have the papers drawn up next week," he told her. "In the meantime, you might want to give Peggy and Gideon and Edie the news. Just in case they hear a rumor and worry. Jan says she won't say a peep, but that's like me saying I won't eat a bite of your pie."

Camille laughed. "Okay. And they needn't worry. I'd never dream of replacing them. They're like family."

Norman nodded, and after they discussed a few more minor details about the sale, he ended the meeting and left for home. Once he was gone, Camille raced into the dining area, where Peggy was just finishing the mopping.

She grabbed her friend around the waist and with a loud whoop, swung her around in a joyous circle.

"Camille!" the waitress exclaimed. "What the heck are you doing? My floor! We're making tracks on my wet floor!"

Laughing, Camille tugged her into the kitchen and after pushing her down on a step chair, explained that she was buying the diner from Norman.

"You're kidding, right?" Peggy asked in disbelief.

"No. I'm very serious. The diner is going to be mine. We're doing the deal next week."

"Oh, my word! This is unbelievable. I knew that you pitched the idea to him about the blue plate special, but I had no idea that you'd tried to buy the place!" Peggy shook her head. "Uh—Camille, are you absolutely sure about this? Look at what running the diner all these years has done to Norman. He's bald and overweight and has high blood pressure."

Undaunted, Camille shook her head. "I understand it will be lots of work. But I intend to run the place a little differently, and if business picks up and we need more help, I'll hire more help. Until then, you and Gideon and Edie will be my extra helping hands. And don't worry, I intend to keep your salaries and benefits as they are. And possibly make them better."

As the reality began to sink in for Peggy, she gathered Camille in a tight hug. "This is just wonderful, Camille. Now I don't have to worry about you leaving and going back to Three Rivers."

Camille smiled wanly. "No. My home is on Red

Bluff now. And I don't expect my family is going to be thrilled with the news about the diner. But I think they'll eventually get used to the idea." The faint smile fell from her face as she suddenly thought about Matthew. Her darling Matthew. In a way, their relationship was just now beginning, but to Camille it felt as though she'd loved him for ages and ages.

Loved him? No, Camille. You don't love Matthew. At least, not yet. You love how he makes you feel. You love to look at him, listen to his voice and have his arms around you. You need to have him near and want to believe that he needs the same from you. But to love him with the deepest part of your heart? To spend all the days of your life with him? No. It's too soon for you to feel that much.

"Camille? What's wrong? You look sad. Are you worrying about your family?"

Shaking her head, she gave her friend a reassuring hug. "No. I'm not worried about them. I was just thinking—about someone and wondering how he's going to take the news."

Peggy's dark eyes narrowed with speculation and Camille blushed under the scrutiny.

"He?" she questioned. "I didn't realize you had a man in your life."

"I didn't realize it, either. Until recently." Pausing, Camille let out a sigh that was both dreamy and hopeless. "I—you see, I've known this man since I was a teenager, but we were never close—I mean, other than casual friends. And since I moved down here to Red Bluff, I'd not seen him in more than two years. Not until he and some of the ranch hands came down this past week to move cattle onto the grazing ranges."

"So he's a cowboy?"

Camille nodded, while thinking the term didn't begin to describe all the things that Matthew was as a man and as the foreman of Three Rivers Ranch.

"He's the foreman of my family's ranch and has been since around the time my father died."

Peggy's lips formed a big round O. "That was several years ago. Why are you just now developing a thing for this man?"

Camille had asked herself that very same question and she'd come to the conclusion that there was not one certain answer. "First of all, he was married a long time ago. That's when I was a senior in high school. She was a fluff head and it didn't last long. After that, he pretty much shied away from women. Which was understandable."

"Hmm. Because after her, he couldn't trust women?" Peggy asked.

Shaking her head, Camille said, "I think it was more like he couldn't trust his judgment in women."

Peggy slanted her a meaningful look. "I've heard you say the same thing about yourself and men. But if you're seeing this guy, then you've obviously gotten rid of that fear."

No, Camille thought, she was a long way from getting over that anxiety. Maybe if she knew for certain that Matthew loved her, she'd feel confident about him, about herself and the future. But since the night he'd gone to bed with her, Matthew hadn't come close to voicing the *L* word to her. In fact, he'd skirted so far around it that sometimes she felt the chasm between them was as wide as the Grand Canyon.

"I'm trying to get past that. And I believe he's trying, too," she said. Then, with a rueful groan, she sank onto the wooden stool sitting near the work counter and covered her face with her hands. "Oh, Peggy, I'm so mixed up. I'm thrilled and happy and worried all at the same time. I don't know what's going to happen with me and Matthew. He'll be going home in another week or so and I have this terrible feeling that he won't be back. Not until next fall."

Frowning, Peggy questioned, "Next fall? I don't know a whole lot about ranching, but if the cattle are here for the winter, won't he have to come back in the spring to get them and take them back to the other ranch?"

"You're right. Come spring, most of the cows and calves will be moved back to Three Rivers. But at that time of the year Matthew doesn't come down here to Red Bluff. It's a terribly busy time at the big ranch. What with spring roundup and branding, my brother, Blake, can't spare Matthew. He sends a different crew of ranch hands down here in the spring. And anyway, seeing a man, even twice a year, couldn't be counted as a relationship."

"I see about the ranching and the cattle. But I don't see everything about you. Or maybe I do," she said. Then, leaving her seat on the step chair, she walked over and placed a steadying hand on Camille's shoulder. "I'm getting the feeling, my dear friend, that you're falling for this guy in a big way."

Dropping her hands away from her face, Camille looked uncertainly at the other woman. "Okay, Peggy, I'll be honest. I'm getting the feeling that I'm falling for him, too. He makes me happier than I've ever been in my life. But he's been divorced for nearly ten years and ever since then he's chosen to remain single. He doesn't want a wife or children. That doesn't leave me with anything except a short, hot affair."

Thoughtful now, Peggy walked to the end of the cabinet and dumped the grounds from the industrial-sized coffeemaker. "Now you're buying the diner. Which means your life is going to be here, while his life is up in Yavapai County. It might be a little hard to have any kind of affair with more than two hundred miles between you."

Sighing, Camille slipped off the stool. "I can't worry about that. I tried giving up my wants and wishes for a man before and it didn't work. I'm not going to give up my dream for this diner, or my home on Red Bluff. I can't see how Matthew and I can happily fit our lives together. But I'm hoping for a miracle. They do happen, you know."

Peggy made a cynical grunt. "Maybe at Christmastime. But today is Halloween. You're a long way off from a Christmas miracle."

Chapter Eight

"You wanta go to Benson with us tonight, Matthew?" Pate asked him as he and the rest of the men unsaddled their mounts. "It's Halloween. We want to see if we can go stir up a bit of mischief."

As TooTall predicted, yesterday they'd captured the last four steers and turned them in with the other sixteen to be shipped to Three Rivers. Today Matthew, TooTall, Pate and Abel had moved two separate herds to the eastern slopes of the ranch. The area had been thick with more chaparral and Matthew knew his horse was probably carrying just as many thorns in his hide as he was in his arms. The notion of going out on the town was enough to make him curse.

"No. Not interested in going to Benson. And the mischief better not be any more than drinking a beer or two," he warned the young cowboy. "I don't aim to bail any of you out of jail."

"Aww, Matthew. Sometimes you act like an old man. Don't you ever wanta have fun?"

"Depends on what you call fun." Matthew hefted his saddle onto his shoulder and started into the tack room, all the while thinking that young Pate wasn't all wrong. In many ways, Matthew was like an old man, because he'd never had the chance to be a child or a teenager. He'd been too busy trying to work at any kind of job he could find to help his mother and sister and himself stay afloat. Fun had always been something for the other kids to have, not Matthew Waggoner.

"Don't worry, Yellow Hair," TooTall said as he followed him into the tack room. "We won't let the little greenhorn do anything silly."

Matthew said, "I'm not worried, TooTall. Just be careful driving. That's all I ask."

TooTall hung a bridle and breast collar on pegs running along one wall, then turned and glanced at Matthew. "You look tired, friend."

"I'm okay," he replied. "We had a long day."

"Yes, but a good day. You should be happy."

"I am happy, TooTall. See?" He plastered a wide grin on his face.

His eyes narrowed shrewdly, TooTall waved a dismissive hand at him. "That's phony. Not honest."

Sighing, Matthew sat down on a low wooden bench and began to unbuckle his spurs. "Okay. Whatever you say, TooTall."

"I say you have a sickness. In here."

Matthew glanced up to see the ranch hand tapping a finger to the middle of his chest. The idea that TooTall could be so damned perceptive was downright annoying and he couldn't help but glare at him.

"I don't have any kind of sickness," he retorted.

"Yes," he countered. "Are you homesick?"

Homesick. That might be the perfect word for what he was feeling, Matthew thought. He was homesick but not for Three Rivers. He was sick from continually longing for something he knew he couldn't have. Like having Camille as his wife and the mother of his children. Like having a real home with her, where they would always be together. Where she would never walk away from him for any reason.

"No. I'm tired and I'm hungry. And I'm thinking we'd better check the water well pumps in Coyote Valley before we put in cattle there."

"Coyote Valley? Are we going there tomorrow?" Abel asked as he entered the tack room carrying a stack of sweaty saddle pads. "That's miles away from the ranch yard."

"That's right," Matthew told him. "So you guys better not get sick tonight on Halloween candy. You're going to have a hard day in the saddle tomorrow."

"Halloween candy?" Pate asked blankly as he joined the group in the tack room. "Who's going to be eating candy? I thought we were going to the Trail's End."

Abel rolled his eyes. "He's talking about the liquid kind, goofy."

"Oh. Well, don't let one little worry go through your head, Matthew," Pate said smugly. "I'll make sure everybody stays in line."

Abel grabbed the young cowboy by the back of the collar and playfully kicked him out the door.

TooTall patted Matthew's shoulder. "You go on to the house, Boss. I'll take care of your horse."

"He has thorns," Matthew told him.

"I'll take care of him," he reiterated. "You go."

Matthew thanked him and left the tack room.

Outside, darkness shrouded the ranch yard and with the disappearance of the sun, cool air had moved in. After working in the heat all day, the drop in temperature put a spring in his step and he turned the long walk to the ranch house into short work.

When he stepped up to the back door, he noticed there were no lights on in the kitchen. Which was unusual. At this time of the day, Camille wouldn't be anywhere else. But to give the men a much-needed break, Matthew had called it a day a little earlier than usual this evening. She might be upstairs in the shower, or changing out of the clothes she'd worn to work.

After letting himself in, he discovered the kitchen was quiet, along with the rest of the house. The cold greeting pointed out just how much he'd come to expect being greeted by Camille's warm smile and even warmer kiss.

Well, you might as well get used to this, Matthew. This is the way it's going to be when you go home to Three Rivers. No dinners or conversation. No teasing or laughter. And especially no loving arms wrapped around you or kisses to send you to paradise. So get used to it, cowboy. You made your bed with Camille, but it's not going to last forever.

Shaking away the miserable voice going off in his head, Matthew quickly stripped out of his dirty clothes and stepped into the shower. At least he'd be clean whenever Camille did show up.

He'd dried off and pulled on a pair of jeans when he heard Camille's light footsteps scurrying down the hallway, and then she was standing in the open doorway, her face a beaming picture of sunshine.

"Knock, knock! May I come in?"

Damn, but it was crazy how just the sound of her voice thrilled him, he thought. He grinned at her. "Sure. I don't think I could stop you anyway."

She walked into the room and didn't stop until she'd smacked a kiss on his lips. "I'm sorry I wasn't here when you got home. I was detained at the diner by my boss. Or I guess I should say used-to-be boss."

He studied her sparkling blue eyes. "Maybe you should explain that part about used-to-be."

With a light laugh, she wrapped her hand around his and tugged him over to the bed. "Let's sit while I explain."

He slanted her a wry look. "You think this is safe sitting here?"

She chuckled. "I think we can control ourselves for a few minutes. So let me tell you what's happened. It's very exciting."

An uneasy feeling rippled through him. "Okay," he said. "What's happened?"

The smile on her face grew even wider. "Norman is selling the diner to me! That's why I'm late. He wanted to talk it over with me to make sure I was still interested."

"And you told him that you were?"

"I couldn't get yes out fast enough!"

Matthew could see she was on the verge of jumping up and down with glee and he wanted to share in her happiness. But her announcement was the same as erecting a fence between them. She was digging her roots here in Cochise County, far away from him. And yet, he couldn't blame her for going after what she wanted in her life.

"This is big news," he said. "So, when will you be making the deal?"

"Sometime next week, after Norman gets the paperwork together." She squeezed his hand. "Oh, Matthew, I'm so excited. There's so much I want to do with the place. Changes I want to make with the menu and the building itself. It's going to be a lot of work, but that just makes something more worthwhile, don't you think? When you invest your all in it?"

Yes, Matthew knew about investing his all into something. For the past fourteen years, he'd invested his whole life into Three Rivers Ranch. He meant something there. His work was important and so was his relationship with the Hollister family. He could never leave it.

He gave her a wan smile. "Sure it does. And I'm happy for you, Camille. I hope it's a huge success for you."

Her beaming expression turned doubtful. "Are you really happy for me, Matthew?"

He cupped his hand to the side of her face and she immediately rubbed her cheek against the callused skin of his palm. She was the most sensual woman he'd ever known and just looking at her turned him on. After making love to Camille, no other woman would do. So where did that leave him?

His throat suddenly felt like someone was choking him. "I meant what I said. Why? You don't believe me?"

She shrugged and looked sheepishly down at their clasped hands. "Yes—but I honestly wasn't expecting you to say that. I thought you'd be chastising me for jumping into something so—well, big. Under the best of circumstances, the food service business is iffy. I could possibly fail."

Her gaze lifted back to his face and the look in her

blue eyes was so tender he almost believed it was love. But what did he know about love? he cynically asked himself. He probably wouldn't know the emotion if it slapped him in the face.

"You're not going to fail, Camille. I have faith in you."

His words put the sunny smile back on her face and with a little cry of joy, she wrapped her arms around his neck. "Matthew, you can't know what that means to me. Especially when I think of what my family is going to say when they get the news. Especially Blake. He's not going like it at all."

He circled his arms around her. "Blake is living his life the way he chooses. You should have the chance to do the same."

She reared her head and looked at him. "I think you honestly mean that."

"Why wouldn't I? Renee tried to change me and made me miserable in the process. No one should try to change you, either."

She gave him another soft, melting look, then pulled out of his arms and stood. "Thank you, Matthew. Now I'd better go find something to fix for supper. It's Halloween! Or have you forgotten about it?"

Rising to his feet, he reached for the clean shirt that he'd laid on the end of the bed before his shower. "No. I've not forgotten. Tonight is for treating. I thought we might drive over to Benson and have dinner out. We've not ever been anywhere together."

She leveled a mischievous look at him. "We've been to bed together," she pointed out. "But that's not like a date, is it?"

He laughed. "Not exactly."

Laughing with him, she hurried toward the open

doorway. "Okay, give me a few minutes to get out of these greasy clothes and fix myself up."

"You got it," he told her.

She vanished from sight, and Matthew could hear her light footsteps racing down the hallway, then climbing the stairs to her bedroom. As he shrugged into his shirt, he walked over to the dresser mirror and stared at his image.

Everything looked the same, he thought. And yet, everything inside him felt different. How in hell could he be so encouraging and thoughtful at a time like this? She might as well have planted a flag out in the court-yard that read, *I'm here to stay and to hell with Matthew Waggoner.*

Muttering a curse under his breath, he reached for a hairbrush and tugged it through his damp blond curls. There wasn't any reason for him to be anything but en-couraging and thoughtful. Just because they were hav-ing a sexual relationship didn't mean she cared about him. Really cared, like I'll-follow-you-to-the-ends-of-the-earth kind of caring. So he needed to snap out of it and get real. This thing with her was just a pleasur-able escapade, a brief break from his days of horses and cattle and corralling a group of cowboys.

Camille and Matthew had dinner at a modest little Mexican café located on the edge of town, not far from the Trail's End nightclub where Pate and the guys had gone to kick up their heels.

The food was delicious, but Matthew could've been eating bread and carrot sticks and washing it down with water and he wouldn't have known the difference. He wasn't sure what exactly Camille had done to herself to-night, but she looked like a piece of treasure all wrapped in a gold-and-brown-patterned dress that clung to her curves and pulled out the fiery glints in her hair. Her hair was different, too. The long strands were looped and pinned to the top of head, while a few of them had been left loose to trail down the middle of her back. Large gold hoops swung in her ears, and red lipstick made her whole face glow.

Hell, he wasn't supposed to be with a woman like this, he thought. She was so far out of his league, it was laughable. But he wasn't laughing. His heart wasn't in the mood for it.

"They make great tres leches cake here," Camille told him. "If you're hankering for dessert."

"I'm full to the brim," he told her. "But you get a piece if you like."

She shook her head. "Actually, there's something else I'd like to do. If you're agreeable, that is."

He pushed his plate away. "What is it?"

She cast him an eager smile. "On the way back to Red Bluff, I thought we might swing by Dragoon. I'd love to show you the diner. It's closed, obviously, but I have a key."

He could see just how much it meant to her, and the fact that she wanted to share this part of her life with him made him feel just a bit special.

"I'd like that."

He motioned to the waiter and after he'd taken care of the bill, they left the café. As Matthew drove his truck east toward Dragoon, Camille put the subject of the diner aside and instead questioned him about his day.

Then she said, "You're probably going to laugh at this, but I've been thinking about getting one of the paints out and riding next Sunday after church. That's about the only day I have for it."

Surprised, he glanced at her. "How long has it been since you've ridden?"

"Oh, not that long ago. When Hannah and Nick come down, I usually try to ride once or twice with them. Of course, you have to be ready for a marathon ride with those two. They never want to get out of the saddle."

Vivian's daughter, Hannah, and Blake's son, Nick, weren't just cousins, they were the best of friends and both shared a love of horses. Occasionally Vivian would bring the two kids down so they could ride over the more gentle areas of Red Bluff.

"I can't recall the last time I saw you on a horse," he said.

She laughed. "It's not always a pretty sight, but most of the time I don't hit the dirt."

They traveled a mile or more in silence before he said, "Actually, Blake has given me another job besides moving cattle."

Camille frowned. "What's come over him? Is he becoming a taskmaster or something?"

"No. He's asked me to stay a few days longer than we'd first planned on. He wants me to look over the whole property. He's thinking about running more cattle down here year-round."

Wide-eyed, she turned slightly toward him. "Seriously?"

"That's right. Three Rivers has been thriving. He wants to invest and broaden its assets."

She shook her head. "But he needs the space down here for winter grazing. That won't work if he has it full of cattle all year long."

"Good deduction, Camille. You are truly a rancher's daughter."

"Thanks. But even a child could see the problem with running out of grazing land."

"Nothing concrete has been said to me, but I'm getting the impression that Blake and your mother are planning on purchasing more land down in this area. If they can find something suitable."

"Hmm. That's very interesting. But what has any of that got to do with me horseback riding?"

"Well, it means I'm going to put you to work. We can ride together and you can help me look the land over."

A wide smile spread over her lips and then she laughed. "Oh my goodness, the foreman of Three Rivers Ranch is going to see how I sit a saddle! Okay. But you promise you won't laugh at me?"

"I promise I'll never laugh at you, Camille. With you. But never at you."

She reached for his hand and when she lifted the knuckles of his fingers to her lips, he wanted to stop the truck on the side of the highway and pull her into his arms. He wanted to tell her all the wants and wishes and feelings that were swirling inside him and tearing at his heart.

But he couldn't expose himself like that to her. She wasn't in this thing with him for the long haul. All she wanted from him was sex.

Yeah, wouldn't it be great, Matthew thought, if he could go back to the days when sex was all *he* wanted.

Chapter Nine

The Lost Antelope was a long, squatty building with stucco walls painted turquoise. The roof was terra-cotta tiles and the window frames and door were stained dark brown. Two large plate glass windows sat on either side of the door. In the left window, a neon sign advertised a popular beer, while in the opposite window hung a metal sign that simply read: Good Food.

The parking area was plain dirt with a faint bit of gravel left over from years gone by. At the back of the building, a rickety windmill was shrouded with mesquite trees.

Camille's beloved diner was like nothing he'd been expecting, and for long minutes after he cut the truck motor, he simply stared out the windshield.

"What's wrong? You're not saying a word," she said.

"No. I'm thinking."

"Well, if you were expecting a fancy café with outdoor seating and half-naked waitresses serving espressos, then you should be disappointed. It's just a simple place with good food—just like the sign says."

"I'm not disappointed," he told her. "I'm surprised, that's all. It just doesn't seem your style."

"Hmm. What is my style, Matthew? Something more modern and expensive-looking?"

"All right, I confess," he said sheepishly. "I was thinking along those lines."

She cast him a reproachful look before she shoved off her seat belt and opened the truck door. "Come on. Let's go in and I'll show you around."

He walked at her side across the hard-packed ground to the back of the building, where a security light illuminated a single metal door.

Since the diner sat on a lonely spot near the highway and wasn't exactly a part of the tiny settlement of Dragoon, Matthew wouldn't be surprised to learn it was often vandalized—although he couldn't see any sign of prior damage to the door or the walls of the stucco structure.

"How many times has this place been robbed?" he asked.

"Never. Norman always takes the money home with him in the evening. I like to believe little desert angels guard the place, because it's never been defaced or damaged. The insurance on the property is outrageous. But that's to be expected."

She unlocked the door, pushed it open and reached around the left wall. Fluorescent lighting instantly flooded a square room with shelves built into the walls on three sides. As Matthew followed her inside, he glanced around at the industrial-sized canned goods, along with an assortment of boxes that were jammed and stacked in every available space.

"This is where we store most of the nonperishable food," she told him. "And a few odds and ends like table napkins and paper towels and that sort of thing."

He was amazed at the volume of stored food. "You actually use all this? Looks like there's enough stock-piled in here to feed a small army."

She looked amused. "Norm is ordering all the time. Otherwise, these shelves would be wiped out."

Motioning for him to follow her, she reached through an open doorway leading into a connecting room and switched on another light. As the two of them moved forward, she said, "In this area is where we keep the refrigerated and frozen foods."

Matthew glanced around at several refrigerators, the sizes ranging from small to large, plus two huge upright freezers. The floor was bare concrete and the cinder-block walls painted pale green. So far, everything he'd seen was impeccably clean and neat.

"One of the freezers is sort of iffy at times. We keep a close watch on the thermometer to make sure the com-pressor isn't going on the blink."

"You don't have a walk-in freezer?" he asked.

Shaking her head, she said, "No. Norm considered it, but the cost of running the thing wasn't going to be feasible."

She flipped another light switch, then pushed through a single swinging door that was colored the same green as the walls. They stepped into a small kitchen and Matthew gazed curiously around him. The space was equipped with a large flat grill and another stove with six large gas burners and an oven below. On the opposite wall from the stoves was a long row of cabinets with a wooden work counter. The scars made from cutting and chopping covered nearly every inch of the worn surface.

"And this is my domain," she said with a proud smile. "It's where I spend my days. Yours is out on the range and mine is in front of one. Only it's a different kind of range."

She was obviously in love with the place. A fact that totally mystified Matthew. She'd always been Joel's little princess and even after her father died, the rest of the family had continued to treat her as such. She'd been the pampered sibling of the Hollister clan and he couldn't ever remember seeing her with grubby hands or wearing dirty work clothes. Apparently that Camille hadn't been the person she'd wanted to be.

"Do you have everything here in the kitchen that you need? Or do you have plans for this part of the diner?" he asked.

"It's enough to get by. Later, if I see that business continues to pick up, I'd like to have a larger oven installed for more baking." She pointed to the cabinets behind him. "That's where we keep all the pots and pans and cooking utensils. Over there on the other wall are the glasses and cups and serving dishes. Although we don't use a lot of the dishes because most things are served in baskets. Which makes Gideon happy. He has less to wash."

"And Gideon is?"

"Our busboy and dishwasher. He's an older gentleman—a widower and a war veteran, in fact. He's lived in Dragoon ever since he got out of the military. Actually, he's throwing a Halloween party for his grandchildren tonight. That's the kind of big-hearted guy he is."

"Your coworker is having a party and you didn't go? Or weren't you invited?"

Her smile turned coy. "Oh, sure I was invited. But I begged off. I wasn't about to miss being with you. It's not like you'll be here much longer and I see my coworkers all the time."

Matthew felt honored that she'd chosen to be with him tonight, but it wasn't enough to overcome the sick little feeling that hit him every time he thought of their dwindling days together. "Then I'm glad we went out for dinner tonight. Your Halloween wasn't a total bust."

She wrapped her arm around his and the soft laugh that passed her lips was utterly sexy. "The night isn't over yet. And I have a few tricks and treats planned for you."

He was trying not to let his mind go there as she urged him forward and through a pair of swinging wooden doors. The security lamps out in the parking area shed plenty of light for him to see the rows of tables and chairs, plus a small checkout counter located in one corner of the room.

"Here's the dining area," she announced. "And this is where I'd like to make most of the changes. Like knocking out the east wall and adding more space. As long as a construction crew can promise to keep the outside looking exactly the same, that is. The simplicity of the place is its charm and I don't want to take that away."

She was right, Matthew thought. If she knocked this building down and replaced it with a fancy new one, she'd end up cooking for herself. "It does have character," he agreed. "What about its name? Are you considering changing it?"

She shook her head. "Not at all. There's folklore behind it. Seems as though back in the late eighteen hundreds there was a prospector camped on this spot, and one night an antelope came up to his campfire. He tried to shoo the animal away, but day after day the antelope kept returning. After a while the prospector figured out the antelope must have gotten lost from the herd and his family and friends had moved on without him."

He slanted her a droll glance. "A lost, lonely antelope, huh? Do you believe that story?"

"Absolutely. And why not? Even wild animals crave company. Like the mustangs and coyotes. They band together in families."

Yes, those wild animals had more of a loving family instinct than any of the Waggoner men had possessed, he thought ruefully. "Have you ever thought the prospector might have shot the antelope and eaten it?" he asked.

She pinched the top of his forearm. "Oh, Matthew, no! The prospector and the antelope became great buddies and lived happily ever after—together. That's how the story goes and that's why this diner will always be The Lost Antelope."

He gazed down at her and as he studied her glowing face, it struck him that her happiness meant far more to him than his own. If that meant he loved her, then he was up to his neck in trouble.

"It fits this place—and you," he said gently.

She looked up at him, and just for a second Matthew thought he saw a tremble on her lower lip. "So, what do you think about the place, Matthew? Do you believe I'm making a mistake to buy it?"

Earlier this evening at Red Bluff he probably would've told her, hell yeah, it was a whopper of a mistake. But now, seeing the diner and her in it, he'd had a complete change of heart. During the last few years she'd lived at Three Rivers, he'd never seen her looking this happy.

"It's not a mistake to follow your heart. I'm glad you've found the courage to do that, Camille. Not all of us are strong enough."

Her expression turned pensive. "You can't be talking about yourself. You're one of the bravest men I've ever known. Not for just the things you do on the job, but for all the things you've survived in your life. That takes enormous courage."

Her praise swelled his chest, yet it also made him feel like the biggest fraud ever born. Even if he'd known exactly how to describe his feelings for her, he wasn't brave enough to try to explain them to her. But then, why bother with that? he wondered cynically. His feelings wouldn't change the fact that their lives were too different to merge together on a permanent basis.

"Let's hope there aren't any Halloween goblins on Red Bluff when we get home," he joked in an effort to lighten the moment. "Then you'll see what a 'fraidy cat I am."

She chuckled. "Sure, Mr. Waggoner. Don't worry, I'll chase them away for you."

As soon as they entered the house back at Red Bluff, Camille took him by the hand, and together they climbed the stairs to her bedroom. Inside the darkened room, Camille methodically went about removing her clothes, while Matthew did the same.

It was bittersweet, she thought, how comfortable and at home they felt with each other. Like a couple who'd been together for a long, long time. Had it been only a week since he'd walked into the house and into her life? And did she only have a week plus a few more days left with him?

The questions left an aching knot in her throat, but she quickly attempted to swallow it away. Tonight was too special to ruin with worries. Like she'd told Peggy, there was always a miracle, and she was going to hold on to that hope.

Behind her, she heard a plunk and then another as his boots hit the floor. The sound was followed by the rustle of his jeans and then, just as she was unfastening the last hoop from her earlobe, he came up behind her and his strong arms wrapped around her waist.

Tossing the earring to the dresser, she turned and, with a groan of pleasure, slipped her arms around him.

"Happy Halloween, Matthew," she whispered.

He kissed her softly. "Happy Halloween to you, Camille."

Bending slightly, he picked her up in his arms and carried her to the bed. Once he was lying next to her, he rolled to his side and pulled her tight against him.

As her gaze soaked in the rugged angles and curves of his features, she traced the tip of her forefinger over his lips. "How did you celebrate Halloween when you were a child? Eat yourself sick with candy?"

He caught hold of her hand and kissed the palm. "I liked the candy, but what I remember most at Halloween was my sister telling me spooky stories. I'd be so afraid I would pull the covers over my head and cry."

"Cry?" She stroked her fingers through his hair. "Oooh, Matthew, that's—awful. Why were you so afraid? Didn't anyone explain that it was all make-believe?"

His lips twisted. "Sis would tell me later that it was all just a story and there weren't any such things as ghosts and goblins. But I didn't believe her. Why should I? All I'd ever known was bad things."

That Matthew should remember such a sad part of his childhood, a period of his life that should have been filled with joyful imagination, tore a hole right through Camille.

"Well, there're no spooky stories tonight. No bad things lurking in the shadows." She smiled gently at him. "But we can get under the covers if you like."

He smiled back at her and then, closing his eyes, he pressed his cheek against hers. "I think we'll be fine just like this."

"We'll be more than fine."

And as the two of them began to make love, Camille held onto that sweet thought.

Fridays were always extra busy at The Lost Ante-lope, and this Friday was no exception. It was ten thirty in the morning before Camille found the time to take a small break.

"Gideon, I'm going out back for a minute or two," she said as she passed the older man, who was up to his elbows in soapy dishwater. "If Edie takes any new orders, yell at me, okay?"

"Sure, Camille. Take your time. Maybe the lunch folks won't start for a few minutes."

Outside, at the back of the building, Camille sat down on a low wooden bench situated beneath the twisted branches of a thorny mesquite tree. The sun was already hot, but the wind was whipping around like a storm was coming, stirring up dust from the dry ground.

She pulled out her phone and, after turning her back to the wind, punched in her mother's number.

The last she'd spoken with Maureen, she and the men had finished moving the cattle from the Prescott area, but that hardly meant that her mother was sitting around sipping tea and painting her fingernails. Most likely she was down at the barns, or out riding with the boys from the bunkhouse to check on cattle.

"Hello, sweetheart," Maureen answered after five long rings. "This is a surprise to hear from you in the middle of the morning. You must've taken off work today."

"No. I finally found a minute to put up my feet. And I wanted to call and share some news with you. Are you very busy right now?"

"No. Actually, I'm here with Blake in his office. We were just discussing some things about the ranch. It's nothing urgent."

Camille let out a long breath. She'd much rather have given the news to her mother while the other woman was alone. But in the end, she supposed it hardly mattered. As soon as Camille hung up the phone, her mother would spread the news to Blake and the rest of the family anyway.

She said, "I'm glad, since I don't have much time to talk."

"Is anything wrong, Camille? You sound sort of strained."

Camille grimaced. "I'm not strained. Well, to be honest, I was dreading making this call. Because I expect you're going to be upset."

"All right. What's happened? Is Matthew okay?"

Matthew was incredible. Long before daylight, she'd woken up with his face next to hers on the pillow and they made love again before the sun had ever crested over the eastern mountains. She didn't know where the man found his energy, and frankly she was wondering where hers was coming from. It was as though being with him energized her whole body and soul.

"Matthew is fine—very busy. It's me that I'm calling about. I've made a deal with Norman—Mr. Kimball. I'm buying the diner from him. We'll be finalizing the deal in the next day or two."

A long, long stretch of silence passed before Maureen finally spoke. "I see. Well, I—honestly don't know what to say."

Disappointment fell like a heavy weight on Camille's shoulders. "Why don't you start with congratulations? That would be the nice thing to do."

Maureen said, "Your mother isn't always nice, Camille. I don't have to tell you that."

No, she thought, Maureen could be a fierce tiger when you got her riled. But Camille could be just as fierce. And determined.

"I wasn't exactly expecting well wishes from you," Camille told her. "But I did want to let you know."

"Thanks for that much," she said with plenty of sarcasm, then let out a rueful sigh. "I'm sorry, Camille. I really am. I want to be happy for you. But you know

what this means to me. I was hoping—even praying—
that you'd be coming home to Three Rivers soon. Everyone here misses you and there's no need for you to
be down at Red Bluff all by yourself. But I guess—you
coming back is out of the question now."

"Yes. My life is here now, Mom. I've been trying to
tell you and the rest of the family that for a long time.
But you've all had this crazy idea that I was down here
pining away instead of actually doing and living."

"Yes, but a diner, Camille. You're going to be sinking money into a questionable business and—"

"Mom, this diner has been a profitable business for
Norm for more than twenty years and it was a money-
maker long before he purchased the place. If I do things
right it's going to remain profitable. Or don't you think
I can manage things as well as Blake or Chandler or
Viv, or—"

"Stop it, Camille!" she interrupted. "This has nothing to do with your brothers or sister. This is about
your mother voicing her concerns about the choices
you're making!"

"I'm going on thirty years old, Mom. I have a right
to make those choices, even if you disapprove. The way
I see it, Red Bluff is an important part of Three Rivers.
I want to be here—on this end of things."

"I want to be happy for you, Camille. I honestly do.
But—"

"Then why aren't you?" Camille interrupted. "Matthew is happy for me. He thinks I'm doing the right
thing. I just wish you would believe in me as much as
he does."

There was another long pause and it struck Camille
that she'd probably said too much about Matthew. But

that was okay, too. She was tired of hiding her feelings and wants and wishes.

"Oh? You've been talking to Matthew about this?"

"Of course. He's living in the house, Mom," she reminded her. "It's not like we stare at each other in stony silence."

"Uh—no, I recall you saying how much you were enjoying his company. Well, at least you have him in your corner."

Camille very nearly laughed. "You make him sound like a traitor just because he wants me to be happy."

"No. It's not that. You just sound so different, Camille. Things are coming out of your mouth that I never expected to hear."

Camille smiled wanly. "Maybe you've just begun to really listen to me."

She sighed again. "Maybe so. But I'm beginning to wonder if I need to make a trip down there. Do I?"

"No!" she blurted, then pressed a hand to her forehead. Normally she loved for her mother to come for a visit. But she and Matthew could hardly be romantic with Maureen in the house. "I mean, yes, you're welcome if you want to come for a visit. But everything is fine here. I'm even going to get on a horse this weekend. That ought to make you happy."

"It does. But Camille, I—"

From the corner of her eye, Camille caught sight of Gideon waving at her. "Sorry, Mom. I've got to get back into the kitchen. The noon rush is about to begin." She made a kissing noise into the phone, then disconnected the call.

"I hated to interrupt you, Camille, but a whole van

of people just pulled up," Gideon told her as she met him at the door.

She grinned at him. "A whole van? That's music to my ears, Gideon."

"Matthew, what in hell is going on down there?"

Matthew pulled the phone away from his ear and stared at it like he'd just picked up a horned toad from a hot rock.

"I just happen to be working my butt off. What in hell is going on up there?" he shot back at Blake.

A stretch of silence passed and Matthew used the pause to put a few steps away from the men who were working on a dead water well pump.

"Okay. I apologize," Blake said after a moment. "I shouldn't have said that."

"No. Not in that tone of voice," Matthew agreed, then said, "But forget it. You must be having a bad day."

"A bad day? Mom just left my office in tears. They were streaming down her face like her heart is broken."

Concerned now, Matthew walked over and stood beneath the skimpy shade of a Joshua tree. "What's happened? Has Joe dug up something new about Joel's death?"

"No. Not that I know of. Dear God, as much as I'd like to have that whole issue settled, I hope nothing turns up right now. I don't think Mom could handle all of this at one time."

"All of this?"

Blake cursed under his breath. "Don't play coy, Matthew! You know what's been going on! And the fact that you're happy about it just blows my mind. Mom's, too, if you want the truth of the matter."

Matthew clutched the phone. Had the family bugged the Red Bluff house with some sort of video cameras? How else would they know about him and Camille sharing a bed every night? She certainly wouldn't have told them. Would she?

"I—uh—guess you're going to have to enlighten me, Blake," Matthew finally told him. "I'm not sure what you're talking about."

After muttering another curse word, Blake said, "That damned diner! That's what!"

"Oh." Relief rushed out of Matthew. Being Blake's right-hand man and helping him run a multimillion-dollar spread was one thing, but making love to his sister was quite another. "Well, what does that have to do with me? Camille already came to the decision that she wanted the diner long before I ever showed up down here."

"Yes, but you didn't have to encourage her, did you? She told Mom you were happy about it. Is that true?"

This was getting ridiculous, Matthew thought, and it was making him a heck of a lot more than annoyed. "You're damned right, it's true. And if you would take a bit of your time to really talk to your little sister, even come see her, then you might understand."

There was no sound on the other end of the line and then the faint shuffle of papers and the creak of a chair. Blake was clearly in his office. A place he didn't actually want to be, but being Joel's first-born had put him there, along with the man's untimely death. Maureen could search far and wide and never find a better manager of the ranch than Blake. But that wasn't where he actually wanted to be. If the truth was known, he'd rather be right here with Matthew, working on a stubborn water pump, or digging up a rotten fence post, than sitting at a desk.

"I'm sorry, Blake. I shouldn't have said any of that. It's not my place to butt into your family affairs."

"You are family, Matthew. You do have a right to say all that and more. I realize you're not down there to control Camille."

Control her? The idea was laughable. She was about as controllable as one of Holt's wild fillies. "Thank God. I'd fail pretty miserably at that job."

"Well, I'm going to try to think in positive terms about this diner thing. If you think it'll be good for her, then I have to believe it. The thing is—we were all just hoping that she'd come home."

A pain crept through his chest. "Blake, I think it's time that you and the rest of the family understand that Camille *is* home."

Chapter Ten

By the end of the next week, Matthew and the men had the cattle all settled and grazing on valley grass. The water pumps were all in good working order and the fences were sound. Their job on Red Bluff was finished.

On Saturday afternoon, as the ranch hands loaded the trucks and trailers to head home to Three Rivers, TooTall was following Matthew around like a lost pup.

"I don't like this, Yellow Hair," he said. "I want to stay here with you."

"You can't. Right now you're needed back at Three Rivers. If the weather takes a turn you men will be hauling hay from morning 'til night. I'm only going to be here at Red Bluff for few more days anyway. Just long enough to look things over."

TooTall didn't look convinced and Matthew could

tell he wanted to argue the matter. But he was a loyal hand and no matter how unhappy he was with the current setup, he wouldn't create a problem for Matthew.

As the two men walked out to where the men were loading the last of the horses, TooTall cast Matthew a determined look. "You remember what you promised," he said. "You'll let me work here with you—whenever you come to stay."

Damn it, he didn't know where TooTall was getting such an idea. It was ridiculous. Even worse, it was grating on his nerves. Trying to hold on to his patience, he said, "I haven't forgotten that I promised. But you need to get that notion out of your head, TooTall. I'll be home at Three Rivers in a few days and then you'll see that nothing is going to change. We'll be working together just like always."

Frustrated, TooTall stopped in his tracks and frowned at him. "I saw a vision, Matthew, and—"

"No, you had a dream, that's all," Matthew interrupted, not wanting to hear any more nonsense from the man. "Now get in the truck with the rest of the men before I put my boot in the seat of your pants."

To soften the order, he patted TooTall's shoulder. "I'll see you in a few days. In the meantime, I'm counting on you to keep the rest of the crew in line. Okay?"

Nodding glumly, the cowboy climbed into the back seat of the truck and shut the door. Matthew walked up to the driver's window and Pate stuck his head out.

"Drive safely, Pate. And send me a text to let me know you all got there in one piece."

"Sure thing, Matthew," he said with a toothy grin. "This couple of weeks has been a hell of a ride, huh?"

"Yeah, a hell of a ride."

He lifted a hand in farewell, then turned and walked inside the barn so he wouldn't have to watch them drive away.

The next morning, Camille was thrilled to have Matthew join her in Sunday services at the little church in Dragoon. As they sat close together on the worn wooden pew, she couldn't help but notice how closely he followed the pastor's sermon and how he knew exactly where to find certain passages in the Bible. From the time he'd become an employee of Three Rivers Ranch, she recalled that he'd attended church with the entire Hollister family. Even so, Camille had never thought of him as a spiritual man. Maybe that was because his rugged exterior had always covered up the softer, gentler parts of him.

After the service she introduced him to Peggy and Gideon, who eyed him with great interest.

"Camille tells us you've been the foreman for her family's ranch for a long time," Gideon said as the four of them stood outside the little white church. "That must be a huge job."

Matthew humbly shook his head. "Not really. I have plenty of ranch hands to help get everything done that needs to be done."

"He's being modest, Gideon," Camille told the older man. "He works long hours and deals with a lot more than punching cows. Blake couldn't run the place without him."

Peggy's all too curious gaze slipped back and forth between Matthew and Camille. "I hope you'll find time to come eat at the diner before you head back to Three Rivers, Matthew," she told him. "You need to try out some of the good things Camille cooks for the customers."

Camille didn't miss the bit of color creeping up his neck.

"I—er—I've tasted a few things that Camille has cooked," he admitted. "But if I get a chance I'll drop by the diner."

"I guess she's told you about buying the place," Gideon said to him. "We're just tickled pink about it, too. Norm is a nice boss, but he's burnt out—he needs a rest."

Peggy let out a good-natured groan. "Gideon, Norm is probably ten years younger than you!"

He laughed and winked at Matthew. "True, but he's not in as good as shape as I am. Anyway, Camille will get the old place hopping. You can bet on that."

"Yeah, we're already planning on a big Christmas around here," Peggy told him. "It would be nice if you could come down and celebrate with us. Do you get a break for the holiday?"

Matthew cast a doubtful glance at Camille and she wondered if he was thinking it was about time for her to celebrate Christmas at Three Rivers. For his sake? No. He wouldn't ask her to do anything like that. Not for him. But he might ask her to do it for the rest of her family. Even so, she couldn't. Not when she was just now taking over the diner.

He said, "Ranchers don't really get time off. This break today is about the most I ever get."

"Oh, that's too bad," Peggy grumbled. "It would be nice for Camille if you could. She gets lonely out there on the ranch, you know."

"Peggy! This isn't the time or place to be talking

about Camille's social habits!" Gideon scolded her, then clamped a hand around her upper arm. "Come on, I'm going to take the kids over to Benson for lunch. You can come along—if you think you can talk nice."

Peggy pulled a face at him. "Talk nice! Gideon, you need a good dose of castor oil and—"

Before the woman could finish, Gideon yanked her away, while giving Camille and Matthew a backward wave.

"Do they always fuss like that?" Matthew asked as they watched the pair walk to Gideon's car.

"Always," Camille said with a fond smile. "They're worse than some old married couple. Except that they're not really a couple in that sense of the word. There's a forty-year age gap between them."

With a hand against the small of her back, he urged her toward his truck. "Hmm. What's a few years? Just look at Sam and Gabby," he said.

Camille laughed. "Why, Matthew, I think you're getting a romantic streak in you."

The faint smile he gave her was more like the wave of a white flag. "You're rubbing off on me, Camille."

Two hours later, Matthew decided this had to be the best day of his life. The sky was vivid blue, the sun was warm and Camille was riding beside him. And from the happy look on her face, she wasn't the least bit worried about her riding skills. In fact, he was surprised at how confidently she handled the paint mare, Daisy.

"I don't think I've ever been this far south on the ranch before," she said as the two of them reined their horses down a shallow wash thickly dotted with sagebrush. "It's very pretty, isn't it? I'll bet if we rode to that next ridge we could see all the way to Tombstone."

"Maybe. I've never been that far, either. But there is a place you might like to see before we get to the ridge. Unless you're too tired to keep going."

"Oh, I'm not the least bit tired. This is lovely, Matthew. And it's so beautiful here."

He had to agree it was a scenic area with the sage and barrel cacti and tall saguaros covering the hills and canyons. "There isn't much grazing for cattle to be had here, but more than you'd think."

Her smile was impish. "I forget this is actually a working ride for you," she said. "So, what are you thinking so far? Think Blake is being foolish to consider putting more cattle on Red Bluff?"

"No. Not from what I've seen so far. And this area basically gets as much moisture during the year as Yavapai County, while the temperature stays warmer, so that's a plus."

They rode up out of the wash and Matthew reined Dahlia, the paint sister to Daisy, in a westerly direction. Camille guided her mount alongside his.

"I think you've been doing some major fibbing to me, Camille. You're riding Daisy like an old ranch hand. I thought you said you rarely ride."

"Thank you for the compliment," she said. "But it's true that I rarely ride."

"You know what I think? You sit the saddle like your father did."

She studied him for long moments. "That's one of the nicest things you've ever said to me."

"Well, I meant it or I wouldn't have said it."

"Yes, I'm learning that much about you," she said.

They rode along in companionable silence for a short distance and then she asked, "Matthew, do you think Major Bob caused Daddy's death?"

Her question caught him off guard and caused a frown to crease his forehead. "Your father's horse would've never intentionally harmed him. Not for any reason. You believe that, don't you?"

Her nod was solemn. "Yes. I believe it. I just wondered what you really thought. I know Mom says you and the hands are still using Major Bob on the ranch."

"That's right. Maureen even rides him on some days."

"I'm glad. Because I have a feeling Major Bob misses Daddy as much as the rest of us do."

He reached over and picked up her hand that was resting against her thigh. Then, squeezing it gently, he said, "I think your feeling is right."

She glanced thoughtfully at him. "Do you believe my brothers will ever find out what really happened to Daddy that day?"

His throat tight, Matthew shrugged. "That's tough to say. I do know that Joe is like a bulldog. Once his jaw is set, he's not going to let go until he's satisfied."

She sighed. "I've not mentioned this before, but about a month ago, Blake told me and Viv about the woman down in Phoenix. I'm sure you know what I'm talking about."

He nodded. "I know. I just wasn't sure if any of your brothers had mentioned it to you. I didn't bring it up because—well, that's your private family business."

"You are family, Matthew," she said. "So tell me, do you think Daddy was cheating on Mom?"

"Hell, no! He adored your mother."

"Strange how you can be so certain," she mused aloud. "When my own brothers have their doubts about our father."

He squeezed her soft little fingers. "It's like I told you before. It's easier to see something when you're on the outside looking in."

She smiled at him and the dark cloud that had momentarily settled over Matthew lifted.

"That's all I want to say about that," she said. "So tell me where we're going."

"We're going to ride around this next hill and then you're going to see how Red Bluff got its name."

Ten minutes later, they rode along a narrow ledge that skirted the hill. Then suddenly the rough trail dropped into a deep valley and there, straight in front of them, a cliff made of slabbed red rock towered into the sky to create a boxed canyon.

Camille automatically reined her horse to a stop and stared in awe at the incredible sight. "Oh my, this is fantastic! How did you know about this?"

"I came here a long time ago with Joel. He said it was a spiritual place. I wanted to bring TooTall here to let him see it, but we didn't have the time. He's a mystical kind of guy. I figure if he ever does see it, he'll tell me he's seeing ghost riders in the sky or something."

"Well, it does strike the imagination," she said. "Let's ride closer and dismount, shall we?"

"Sure. Follow me. From here on the trail gets narrower."

Five more minutes and they were at the base of the bluff. Camille was delighted to see a pool of water beneath a trickling spring. Nearby pines seemed to be growing straight out of the rocks.

They dismounted and tied the two horses to a desert willow growing near the edge of the water. Butterflies flittered around its purplish blooms, while high above the bluff, a hawk tilted its wings in the desert wind.

Camille sat down in the cool shade and patted a spot on the rock next to her. "Come sit next to me."

He sank down beside her, then pushed the brim of his hat back on his forehead. "This is nice."

"I could stay here forever," she said with a wistful sigh, then added with a chuckle, "Until I got hungry."

"I just wonder if this is the way it looked years ago— back before gold was discovered."

"Hmm. Probably something like this," she said thoughtfully. "Did you ever think that maybe Billy the Kid roamed through this land?"

"No. His stomping ground was New Mexico. But Wyatt Earp might've. We're not far from Tombstone. Before then, some of the Spanish expeditions could've traveled through here."

She glanced curiously at him. "You know about history?"

"A little."

"I noticed today at church that you're very familiar with the Bible."

"Yes, my mother often read passages to me and my sister. When things were really tough that seemed to bring her more solace than anything."

She reached over and laid her hand on his forearm, but there was nothing she could really say to wipe away his sad memories. All she could do was to let him know that whatever hurt him, hurt her, too.

"I hear your phone dinging," he said after a moment.

"A message," she said. "I really don't want to bother with it now. But maybe I should—just to make sure it's not an emergency."

She pulled the phone from her shirt pocket and punched open the new message. "Oh, it's from Viv. She says congratulations on buying the diner. Gosh, I do love my sister."

Camille started to put the phone back into her pocket when it dinged again and she looked to see Vivian had sent a pair of photos. One was of her and Sawyer's twin boys, Jacob and Johnny. The toddlers were both dressed like pumpkins for Halloween. The second pic caused her to gasp out loud.

"Oh, oh, Matthew, look! Roslyn and Chandler's baby was born this morning! It's a boy! Look at that precious little face!" She moved the phone over so that he could see the screen with her. "That's Chandler's hands holding him. I can tell."

"Hmm. He's bald and his eyes are squinted, but if you say he looks precious, then he does," Matthew said. "I wonder what they've named him."

"William Chandler. But Viv says Chandler is already calling him Billy."

"Chandler never was big on formalities."

Camille laughed and then suddenly, before she could do anything to stop it, the joyful sound turned to a broken sob.

Hearing it, Matthew wrapped an arm around her shoulders. "Camille, what's wrong? I thought you were happy about the baby."

Blinking back her tears, she returned the phone to her shirt pocket. "I am. I'm thrilled for my brother and for the whole family. It's just that—" She looked at him and did her best to smile. "It's like you when you talk about standing on the outside looking in. That's what I'm doing, Matthew. I see my siblings with spouses and children and I don't have that. I'm not sure I'll ever have it."

"Camille, you're still very young. Your life is just beginning."

Now was the time, she thought, if he was ever going to say that he loved her, that he wanted a life with her and the children they'd hopefully have together. But nothing like that was going to come out of his mouth, she thought sadly, and she was beginning to realize it never would.

You can't be angry about that, Camille. You can't even be sad. You knew all along that Matthew was in your life on a very temporary basis. But you wanted him. Now you want to believe in miracles. But they don't happen. Not for you.

Sighing, she nodded and forced another smile to her face. "Yes. You're right. I don't have any reason to be sad. I'm young and my dream of owning the diner has just come true. I couldn't possibly hope for more."

They remained at the bluff a few more minutes and allowed the horses to drink and doze in the shade. By then, Matthew determined there wasn't enough time before dark to make it to the last ridge marking Red Bluff's most southern boundary, so they headed back to the ranch.

For most of the ride, Camille was quiet and pensive. Matthew didn't push her to talk. He understood that the news about Chandler's baby had turned her mood melancholy and there wasn't much he could say to lift her spirits. She wanted and needed things in her life that he couldn't give her.

"I'll take care of the mares, Camille. You go on to the house," he told her as they led Daisy and Dahlia into the barn.

She frowned at him. "No. That's not the way this works. I'm going to help you," she insisted. "We're in this together."

In this together. Yes, for now, he thought. For tonight and tomorrow. That was all he could let himself think about.

"Okay," he said. "If that's the way you want it."

"I do."

She led the mare over to a hitching post and looped the reins loosely around the worn wood. Matthew followed, and side by side they unsaddled the horses and put everything away in the tack room.

After they'd finished pouring out feed and spreading hay, they walked to the house, where Camille immediately excused herself and went upstairs for a shower.

While she was gone, Matthew searched around in the refrigerator for whatever leftovers he could find and went to work heating everything and setting the table.

He was pouring tea into iced glasses when he heard her footsteps enter the kitchen, and he glanced over his shoulder to see her standing a short distance away, staring in surprise.

"What is this? You've fixed us something to eat?"

"No, you did. I only heated it up. We're having spaghetti again."

She joined him at the table. "You made salad and skillet toast," she observed.

She seemed genuinely amazed, and he grinned at her. "I can be handy whenever I put my mind to it."

"Well, I'm glad you put your mind to it. But you didn't have to do all this."

He pulled out her chair. "We're in this together. Remember?"

Her eyes were watery as she lifted her gaze to his face and for one second Matthew considered drawing her into his arms, holding her tight and letting all the things he was feeling pour out in whatever words he could find. But that wouldn't do anything, he decided, except complicate things even more than they already were.

She leaned close enough to place a kiss on his cheek. "Yes, I remember," she murmured.

Clearing his throat, he helped her into the chair, and as they began to eat, Matthew was relieved to see she was collecting her ragged emotions. Still, through the remainder of the meal, he carefully avoided mentioning her family. Instead, he urged her to talk about the diner and the friends she worked with. Gradually, she began to smile again, and so did he on the outside. On the inside, he wondered how much longer he could deal with this chronic pain in his chest and the dreadful sense he was never going to recover from this trip to Red Bluff.

Once their plates were empty, Camille rose and began to gather the dirty dishes. "I think there are brownies left. I'll make coffee to go with them."

"That would be good. I'll clear the rest of this from the table."

He'd barely gotten the words from his mouth when his phone rang. As expected, the caller was Blake and he had no choice but to answer.

"Sorry, Camille. It's Blake. I'll have the coffee later."

He carried the phone into the living room and took a comfortable seat in one of the armchairs. For the next fifteen minutes he listened to everything Blake had planned for the next month. The ranch manager's agenda didn't include Matthew spending more than a few more days here at Red Bluff.

"I don't suppose you've had much time to look at some of the remote areas yet," he stated rather than asked. "This is the first day you've had without you and the guys pushing cattle."

Matthew leaned his head back against the couch and rubbed a hand over his eyes. "Camille and I took a long ride today on one of the southern sections. The grass looked good there. We didn't have time to go all the way to the boundary fence, though. I'm thinking the eastern range should be somewhat better. It's not as hilly."

"That's the way I remember it, too," Blake said.

He didn't add anything to that and Matthew waited, expecting him to continue with the subject of the grazing land. Instead, silence stretched between them.

"Blake, are you still there?" Matthew finally asked.

"Uh—yeah. Sorry, Matthew, my mind is pretty jammed right now. Too much has been going on around here. Did I hear you right? That Camille rode with you?"

"She did. You sound surprised."

"Hell, I'm not surprised. I'm flabbergasted. What have you done to my little sister? Put some kind of spell on her?"

Matthew dropped his hand away from his eyes and stared around the shadowy room. Everywhere he looked he saw Camille's lovely face smiling at him, her eyes twinkling like the desert stars. Would it be like this, he wondered, when he got back to Three Rivers? If so, he didn't know how he'd live with it.

"No. I've not put a spell on her," he said crossly. "I've just tried to encourage her. It's not that she never wanted to be a part of the ranch, Blake. She just lacked self-confidence. Your mother and all of you siblings are a pretty hard group for her to measure up to."

Blake blew out a heavy breath. "We never expected Camille to be a ranch hand. We just want her to be a part of the family."

"She is a part of the family. In her own way—the best way for her."

Blake snorted. "If you ask me, she's still hiding and unable to face her failure."

Matthew felt like reminding Blake how he'd faced his own failure when Lenore had jilted him several years ago. For a long, long time, he'd buried himself on Three Rivers and sworn off women completely. But cutting into the man wouldn't help matters. It would only cause resentment.

"Think about this, Blake. Her brothers and sisters all have things that she doesn't have. That makes her feel lost and alone. That's why—I hope that all of you will be happy for her about the diner. That's the only thing of her own that she truly has. And she's proud of it."

Blake didn't immediately reply and after the silence continued to stretch, Matthew expected him to come back with some sort of scathing retort. But he didn't. Instead, he sounded very thoughtful and almost apologetic.

"I guess I never stopped to think about my little sister in that way. And just because I'm running the ranch doesn't mean that gives me the right to rule over the whole family. Sometimes, Matthew, I wish—"

"That Joel was still alive. And you weren't having to do some of the things you're doing now," he finished tactfully.

"Yeah," Blake said gently. "The longer I do this, the more I realize that Dad was a superman. He saw everyone as they really were and always dealt with them in the right way. Every problem that came along, he handled like a man. I can't live up to him, Matthew. It's impossible."

"You shouldn't be trying. You're Blake Hollister. Not Joel or anyone else."

"No, I'm just me," he said in a pensive voice, then cleared his throat and asked, "Did you get the news about Chandler and Roslyn's baby?"

"Yes, Viv texted Camille and sent her a photo. I'm sure they're over the moon."

"We all are. I had a hell of a time tearing Kat away from the hospital. Seeing baby Billy has sparked her maternal instincts. Before the night is over I'm expecting to hear an argument for another baby."

"Another baby? But the twins aren't that old yet!" Matthew exclaimed.

Blake chuckled. "What can I say? She loves me and she loves children. How could I possibly deny her?"

"I—uh—see your problem."

Blake let out another laugh. "Problem? Hell, Matthew, I only wish you had this kind of problem."

The two men talked for a couple more minutes before Blake ended the call. Matthew slipped the phone into his pocket and walked back out to the kitchen. The room was dark and quiet and he decided Camille must have given up on him and dismissed the plan to have coffee and brownies.

He climbed the stairs and found her in the bedroom, sitting on a vanity stool in front of the dresser mirror. She was pulling a hairbrush through her long hair, and after watching her for one brief moment, he walked up behind her and placed his hands on her shoulders.

"Let me do that for you," he offered.

Smiling faintly, she handed him the brush and Matthew began to stroke the silky strands from the crown of her head all the way down to her waist. It crackled beneath his hands as though it had a life of its own and he thought how the fiery shades of copper and ginger mixed amidst the browns fit her temperament.

"Mmm. That feels good," she said.

"My horse tells me the same thing," he teased.

She made a playful face at his image in the mirror. "I'll bet he does," she said. Then her expression turned sober. "So, what was Blake's call about? Is he needing you back at Three Rivers?"

"Not yet. He told me to stay until the end of the week. If he needs me before then, he'll let me know. In the meantime, he's sending down a skeleton crew next Monday. They'll be tending the cattle for the duration of the winter."

Her face brightened. "Until the end of the week? Really?"

He nodded, while thinking how closely his happiness was now tied to hers. As long as she was smiling he was smiling, too.

"Yes. Really."

She plucked the hairbrush from his hand and tossed it on the dresser, then rose and slipped her arms around his waist. "Then we need to make every minute count, don't you think?"

"I thought you were feeling too sad to want me in your bed tonight," he murmured.

She brought her lips within a fraction of his. "Sad? I could never be sad as long as you're here with me."

As soon as the last word died away, her lips were moving over his. Matthew closed his eyes and gladly let her kiss blot every doubt and worry from his mind.

Chapter Eleven

The next day Camille came down with the sniffles, but she didn't let it stop her from going full throttle. By Wednesday Norman had everything ready to finalize the sale of the diner and the two of them drove the twenty-minute drive over to Benson to sign the papers in front of witnesses at the title company.

In spite of constantly wiping her nose with a tissue, she was in high spirits when she arrived home that evening and she couldn't wait to show Matthew the legal paper showing she was the new rightful owner of The Lost Antelope.

When she didn't find him in the house, she immediately walked down to the barn and found him in the feed room sitting on a bale of alfalfa with his cell phone jammed to his ear.

As she entered the dusty room stacked with bags

of feed and bales of hay, he acknowledged her with a glance but continued with the conversation. Which told her the call held some importance.

Deciding to wait, she walked some distance away from him and took a seat on a ledge of feed sacks.

"Yes," he spoke into the phone. "I'd like that, too. But if you need me—yeah, I understand. It can't be helped. I'll be there in the morning—as early as possible."

He hung up the phone, and the look he directed at Camille was dark and hopeless. "That was your mother. Blake has come down with the flu and the doctor has ordered him to bed. I have to leave for Three Rivers in the morning. Somehow I'm going to have to try and fill in for him until he can get on his feet."

Camille felt as though the roof of the barn had just collapsed on top of her. "But what about Mom? She can fill in for Blake!"

He shook his head as he slipped the phone back into his shirt pocket. "Cattle buyers are coming tomorrow afternoon. But Maureen and Chandler have to go to the Prescott range. Something about a sick bull they'd had to leave behind. So that means Chandler is going to have to take time off from the clinic. And it also means that I'm going to have to leave early in the morning."

"Oh." It was the only word she could manage to say.

With stiff, jerky movements, she rose and walked toward him. "But Matthew, I was planning on you staying until Saturday morning!"

He shook his head. "I was planning on it, too. But this has put a kink in things. I'm foreman of Three Rivers, Camille. I'm needed there. To do my job and part of Blake's."

"Yes," she said dully. "It's your job. I understand."

"Do you?"

Camille did understand all too well. In simple words, Matthew's life was at Three Rivers. Hers was here at Red Bluff and never the twain would meet again. Not as they had these past couple of weeks. The short period of time had changed everything for her. She'd fallen totally and irrevocably in love and no amount of time or distance was going to change that.

"I do." Tears suddenly blurred her vision and she quickly turned and started out of the feed room. "I— I'm going to the house."

Jumping from the hay bale, he caught her by the shoulder. "Camille, you came out here to the barn for some reason. What was it?"

She dabbed her watery eyes with the tissue she'd been carrying. "Nothing important. I just wanted to show you this."

She pulled the folded document from a pocket on her jacket and handed it to him.

As he unfolded the paper and scanned the contents, she watched a myriad of feelings parade across his face. He seemed pleased and regretful all at the same time.

"I'm thrilled for you, Camille."

Was he? She wouldn't describe the look on his face as thrilled, but then Matthew had never been a man to wear his feelings on his sleeve.

What feelings, Camille? The man likes your company. He enjoys the meals you cook and the sex even more. But that's all the feelings he has for you. Don't expect to read them on his face or anywhere else. In the morning you need to tell the man goodbye, then forget him.

Wanting to scream at the hateful voice going off

in her head, she took the property title from him and stuffed it back into the jacket pocket.

"Thank you," she said stiffly. "That means a lot to me."

She started to pull away from him, but his fingers tightened on her shoulder, preventing her from taking a step.

"Camille," he said softly. "Don't you think we need to talk about this?"

Her heart pounding sickly in her chest, she forced her gaze to meet his. "About this? What is there to talk about?"

His gray eyes were suddenly full of shadows. "I don't know. I thought—" He continued to look at her while a hopeless expression crept over his face. "Well, I guess you're right. There isn't anything for us to talk about. I'd just like to ask if you think you might be coming up to Three Rivers anytime soon."

He might as well have picked up the pitchfork behind him and rammed it straight into her chest. She was hurting so badly she thought her breathing was going to stop, literally.

"No. Not now. Maybe in a few months—if all goes well with the diner," she said, her voice little more than a hoarse whisper.

A muscle in his cheek flinched, but otherwise, his expression didn't change.

"I thought you would say that."

Hoping he couldn't see the pain she was feeling in her eyes, she asked, "What about you, Matthew? Will you be coming back to Red Bluff before next fall?"

"That's a whole year from now. I can't say if I might be here before that time."

She let out a long, shaky breath and did her best to smile at him. "Well, it's been special, hasn't it? And we still have tonight."

"Yeah," he said. "We still have tonight."

Long before daylight the next morning, Camille was still sound asleep when Matthew slipped out of her warm arms, dressed quietly so as not to wake her, then walked out of the house and drove away from the ranch.

The rough dirt road carrying him away from Red Bluff was narrow and often filled with wildlife. Matthew didn't allow himself to think about anything except driving the truck safely through the cold dark morning. For several miles, Hollister land remained on both sides of him, until finally, just before he reached I-10, he passed under a formal entrance and the ranch was in his rearview mirror.

When he finally merged onto the interstate, he tromped on the accelerator and focused on one single objective. Get to Three Rivers as fast as he could and back to being the Matthew Waggoner he'd been before Camille opened the door and welcomed him inside the Red Bluff hacienda.

At the speed he was driving, he reached Benson in record time, and as the lights of the town twinkled off to his left, he was glad the highway looped around it. He didn't want to see the little café where he and Camille had gone for dinner on Halloween night. No. The sooner he forgot, the quicker he could rid himself of the hollow feeling that had settled in his chest.

Yet by the time the sun started peeping over the mountains behind him and Phoenix appeared on the horizon, the pain in his heart was unbearable and the only thing he could think about was all that he'd left behind him.

So what are you going to do, Matthew? Be like that little boy back in Gila Bend and cover your head up and cry? You knew going to bed with Camille Hollister was going to be a mistake, but you couldn't resist her. You couldn't find enough common sense to walk away from the woman. No, you had to go and fall in love with her.

Determined to drown out the mocking voice in his head, Matthew punched on the radio and turned up the volume.

Damn it, he hadn't fallen in love with Camille. A man like him didn't have the ability to give that much of himself to anyone. Not when the only two things he'd ever really known in his life were hard work and surviving. And he would survive this, he mentally contended. He had no other choice.

An hour and a half later, he drove into the Three Rivers ranch yard and parked his truck near the cattle barn where Blake's office was located. The morning was still early and as he climbed down from the cab, he noticed the ranch hands were still tending to barn chores. A few yards away from the building, Chandler's diesel truck and trailer rig was idling and ready to go.

Maureen must have been watching from the window and had seen Matthew's arrival. He didn't have time to reach the office door before she burst out of the building and ran straight to him.

Hugging him tight, she said, "Matthew, you can't know how happy I am to see you!"

Maureen had always treated him as a son and considering that he'd been here on Three Rivers since he was nineteen years old, she was more like a mother to him than an employer.

He patted her shoulder, then eased her back far enough to look her in the face. "It's good to see you, too, Maureen. But I haven't been gone that long."

"It seems like ages to me," she contradicted. "And without you here to hold things together, the men act like scattered chickens."

Maureen always did give him more credit than what was due. But what would she think if she knew he'd been spending his nights in Camille's bed? Hate him? Fire him? Yes, the woman treated him like a son, Matthew thought, but Camille was her and Joel's baby.

It was too late to be thinking about that, Matthew chided himself. Besides, everything with Camille was over. He wouldn't see her again until next fall. And by then she'd probably have a man in her life. One who would be more than willing to put a ring on her finger and give her as many babies as she wanted.

Trying to shake away those dismal thoughts, he asked, "How's Blake?"

"Confined to his bed. We're trying to keep everyone, especially the kids, away from him as much as possible. Thankfully this morning he appears to be a bit better. At least, he managed to get some juice down and a piece of toast." She shook her head. "I'm sorry you had to cut the stay at Red Bluff short. Especially when we needed you to take a closer survey of the grazing situation."

"Well, when the skeleton crew gets down there they can give Blake a report."

"Ha! Do you honestly think he's going to trust their judgment? You're his eyes and ears, Matthew. You always will be."

He didn't have the opportunity to make any kind of reply to that as Chandler walked up to join them.

"Welcome home, partner," the other man said, thrusting his hand out to Matthew as though they'd not seen each other in two months rather than a little more than two weeks.

"Thanks, Doc. It's good to be home." Normally those words would have come straight from his heart, but this morning, he wasn't even sure his heart was beating. Nothing felt the same. "Congratulations on the new baby boy. You and Roslyn must be thrilled."

Chandler's grin was ear to ear. "Oh, we kinda like the little guy. Even if he does keep us up at night."

Even in his weary state of mind, it was easy for Matthew to see that Chandler was walking on a cloud over his new son. And why not? He had an adoring wife, two beautiful children and a job he loved. The man had everything that meant the most in life and suddenly Camille's words whispered through his head.

I see my siblings with spouses and children and I don't have that. I'm not sure I'll ever have it.

Funny how clearly he could now understand why she didn't want to live here. No matter how much she loved her family, the constant reminder would be too much for her to deal with. It was almost too much for Matthew to handle.

"I'll go by the house and see the baby when I get a chance," Matthew told him.

Maureen reached over and patted his cheek. "That'll be tonight, Matthew. I'm telling Reeva to set an extra plate for you at the dinner table. I want to hear all about Red Bluff and Camille."

Oh God, how was he going to endure this?

Maureen must have caught the uncomfortable look on his face because she suddenly leaned closer and studied him through squinted eyes. "Now that I'm seeing you up close, you look piqued. Are you coming down with the flu, too?"

The Hollister matriarch was right. He was coming down with something, all right. But it wasn't the influenza. There was something broken inside of him and he had the uneasy feeling it was his heart.

"Mom, Matthew has just driven more than two hundred and sixty miles. He's tired. Quit pestering him. You and I need to get on the road and see if we can get that bull home before it comes a blizzard up there."

Matthew frowned. "Blizzard? What are you talking about? It rarely snows up that way."

"Right. But the weatherman is predicting a chance of heavy snow. And we don't want to leave old blue boy up there with a bunged up leg and no shelter," Maureen told him, then motioned to the building behind them. "Go on in the office. Flo's already at work. She'll tell you all about the cattle buyers."

Taking his mother by the arm, Chandler led her off to the waiting truck, and Matthew walked into the office building.

At the end of the room, his secretary, Flo, a red-headed divorcée in her sixties, was sitting at a large desk. She looked up. Then, seeing it was Matthew who had entered her domain, she left her chair and walked over to greet him.

Not only did she give him a hug, she gave him a kiss on the cheek. Something he'd never seen her do with anyone else.

He did his best to give her a smile. "This is some kind of welcome. What did I do to deserve this?"

"You're the only man around here with enough cow sense to fill Blake's boots. Besides that," she added cheekily, "I've missed you."

"I've missed you, too, Flo."

She laughed at that, then pinched his arm for good measure. "Come on over here and sit down at my desk. You can have some coffee and pastries while I give you all the information about the cattle buyers. They should be showing up in the next hour or so."

After filling a cup with coffee and a paper plate with a bismarck and a chocolate-covered donut, she carried the lot over to where he'd taken a seat. He wasn't hungry, but the coffee was welcomed.

Matthew thanked her, then asked, "Have these men purchased cattle from Blake before?"

"No. They're two brothers from somewhere around Modesto, California, so they've traveled a far distance to buy Three Rivers' cattle. And from what Blake says, they have plenty of money to back it up. So do your best not to blow this sale, Matthew."

She returned to her seat behind the desk and he shot her a dry look. "Well, thanks Flo, for taking off all the pressure."

"You can handle it," she said, then frowned as she ran a speculative glance over his face. "By the way, you look like hell. What have you been doing down there at Red Bluff?"

Making a big mistake? The taunting question instantly rolled through Matthew's head, but he quickly dismissed it. No matter what happened in the future, getting close to Camille wasn't a mistake. He had a mind full of precious memories now. That was more than he had before.

"The same thing I do up here," he told her.

She pursed her lips with disapproval. "Then you're doing too much of it."

She pulled a manila folder from a drawer and handed it across the desktop. "Here's most of the specifics of the pending sale. If you run into any trouble, I can get Blake on the phone. But I'd rather not unless it's an emergency."

"Don't worry, Flo. There won't be any trouble."

"Camille, this order for table nine was supposed to have fried eggs, not scrambled," Peggy told her as she carried the plate of breakfast food back into the kitchen. "Did I not write the order down right?"

Turning away from the grill, Camille searched rapidly through the stack of orders until she found the correct one. "You wrote it down right, Peg. I'm the one who messed up. For the second time this morning. I'm sorry. You probably won't get a tip out of this one, either."

"I'm not worried about a tip," Peggy assured her. "I'm more concerned about you."

Camille shook her head as she cracked three eggs onto the grill. "Don't be. I'm just having a little trouble staying focused today, that's all."

"Well, I know you've come down with a cold, but you seem really off today. Has something happened at the ranch? Or with your family?"

On the opposite side of the grill, she flipped three pancakes. "The only thing that's happened is something good. Chandler and Roslyn have their new baby now. It was a boy. William Chandler Hollister. Seven pounds and four ounces and very little hair. When we get an extra minute, I'll show you a picture on my phone."

"Oh, that's exciting. You have a new little nephew! So why is your face so glum?"

Glum? She wasn't just glum, Camille thought. She was dead. At least, dead on the inside.

Matthew was gone.

This morning at five she'd woken to find her bed empty and a simple little note left on the kitchen table.

It's been nice. Matthew.

Nice! Was that how he'd thought about all the time they'd spent together? The sweet intimacy they'd shared? It had just been—nice? And couldn't he have woken her and told her goodbye? Or had she not deserved that much from him?

Oh, Lord help her, she prayed. She wasn't sure she was going to make it through the day, much less the rest of her life.

"I'm not glum. Just trying to deal with these sniffles. And the ranch is quiet now. The whole crew is gone, including Matthew," she forced herself to say.

As Camille scooped up the eggs and slid them onto the plate, Peggy cast her a shrewd look. "I thought he was staying until the weekend. That's a bummer. He was going to come by the diner."

"Couldn't be helped. My brother, Blake, has come down with the flu and Matthew was needed back at Three Rivers," she explained, then thrust the plate of food at Peggy. "Here. Maybe this will make the customer happy. I gave them an extra egg—at no charge."

"I'll make sure to tell the woman," Peggy said, then hurried away with the food.

As soon as she disappeared from the kitchen, Edie stuck her head through the swinging doors. "What about my pancakes, Camille?"

"They're ready." She dumped crisp bacon atop the pancakes and handed it to the second waitress. "What time is it, anyway, Edie? It feels like I've been cooking breakfast food for hours."

The young blonde woman glanced at the watch on her wrist. "Nine thirty-five," she announced. "We ought to be getting close to the end of the breakfast run."

Edie hurried away with the pancakes, and seeing she was caught up for the moment, Camille sat down on the wooden stool and pressed a tissue to her running nose.

Nine thirty-five. She had no way of knowing when Matthew had left the house, but by now he'd had plenty of time to make the four-hour trip to Three Rivers. No doubt he was already back in the swing of giving orders to the men and dealing with whatever Blake needed to have done around the ranch.

He loved his job. It was his life. Just as this diner had become her life. She couldn't expect things to be any other way. So why was she having to fight like hell just to keep tears from rolling down her face?

Because she understood that this was nothing like being jilted by Graham Danby. The only thing she'd suffered over that incident was squashed pride. Her feelings for Matthew were deep and real. The kind that lived on in spite of time or distance.

Perhaps she'd made a mistake in not telling him that she loved him. But she didn't think so. Matthew had no desire to be a husband or father. He'd not been raised to embrace such roles in his life. And Renee's desertion had only reinforced his doubts about being a married man. No. He didn't want to hear about love. Not from her or any woman.

When Peggy returned to the kitchen, Camille was dabbing her seeping eyes with a napkin. The waitress shook her head with dismay and wrapped a comforting arm around Camille's shoulders.

"Oh honey, don't tell me you're crying because Matthew has gone home! Before he came you were dreading having to put up with the man!"

She sniffed and lowered the napkin from her eyes. "I'm not crying about Matthew," she said stubbornly.

"Sure you aren't. Just like Thanksgiving never falls on a Thursday," she said dryly. "Who are you trying to fool? Yourself?"

Camille dropped her head and mumbled, "No. I'm just teary-eyed because—well, things can't be the way I want them to be, that's all. I have my life here with the diner. And he has his on Three Rivers. It's as simple as that."

Peggy went over to the huge coffee urn and filled a cup. When she handed it to Camille, she said, "Doesn't sound simple at all to me. Unless you've come to the conclusion that the man is worth more than this place."

She waved her arm around the kitchen, and Camille shot her a droll look. "There's no question about it, Peggy. Matthew is worth a hundred diners. But it wouldn't do me any good to give up this place. That wouldn't make him fall in love with me."

"Is that what you believe? That he doesn't love you?"

"I don't just believe it, Peg, I know it. So the only choice I have is to stiffen my spine and get over him."

Peggy rolled her eyes. "Oh boy, now that might be easier said than done. From what I saw the other day, Matthew is one hunk of a man. Quiet. But sexy as heck. He'd make any woman's heart flutter."

And no doubt there were plenty of women back in Yavapai County who'd be more than happy to get a few hours of his company from time to time. The thought stirred nausea through the pit of Camille's stomach.

"There's a foolproof medicine to cure that kind of heart problem," Camille told her firmly.

Peggy's brows arched in question. "What's that? A double shot of Scotch?"

Camille put her tissue away and returned to the grill. "No. Hard work. And that's what I plan for all of us to be doing here at The Lost Antelope. The holidays are coming and I have all kinds of ideas to make them special for our customers."

"Holidays? Did someone mention the holidays?" Edie asked as she bounced into the room and handed Camille another breakfast order.

"I did," Camille answered as she slapped several thick slabs of bacon on the grill. "Why?"

"Because I think we should have a traditional turkey dinner with all the trimmings and give the meals away to anyone who wants one—uh, until the food runs out, that is."

Peggy was flabbergasted. "Give the dinners away! Camille just bought this place. She can't make money like that!"

Camille glanced over her shoulder at the two waitresses. "Edie, I think you have a great idea. It would be the perfect way to show the customers how much we appreciate them."

Grinning smugly, Edie patted the blue bandana tied over her head. "See, sometimes I'm more than a ditzy blonde."

Peggy let out a good-natured groan while Edie giggled, but Camille couldn't summon up anything more than a wan smile. Would she ever be able to laugh again? she wondered.

"Okay, genius," Peggy teased. "Better go warm up the customers' coffee or you're going to hear some loud grumbling out there."

Humming a happy tune, Edie grabbed up the coffee carafe and headed back to the dining room. Peggy walked over to Camille and gave her shoulder an encouraging squeeze.

"I understand you're feeling down right now. But aren't you the woman who told me she believes in miracles?" she asked.

Camille sighed. "Yes. But—"

"No buts," Peggy interrupted. "You either believe in miracles or you don't."

With that bit of advice, Peggy left the kitchen, and as Camille continued to cook the rest of the breakfast order, she realized that she had to believe a miracle would bring Matthew back to her. Otherwise, her hopes for a happy future were over.

Chapter Twelve

Thanksgiving turned out to be an exhausting work day for everyone at the diner, but it was a huge success with the customers. Camille decided she was on the right track with the idea of the blue plate special, and the following week she worked tirelessly to implement all the changes the diner needed before they could actually begin offering it on the menu.

By the middle of the following week, Camille could hardly put one foot in front of the other and she was struggling just to keep a few bites of food in her queasy stomach.

"I think you're coming down with that nasty flu bug, Camille," Gideon said as he placed a tub full of dirty coffee cups into the sudsy water. "And it's only going to get worse if you don't get yourself to the doctor."

"I don't have time for a doctor's appointment,

Gideon. Peggy can't cook and waitress at the same time. And Edie had to take off today to take her mom to the doctor. Seems the woman has the flu or something like it."

"See, that's what I'm telling you." Gideon pointed a dirty fork at her to emphasize his words. "Edie has probably carried the germs here to you. So go get your coat and head over to Benson to the doctor."

Camille glanced at the clock hanging on the wall above the double sink where Gideon was washing dishes. "It's two o'clock. The lunch customers have let up." She pondered for a moment. "Now might be a good time to go."

"That's right. If anyone shows up, I'll cook. It won't be as good as your stuff, but it'll be edible."

"All right," Camille reluctantly agreed. "I can't afford to get sick and miss work. And I sure don't want to spread a stomach virus through the diner."

"Now you're talking," Gideon said with a vigorous nod.

Peggy walked into the kitchen just as Camille was pulling off her apron.

"Talking about what?" Peggy asked, then cast a concerned look at Camille's pale face. "Honey, you look awful. Are you going home for the rest of the day?"

"She's going to the doctor," Gideon answered for Camille. "And high time, too."

Peggy didn't waste any time fetching Camille's coat and handbag from the little office off the kitchen.

As she helped her on with the coat, she said, "If the wait at the clinic turns out to be long, don't worry about the diner. Gideon and I will close up. I'll let him take the cash home."

Camille shook her head. "I'm coming straight back here no matter how late it is. I have to put in some food orders for next week's menu."

The wait at the clinic wasn't quite as long as Camille was anticipating. An hour and a half after she entered the medical building, she walked out in a mental fog.

She wasn't coming down with the flu or anything close to a virus. The family practitioner had pronounced her six weeks pregnant! She was going to have Matthew's baby!

With an appointment card to her regular gynecologist stuffed in her purse and a prescription for nausea, she climbed into the car and stuck the key into the ignition. But that was as far as she got.

For long moments, Camille was too stunned to do much more than stare blindly out the windshield at the people coming and going through the front entrance of the medical building. Never in her wildest dreams had she anticipated something like this. She'd been taking the Pill, yet here she was on her way to being a single mother!

It happens occasionally, the doctor had explained to her. But how was she going to explain that to Matthew? What was he going to think? That she'd deliberately misled him about the birth control?

No. She felt sure he knew her better than to think she'd been lying about something so important to both their lives. But she was also fairly certain that he had no plans to become a daddy. Not to Camille's child, or any other woman's child.

On the drive back to Dragoon, Camille tried to collect herself. But the minute she walked into the diner and looked at Gideon's and Peggy's concerned faces, she burst into tears.

Rushing to her side, Peggy clutched her arm. "Oh honey, what in the world?"

Gideon put down his dish towel and in fatherly fashion led Camille over to the step chair sitting at the end of the work counter.

After gently removing her coat and handing it and her handbag to Peggy, he urged Camille into the chair.

"Now, what are all these tears about?" he asked in a firm but caring voice. "Do you have something worse than the flu?"

Camille looked at Peggy's worried face, then up to Gideon's. "I'm not sick. The doctor says I'm as healthy as a horse."

Peggy cursed. "What kind of idiot did you see? I'm about as far away from being a doctor as you can get, but even I can see you're sick as a dog! You can't hold a thing on your stomach!"

Camille drew in a long breath, then blew it out. "That's because I'm pregnant."

Peggy and Gideon exchanged stunned glances.

"A baby?" Peggy asked in an awed voice. "Matthew's baby?"

Camille scowled at her. "Who else?"

Peggy spluttered. "Uh—sorry—I—didn't mean it like that! It's—well, I realize you'd gotten close to Matthew—I just didn't know you'd gotten *that* close."

Camille groaned and then another fresh spurt of tears streamed from her eyes.

Gideon shot Peggy an annoyed glare. "Peg, would it kill you to use a little more tact sometimes?"

The waitress rolled her eyes at him. "Tact isn't going to change the fact that Camille is going to have a baby!"

"She's right, Gideon," Camille said dully. "I don't expect to be coddled. And I sure don't want you two to have to tiptoe around the obvious. I had an affair with Matthew and because of it we're going to be parents. Or should I say, I'm going to be a parent."

Peggy and Gideon exchanged more strained glances before Gideon placed a hand on her shoulder. "Why do you say it like that, Camille? Don't you think your young man will want to be a father to the child?"

Would he? Yes. He'd been too hurt by his own father to ever let a child of his feel unloved and unwanted. Yet she couldn't see him having anything more than a long-distance relationship with his son or daughter.

"He'll be a father," Camille admitted. "Just not on a daily basis."

"Does that mean you're not going back to Three Rivers?" Peggy wanted to know.

Frowning, Camille shook her head. "The thought never entered my mind. My home is on Red Bluff. This diner is mine now. I'm not leaving. I'll be raising my child here."

Gideon didn't look a bit relieved. "But you are going to tell the man about the baby, aren't you? It wouldn't be right to keep it from him."

Camille dabbed a tissue to her eyes. "Yes, I'll be telling him. I just don't know how or when."

Peggy's pained expression suddenly transformed into a smile. "What are we all looking so glum about? You've wanted a baby of your own for a long time. Now you're going to have one! This should be a celebration!"

Gideon nodded in agreement. "Peggy has the right

idea now. This is a joyous occasion. We've already locked the front door for closing time. Let's have a toast with a beer."

"Gideon, what are you thinking? Camille can't have beer!" Peggy scolded him.

Recognizing his mistake, he snapped his fingers. "Oh shoot, that's right. Okay, let's have milkshakes. I'll make them."

Gideon left to go after the ice cream and Camille gave Peggy a half-hearted smile. "In spite of these tears, Peggy, I'm really happy about the baby. I already love it—more than anything."

"Well, sure you do, honey. And you're going to be the best of mothers." She gave Camille's shoulders a hug, then stepped back and eyed her curiously. "So, what do you think your family is going to say? Especially your mother?"

Camille shook her head. "I honestly can't say. Any other time Mom would be crying and laughing and hugging me with joy. But now—I'm not so sure. She's been so different this past year. And then there's the fact that she's very close to Matthew. She considers him her fifth son. I don't know what to expect from her or any of the family. I do know that I can't breathe a word of this to my mother or my siblings. Not until I talk with Matthew."

"And when do you plan on doing that? Tonight?"

Camille gasped. "Not hardly! I'm not yet ready to deal with him."

"You think putting it off is going to make it easier?" Peggy asked.

"No. But it will give me time to plan what I'm going to say to him." Like how she didn't expect anything

from him. Like how she understood their time together
was nothing but sex to him and therefore he had no
emotional investment in her.

The thought put a hard lump of pain in her throat,
but she did her best to swallow it away.

"You might just be surprised by Matthew's reaction to the baby," Peggy gently suggested. "He might
be thrilled."

Camille's short laugh was a cynical sound. "Oh,
Peggy, sometimes I think you should have been a stand-
up comedian."

A week later the weather turned unusually cold for
Yavapai County. Matthew and the men had been extra
busy keeping a closer eye on the cattle and making sure
none of the pumps at the watering tanks had frozen.

The Three Rivers Ranch house was decked out with
Christmas decorations, and the festive season had carried over into the horse barn, where each stall was
adorned with evergreen wreaths and bright red bows.
Colorful lights blazed in the front yard and also decorated the patio in the back.

Christmas was always a joyful season at the ranch,
and this year the Hollisters had been especially blessed
with all the new little family members. Yet Matthew
didn't have to wonder if one certain Hollister would
be here for the holiday. He already knew that Camille
would be at Red Bluff.

She had the diner to run. And even if she didn't, he
could hardly imagine her wanting to drive up here to
Three Rivers and be faced with her siblings and their
families.

Inside the huge horse barn, Matthew and TooTall

were unsaddling the horses they'd ridden today when Matthew's phone dinged with a message.

He tossed the loosened breast collar over the seat of the saddle and pulled the phone from his jacket pocket.

The message was from Blake: Come by the office before you leave.

Across from him, TooTall asked, "You going to eat with us at the bunkhouse before you go home?"

Normally Matthew made a point of eating with the crew of men at least three or four times a week. The shared time gave him a chance to hear their ideas or grievances and let them see that he considered their feelings important. But tonight he wasn't in the mood for food or talk.

"I'm not really hungry, TooTall. And anyway, I've got to go by the office and see Blake."

The cowboy frowned. "You're getting as thin as a snake, Matthew. You need to eat."

He tried to eat, Matthew thought. But every time he sat down at the dinner table, he started thinking about all the meals Camille had prepared for him, and his throat would close up to the point that swallowing the smallest bite of anything was painful.

"I'll get something to eat when I get home," he told TooTall. "You don't need to be worried about me."

TooTall pulled the bridle from his horse, then tossed it over his shoulder before he turned and looked at Matthew. "Maybe no one else around here knows you're hurting. But I do."

The suggestive remark was the first one that TooTall had made to him since they'd come home from Red Bluff, and it caught Matthew by complete surprise.

"I don't know what you're talking about," he muttered. "And I don't want to know."

"You're not happy."

For the past few weeks since he and the men had returned to Three Rivers, Matthew had been careful to behave as though nothing had changed with him. He'd been determined not to let anyone suspect that he was dying inside. But TooTall was a different matter. It was like the man could see right through a person.

Jerking loose the leather cinch strap, Matthew mindlessly wrapped it through the keeper on the saddle. "What would you know about it?"

"I know you don't belong here anymore," TooTall told him. "You know it, too. That's why you're unhappy."

Damn. Damn. Damn.

He scowled at the cowboy. "Do you know how mad you make me when you start this nonsense?"

TooTall shook his head. "Not mad at me. At yourself."

Matthew wasn't going to argue with the man. For one thing, he didn't have the energy. Nor did he have the heart for it.

"I suppose you've been having more of those visions," Matthew grumbled.

"No. They only come to me once in a while. Like when my mother died."

TooTall turned back to his horse and Matthew felt even worse than he had before. Like him, TooTall had endured a tough childhood, and both men had lost their mothers at a very young age. They each understood what the other had gone through and the connection had bonded them in a way that was more than mere friendship.

"Damn it, TooTall, I'm sorry," he said gruffly. "You're right. I am miserable. But there's nothing I can do about it."

The cowboy glanced over his shoulder at Matthew. "A way will come. You'll see."

Matthew wasn't going to bother asking him what he meant by that. Instead, he finished caring for his horse and walked over to the cattle barn to see Blake.

Inside the office, Flo was still at her desk. She looked up at Matthew, then quickly motioned him toward the door that opened to Blake's office.

"He's in there."

"And you're obviously burning the midnight oil," Matthew said to the woman. "Isn't it time for you to go home?"

She shrugged. "I don't have anything there except a spoiled cat and a TV. They can wait."

Matthew gave her a dismissive wave, then entered Blake's office. The man was on the phone, so Matthew used the time to pour himself a cup of the syrupy black coffee that had been left over from earlier in the day.

By the time Matthew made himself comfortable in one of the padded chairs in front of Blake's desk, the other man tossed the receiver of the landline back on its hook.

"Damned hay grower! Just because we're headed into winter, he thinks that gives him reason to price-gouge us ranchers. Well, I've got news for him. I can get it shipped in from California cheaper than what he's asking."

Matthew took a careful sip of the coffee, then grimaced at the taste of the gritty liquid. "This stuff could probably run a diesel for twenty miles."

"Sorry. Flo thinks she's above making coffee for me and I've been too busy." Linking his hands at the back of his neck, he stretched, then leaned back in his executive chair. "Have you seen the weather forecast?"

"No. We've been checking cattle all afternoon and my phone didn't have a signal until we got back here to the ranch yard. Why? Is it supposed to get colder?"

"Worse than that. Snow is being predicted for the southern part of the state. I'm worried about the calves at Red Bluff."

Red Bluff. Just hearing the ranch's name caused his insides to twist into unbearable knots.

Shaking his head, Matthew repeated the key word. "Snow? I don't believe that for a minute. It would be a cold day in hell before snow fell at Red Bluff."

Blake thoughtfully rubbed a hand along his jaw. "I wouldn't say that. I remember Dad talking about snow down there years ago."

"Years ago isn't now. You're worrying for nothing."

"I'm not worrying, but I am going to be cautious. That's why I'm sending you back down there. If it does snow I want you to make sure the cows can get their calves to some sort of shelter. There's four men already down there. If you—"

Matthew felt as though his whole body was turning to a chunk of ice. "No! There's no need for me to go to Red Bluff, Blake. You're making a mountain out of a molehill."

Blake stared at him as if he'd lost his mind, and Matthew figured he had gone a little crazy. Just the thought of seeing Camille again, of hearing her voice, touching her and then saying goodbye all over again, was too much for him to bear.

"What the hell has come over you, Matthew? It isn't like you to argue about something like this. In fact, it isn't like you to argue at all!"

Rising from the chair, Matthew walked over to the large picture window behind Blake's desk. Beyond the glass he could see a portion of the ranch yard and a cluster of smaller barns and corrals illuminated by security lights. This had been his home, his life for so many years, he could find his way through the maze in the blackest of nights. And yet it was like TooTall had said. Matthew didn't belong here anymore. Not when his heart was elsewhere.

"Sorry, Blake. I realize you have enough problems on your hands without me adding to them. But—I—don't want to go to Red Bluff. It's that simple."

"Simple." He repeated the word softly as though it was something foreign coming out of Matthew's mouth. "That's right! I give you a simple order and you act as though I'm asking you to march into a war zone without a weapon to defend yourself! I don't understand you, Matthew. And now that we're speaking frankly, I'll just come out and say it—I'm worried about you. You look awful and you're acting even worse and—"

"Okay, Blake," he interrupted harshly. "I'll tell you what's wrong. I don't want to go back to Red Bluff because—of Camille."

When Blake didn't immediately reply, he turned to see the man was staring at him in stunned silence. "Camille? I don't understand. Did you two get into it about something while you were down there?"

Matthew felt his face turn as hot as a furnace. "No.

It's not anything like that, Blake. You see, I did something stupid while I was down at Red Bluff. I—uh, fell in love with your sister."

Blake's eyes narrowed to shrewd slits and Matthew braced himself for the worst. Yet instead of the man spewing out a long tirade about betrayal and misconduct, a wide smile spread across his face.

Finally, he said, "Well, thank God. I was afraid something was really wrong with you."

Groaning, Matthew lifted his hat and shoved a hand through his hair as though the act would clear his jumbled brain. "What are you talking about, Blake? Something *is* really wrong!"

The misery in Matthew's voice turned Blake's smile into a concerned frown.

"Why?" he asked. "Camille isn't interested?"

Once again Matthew felt like a torch had passed over his face. "What do you mean—interested?"

Blake shook his head in disbelief, then followed that with a chuckle. "Okay, let me put it this way—does she like you?"

Like? After all that he'd shared with Camille, the word seemed downright silly. But how, exactly, did she feel about him?, Matthew wondered for the umpteenth time. True, she'd made it very clear that she enjoyed his company in bed and even out of it. But she'd never talked about love or said that she might want him in her life for the long haul.

"Well, yes. She likes me. I mean—we got along fine. Really fine."

"Then what's the problem?" Blake questioned. "Seems to me if you're that crazy about the woman you'd be jumping at the chance to go to Red Bluff."

Unable to look the man in the face, Matthew rested his hip on the corner of Blake's desk and stared at the intricate design on the tiled floor. "I don't want to go—because it hurts too much. I'll—" He drew in a long breath and blew it out. "After a few days I'll have to leave again and that's not an easy thing to do."

Somewhere inside him, he found the courage to look Blake in the eye. "Can you imagine driving away from Katherine and not knowing if, or when, you might see her again?"

Sudden dawning passed over Blake's handsome face, followed by a wealth of compassion. "You really do love my sister," he said gently.

Matthew nodded. "I didn't want to. It just happened."

"Yeah. It's something a man can't stop." Blake's perceptive gaze continued to study Matthew's face. "So what are you going to do about it?"

"There's not much I can do. She's made a life for herself there. I couldn't ask her to leave it. I know what that's like, Blake. Renee did it to me and—I resented it like hell—and that's when I knew it was over between us. I'm not about to do that to Camille."

Blake remained thoughtful. "Sounds like you're in a mess. Does she know how you feel about her?"

Matthew gave him a noncommittal shrug. "I think she does."

"Think! Man, you can't just let a woman wonder about such things! That's dangerous!"

Matthew was amazed that Blake couldn't fully comprehend the situation. Telling Camille how he felt wasn't going to change anything. It was only going to make matters far more miserable.

Matthew walked over to a wastebasket and tossed away the foam cup and bitter coffee. "So you say."

From his seat behind the desk, Blake continued to watch him, and Matthew got the feeling the man was calculating something. He just couldn't imagine what it might be.

"Matthew, are you afraid Camille might not be over Graham Danby?"

I want to laugh until my sides hurt.

Camille's words suddenly waltzed through his mind and he barked out a loud laugh. "Not in the least."

Blake shot him an odd look, then said, "Okay. I want you to go pack your bags and head to Red Bluff in the morning. And I expect you to stay until the weather clears. Got it?"

"Yeah. I got it. I'm just going to ask one thing of you. Can I take TooTall with me?"

Blake gave him a single nod. "I'll call him right now and let him know to be ready."

Matthew started to the door.

Behind him, Blake added, "And Matthew, things have a way of working out. So no more worrying about anything. Hear me?"

Hardly encouraged, Matthew nodded and left the office.

Chapter Thirteen

Camille stood in the middle of the living room of the Red Bluff hacienda and surveyed the Christmas decorations she'd been slowly putting up this past week. Red, pink and white poinsettias adorned the tables and flanked the hearth of the fireplace, while on a wall table, she'd erected a small nativity scene complete with wise men, shepherds and barn animals. In front of the window overlooking the back courtyard, a tall pine was covered with twinkling lights, sparkling tinsel, bows and ornaments of all colors, and a pretty angel sitting on the highest bough. The festive tree gave her a measure of comfort, but it couldn't take away the dark doubts weighing on her shoulders.

Today she'd come to the conclusion that she couldn't put off seeing Matthew any longer. Christmas was rapidly approaching and before the parties at Three Rivers began in earnest and The Lost Antelope was jammed with holiday travelers, she needed to make a trip to Yavapai County and give Matthew the news about the coming baby.

Since her fiasco of an engagement with Graham had ended more than two years ago, Camille hadn't stepped foot on Three Rivers. For the first few months after she'd left the ranch, she'd been afraid to go back, afraid to face her family and the failure of being unable to hold on to her fiancé. However, it hadn't taken her long to see that sort of thinking was ludicrous. Graham hadn't been worth a second thought. Besides, everyone failed at something at some point in their life.

But this thing with Matthew was a whole different matter. She loved him with all her heart and she was going to have his baby. Even if he didn't want to be in their lives on a daily basis, she wanted him to know how she felt about him, and about the baby they'd created together. She could go back to Three Rivers for all those reasons.

Squaring her shoulders, she climbed the stairs to her bedroom and pulled out a pair of suitcases from beneath the bed.

Both of them were nearly filled with the clothes and toiletries she thought she'd need for the short stay, when her cell phone rang.

Moving over to the nightstand, she picked up the phone, and then, seeing the name of the caller, promptly placed it back on the tabletop. Ever since elementary school, Emily-Ann had been her best friend, and normally she would be happy to chat with her. But the two of them had always shared their ups and downs with each other. Camille feared that once she started talking she wouldn't be able to quit. She'd end up telling her about Matthew and the baby, and Camille couldn't risk the chance of him getting the news from anyone other than herself. Not that Emily-Ann was a gossiper, but things slipped out accidentally sometimes.

The phone stopped ringing and Camille went back to her packing. But less than two minutes later, it started ringing again. Only this time the caller wasn't Emily-Ann. It was Peggy.

Camille quickly answered it. "Peg, I'm glad you called because I needed to talk to you about the diner."

"Well, I'm calling about the diner, too," the woman explained. "Edie needs off in the morning, so I told her I'd fill in for her. If that's okay with you."

Camille sank onto the edge of the bed. "It's okay. It just means that Gideon will have to help you cook."

"Me and Gideon cooking together, oh Lord. That's going to be fun. Uh—why, are you too sick to come in or something?"

"I'm feeling okay. But I'm going to take off for a day or two—three at the most. Do you think you and Gideon can handle the place? If Edie is going to be off for very long—"

"No. She only need a couple of hours in the morning. Otherwise, she'll be at work. But why do you need to take off? Are you keeping something from me, Camille? Is something wrong with the baby?"

"No. No. Quit worrying. I've decided to drive up to Three Rivers and tell Matthew about the baby."

"Oh."

"Yes. Oh. And I want to get it done and over with before Christmas."

"That's a good idea, Camille," Peggy replied. "You're doing the right thing."

Camille pinched the bridge of her nose and willed away the tears that were always near the surface of her emotions. "I know, Peg. It's just going to be—difficult. And not only with seeing Matthew, but facing my whole family. They're all going to be whispering that little Camille has messed up again."

"Who says you've messed up? I don't."

From Peggy's standpoint, Camille was blessed. Husband or not, she was going to have a child of her own. "Well, you're just a bit biased, Peggy. But thanks for your support."

"So, when are you leaving for Three Rivers?" Peggy asked.

Camille answered, "As early in the morning as possible."

"That might be wise, to get up there before the weather turns bad," Peggy advised. "I keep hearing we're going to get snow or possibly freezing rain in our area. Can you believe it?"

"I'll believe it when I see it. But say a little prayer for me anyway. The last thing I want is to get stranded on a slick highway."

"I'll say two prayers for you, Camille. For safe, clear driving and for good luck with Matthew."

"Thanks, Peggy. As far as Matthew is concerned, I'm going to need that miracle we've talked about."

The two women talked a few more minutes about the diner and then ended the call.

Camille went to work finishing her packing, but before she zipped the lid shut on the last case, she fetched a little Christmas angel from the nightstand and dropped it among the folded clothing.

The next morning before daylight, Camille jumped out of bed as soon as the alarm went off, but she didn't get the early start she'd been planning on. As soon as her feet touched the floor, nausea hit her in giant waves.

After fetching a few crackers from the kitchen, she lay back down in the bed and slowly munched on the dry food in hopes it would settle her roiling stomach.

By the time sunshine was beginning to peek through the curtains on the window, she'd eaten the crackers and to her great relief was feeling well enough to get up and dress.

She was about to remove her robe when she heard a faint rattling noise that sounded very much like a stock trailer going by the house. Which would be strange, she thought. At this time of the year, Blake didn't purchase or sell cattle, nor did he move them from one place to the other. So why was a trailer being used at this early hour in the morning?

Telling herself that the comings and goings of the ranch hands were hardly her business, she reached for the jeans she'd laid out to wear when a faint knock sounded on the kitchen door at the back of the house.

Annoyed at the interruption, she tossed the jeans back onto the bed and, tying the sash of her robe back around her waist, she hurried downstairs and out to the kitchen.

Before she managed to reach the door, the knock sounded again, only longer this time. With an impatient shake of her head, she called out, "Just a minute. I'm coming!"

Flinging her tousled hair back off her face, she unbolted the door and pulled it open, then nearly fainted.

"Matthew!" His name was all she could manage as she stared at him in stunned fascination. He was wearing his normal work clothes, only this morning his shirt was covered with a brown canvas jacket. The dark leather collar was turned up against his neck and the brim of his gray hat was pulled low over his forehead. Cold wind had left his skin splotched with red.

"Hello, Camille."

Her mind whirling with a storm of questions, she pushed the door wide and gestured for him to come in.

He stepped into the kitchen and she shut the door against the freezing air whooshing in behind him.

He said, "I—uh—guess you're wondering what I'm doing here."

Clamping her trembling hands together, she turned to face him. "Since I've not talked to Blake, I have no idea why you're here."

He grimaced, and as Camille's gaze slipped over him, she thought he looked gaunt and just a bit haggard. The idea that he might've been ill sent fear spiraling through her. Even though the man was breaking her heart, she wanted him to be healthy and happy and safe. That was the true meaning of loving someone. And she truly loved Matthew.

"The weather," he said.

When he didn't explain further, she looked at him blankly. "Uh—what about the weather? Other than it's cold for Cochise County."

"And it's going to get colder. It might even snow. So Blake sent me down to watch over the cattle for the next few days. If worse comes to worst we might have to herd as many as we can into the barns."

She released the pent-up breath she hadn't realized she'd been holding until now. "Oh, I see. Peggy mentioned something to me last night about snow. I honestly didn't take her seriously."

"It's serious. Otherwise, I wouldn't be here."

She practically flinched at that, but managed to keep a stoic look on her face as she turned and walked over to the cabinet. "I'd offer you some coffee, but I've not made any yet. I'm running late this morning."

"I need to get down to the barn anyway and help TooTall unload the horses."

"Okay." She glanced over her shoulder to see him wiping a gloved hand over his face. Just looking at him made her ache to throw herself into his arms. "Uh— while you're here, will you be staying in the house?"

"The bunkhouse is full," he said. "But if my being in the house bothers you, I can probably wedge another cot in somewhere."

Were they crazy? Camille wondered. They were talking to each other like two strangers awkwardly trying to communicate in different languages.

Marching back over to where he stood, she frowned at him. "It's a little late to be worrying about something like that now, don't you think?"

"Camille, I don't have time to discuss sleeping arrangements right now! I—"

It was all she could do to keep from slapping his face. "I'll bet you don't," she muttered. "Just like you didn't have the time or the courtesy to wake me and tell me goodbye."

His face turned a sickening gray color. "I had my reasons for leaving like I did."

"Sure you did. The main one being that you're a coward!"

His jaw grew tight and then he looked away from her. "You're right," he said stiffly. "When it comes to you and me, I'm a big coward."

She wasn't exactly sure what he meant by that and trying to figure it out could wait until later, she thought. Right now, there was something far more important on her mind.

"Matthew, maybe you're curious as to why I'm not already at the diner this morning. And maybe you're not. But I'll explain it anyway. I was planning to leave in a few minutes for Three Rivers."

She had never seen him looking so shocked, or seen so many questions swirling in his gray eyes.

"Three Rivers! I don't believe it!"

She could understand his disbelief. Like him, she'd been a coward for far too long. But she was well and truly over that now. "If you don't believe me, go look in my car. My bags are already loaded in the back seat."

His lips parted. "But why? It's still a few weeks before Christmas," he said, and then his eyes suddenly narrowed. "Does your family know you're going up there?"

She shook her head. "No. Seeing them wasn't my main reason for going. And now that you're here there's no need for me to go at all."

He looked confused and suspicious at the same time. "Why?"

"Because you're the one I was really going to see."

"Me?"

She nodded, and as luck would have it, a pang of

queasiness shot through her stomach. Her hand un-wittingly pressed against her abdomen as she fought against the urge to rush over to the sink and throw up all the crackers she'd eaten.

"Yes, you," she said hoarsely. "I thought you needed to know that you're going to be a daddy."

His eyes grew wide and then his jaw dropped. "Are you saying—are you telling me that—"

Nodding, she said, "Yes, I'm pregnant. In roughly seven and a half months you'll be more than Three Rivers's fore-man. You'll be the father of a Hollister baby."

The sickly gray color of his face was suddenly blotched with spots of bright color. Other than the changes in his complexion, his face was a mask, making it impossible to determine what he was thinking.

"How long have you known?" he asked quietly.

"Only a few days. I never suspected I was pregnant. I was on the Pill and thought it was impossible for me to conceive. But I've been so sick I had to go to the doctor to find out what was wrong," she explained.

"Sick? Are you all right now?"

His hands curved over the tops of her shoulders and it was all Camille could do to keep from flinging herself into his arms and sobbing out how much she loved him. But she should've done that weeks ago, before he left Red Bluff, she thought miserably. Now it would look far too convenient and contrived to start talking about love.

"Not exactly," she answered. "I'm having a heck of a bout of morning sickness right this minute."

"Oh." He let out a heavy breath and then, taking her by the arm, led her over to one of the chairs at the kitchen table.

Camille took a seat, and he walked over to the sink

and tore off several paper towels. After he'd wet them in cold water he carried them back to her.

"Here," he said. "Wipe your face. It might help."

She did as he suggested, then pulled in several deep breaths before she turned her attention back to him. As she watched him tug off his gloves and remove his hat, Camille decided he actually looked sicker than she was. Undoubtedly, he was still in a state of shock over the news.

He laid the items on the tabletop, then assessed her with a piercing look. "What do you think your family is going to say about this—about the baby?"

"I don't have to wonder about that, Matthew. They'll be very happy for me."

"And what about you?" he questioned, his face still an unreadable mask. "How do you feel about it?"

His stilted questions were annoying the heck out of her. This wasn't the Matthew she knew. Or the Matthew she'd fallen in love with. This man was as cold and stiff as a board out on the cattle barn. Had learning he was going to be a father done this to him? Or had the past weeks he'd been back at Three Rivers made him forget every tender moment they'd shared together?

"How do you think?" She shot the question back at him, and then, with a rueful sigh, added in a softer voice, "I'm in love with this baby. Totally and completely in love with it."

"Then that's all I need to know. Tomorrow we're going to drive down to Bisbee and get married at the courthouse," he told her in no uncertain terms. "I want this child to have legal, legitimate parents."

Camille stared at him while the pain lancing through her chest made her forget all about the upheaval in her stomach. No words of love. No proposal of marriage. Or vows to be at her side for the rest of his life. This had to be the coldest, cruelest thing he or any man could ever say to her.

"Matthew Waggoner, no man is going to *tell* me I'm going to marry him. And that includes you! As far as I'm concerned, you can forget about me and this baby. You can go right back to Three Rivers and stay there— it's where you belong!"

Her outburst momentarily stunned him and then his face turned colder than a piece of granite. Was this the same man who'd held her so tenderly in his arms? The man who'd brushed her hair and whispered sweet words in her ear? It couldn't be, she thought sickly.

His jaw tight, he said, "In case you've forgotten, I was sent down here to do a job. And I'm not leaving until it's done. So until then, you'll just have to put up with me." He jerked on his hat and gloves and stalked to the door. "Maybe you're the one who ought to run back to Three Rivers, Camille. That's what you want to do when trouble pops up, isn't it? Run and hide?"

She glanced around for something to throw at him and realized there wasn't anything close enough to get her hands on. "I must have been out of my mind to think you could deal with this in a sensitive way!"

His brows arched in sardonic fashion. "Sensitive? If that's what you want you should've tried to hold on to Graham Danby. Not go to bed with a cowboy!"

Her teeth clamped together. "I can tell you what I don't want, Matthew, and that's you!"

Late that afternoon as Matthew and TooTall rode their horses back to the ranch, fat flakes of snow began to fall from the high ceiling of gray clouds. The sight of the ominous weather didn't surprise him. It seemed everything today was supposed to go from bad to worse.

"Look, Yellow Hair, the ground is already turning white," TooTall exclaimed as he turned up the collar of his old plaid coat and hunched down in the saddle. "I hope those mama cows in the south pastures have sense enough to take their babies to the bluff. That's the only decent shelter on that range."

"Hope is the best we can do for now. It's so far to that section of the ranch, it would be dark by the time we reached the herd. First thing in the morning we'll head down there."

Tugging the brim of his hat lower on his forehead, Matthew peered through the falling snow toward the ranch yard and the house beyond. Whether Camille would be home whenever he got there was questionable, but one way or the other they had to talk tonight. And not like a pair of sparring birds, warily circling each other, but like two adults with a baby to consider.

He'd never been so blindsided in his life when she'd told him she was pregnant. And now that he'd had several hours to think about it, he had to admit that a huge part of him was thrilled to the very core of his being. He'd never thought he would be a father, and to think the woman he loved more than anything was going to bear his child was incredible. Even if she didn't want him as a husband, the connection to her was more profound than anything he'd ever expected to have.

"How was Camille this morning?" TooTall asked. "You never said."

It had taken Matthew most of the day to absorb the

news about the baby, much less talk to anyone else about it.

"She was kinda sickly."

TooTall grunted. "That's the way it is for a woman. She goes through a lot for a man."

Matthew's head jerked over to the cowboy riding by his side. "How did you—"

"I had a—"

"Vision," Matthew finished before TooTall could get the last word out. "Sometimes, TooTall, I wish you'd keep these things to yourself!"

The other man didn't bother to look in Matthew's direction. "And sometimes I wish I didn't see them," he retorted, then cast Matthew a wry look. "Don't fret. It's all going to be good, Matthew."

Good, hell! Camille was carrying his child and she didn't want to marry him. Just mentioning the word marriage to her had sent her into a furious frenzy. But then, he should've expected that. He was a Waggoner and she was a Hollister. Such things didn't happen. Not in his world.

Camille rapidly counted the stack of bills in her hand and placed them on the desk along with the remainder of the money the diner had taken in for the day. Because of the worsening weather, she'd decided to close up an hour early to give Peggy and Gideon plenty of time to drive home before dark. As for herself, she was dreading the idea of going to Red Bluff and facing Matthew tonight.

"Everything is shut down," Peggy announced as she stuck her head in the open door to the office. "And

Gideon has already left. He wanted me to remind you to drive carefully on the way to the ranch."

Camille glanced over to see Peggy had already pulled on her coat and tugged a sock cap over her black hair.

"I would be more than grateful, Peg, if you'd let me bunk in your spare bedroom for the next few days. Just until Matthew leaves."

Frowning, Peggy stepped into the room that looked spacious and neat since Camille had cleaned out Norman's clutter. "Of course you're welcome to stay at my place. You didn't even have to ask. But don't you think you're being a little hasty? And a bit stubborn?"

Camille whirled the swivel chair around so that she was facing her friend. "No! The man doesn't want a wife. All he wants is to give the baby two parents—legally bound by a piece of paper!"

Peggy made a palms-up gesture. "Isn't that what married people are?"

"Yes, but that's not enough. Not for me. The man demanded that I marry him! Demanded! How do you think that would make you feel?"

Peggy looked at her for a moment and then rolled with laughter. "Listen, Camille, if a man like Matthew ever demanded that I marry him, I'd think I was dreaming. And I probably would be. But one way or the other, I'd be standing in front of the altar letting him slip a ring on my finger."

Camille groaned with frustration, then dropped her face into both hands. "I don't want him that way."

"I thought you'd gotten over all that wounded pride business you were suffering from when you first came down here. What are you going to do? Let it take over again and ruin everything with Matthew? Okay, so he didn't approach the matter in a romantic way, but give him time. He's probably still in shock."

Dropping her hands from her face, Camille began to stuff the counted bills into a money bag. "Nothing shocks Matthew. That's what my father understood about him all those years ago. He realized that Matthew had the cool demeanor that would stand well as foreman of Three Rivers. And that hasn't changed—he's cool under the worst of conditions."

"You're talking about work now," Peggy reasoned. "I have a feeling this matter with you and the baby is very different for him."

The lump in her throat made it nearly impossible to speak. "Oh, Peg, maybe I am behaving childishly, but I—I don't think it's wrong for me to want real love from Matthew. Yet that's only a part of it. I'm very afraid that he might think I purposely got pregnant to trap him."

"Oh, Camille, that old ruse doesn't fit you at all. Matthew should be able to see that."

Maybe, Camille thought drearily. But she was the one who'd assured him that a pregnancy couldn't happen and he'd trusted her. Now she felt as though she'd betrayed him in some way. Which was even more stupid of her. No matter how much protection was being used, any time a man had sex with a woman he was running the risk of creating a child.

"I don't know anything anymore," she said miserably.

Peggy patted her shoulder. "You're not going to figure everything out about the baby and Matthew sitting here in this office. Let's get out of here and go home before the roads get too slick to travel."

Pushing herself up from the desk chair, Camille grabbed up her handbag, the day's take and her coat.

Peggy was right. She needed to get home to Red Bluff. She needed to face Matthew all over again. And this time she was going to make it clear to him that she wanted a marriage proposal spoken from his heart. She wanted his love. Nothing less would do.

Chapter Fourteen

When Matthew finally returned to the ranch house, it was dark and snow had covered everything in the courtyard, including the lounge chairs sitting under the branches of a Joshua tree.

It seemed like months had passed since he and Camille had lain together on one of the loungers. The stars had been bright that night and her kisses had been as hot as a red pepper baked in the sun. And later that evening, when he'd taken her to bed, she'd not hesitated to show him how much she'd wanted him.

But those times were over, he thought ruefully. This morning, she'd made it perfectly clear that she wanted nothing to do with him. Is that what having a baby did to a woman? Caused her feelings, her whole personality to take a one-hundred-eighty-degree turn? If so, Matthew didn't know how the Hollister men had endured their pregnant wives.

Except for a night-light over the gas range, the kitchen was dark. There were no delicious smells of cooking food or a smiling Camille setting the table for two. There was no kiss to greet him or promises of loving him through the night.

That idyllic time in his life had ended the morning he'd driven back to Three Rivers. And understanding that he'd never have the chance to regain those days again had made the long trip even more devastating for Matthew. But that didn't mean he was going to let her move completely move out of his life. Not with his baby. No, it was his child, too, and he wasn't going to be bashful about reminding her of the fact.

Still bundled in his hat and coat, he walked through to the living room, only to find Camille wasn't there, either. One small lamp illuminated a portion of the large space, and as his gaze took in the Christmas decorations and pine tree loaded with ornaments, a heavy weight of regret fell over him. They should be spending the holiday together, he thought, and celebrating the news that she was pregnant. Instead, she didn't want him near her.

Deciding she had to be in her bedroom, he climbed the stairs and entered through the partially opened door. After three steps into the room, he stopped and looked over to where she was standing at the side of the bed. An open suitcase was lying in front of her and one by one, she was folding pieces of clothing and stacking them carefully inside the case. The sight angered and sickened him at the same time.

Striding to her side, he asked, "What are you doing?"

She didn't make the effort to look at him. Instead, she stared at the inside of the suitcase and spoke stiffly, "That question is rather irrelevant, isn't it? I'm packing more of my things to go with what's already loaded in the car. I'm not going to stay another night in this house. I thought I could—I thought I could force myself. But you've ruined everything I ever loved about Red Bluff!"

Her last words snapped something inside him and before he could stop himself, he closed the lid on the suitcase and shoved it aside. Then, wrapping a hand around her upper arm, he turned her toward him.

"Forget the packing," he ordered gruffly. "You're not going anywhere! Snow is still falling out there and I'm not about to let you get on the highway and put yourself and our baby in danger! Just because you've decided you don't want me around anymore!"

Her mouth fell open and for long moments she studied him with wide, wondrous eyes. And then suddenly, as if a switch had been flipped, her features softened and her hands were clutching his forearms.

Lifting her chin to a challenging angle, she asked, "Why should my driving on a snowy road worry you, Matthew?"

He muttered an impatient curse under his breath. "That's a stupid question. It should be obvious to you!"

"There's nothing stupid about it. Or obvious. You wouldn't order anyone else to stay off the road. So why order me?" she persisted, while her fingers tightened their hold on his arms. "You have a mouth. Tell me."

If he'd been standing there naked he wouldn't have felt any more exposed than he did at this moment. Something inside of him was crumbling away like a weathered brick wall. And as it fell, it was revealing every emotion, every fear and doubt he'd carried around in his heart.

"I don't—damn it, Camille, if something happened

to you or our baby I couldn't bear it—because I love you. I've loved you for a long, long time. I just didn't recognize it until these past few weeks. Or maybe I did recognize it, but I didn't have the courage to really face my feelings head on."

She closed her eyes, but tears leaked onto her cheeks anyway. "Oh, Matthew, why didn't you tell me? That's all I needed to know. That's all I've ever wanted from you."

He pulled her close and buried his face in the curve of her neck. She smelled like lily of the valley and the scent evoked all the tender moments they'd shared in the past and would hopefully share in the future.

"You were right this morning when you called me a coward, Camille. All this time—all these years I've been afraid to admit my feelings for you—even to myself."

She eased his head back and smiled into his eyes. "But why, Matthew? If I'd only known I—"

He cradled her face between his hands. "You're a Hollister, Camille. I've never been good enough for you. I'm not sure I am now. But I have to believe that I am—because I can't let you go. Not now, or ever."

Shaking her head, she slipped her arms around his waist and drew herself closer. "I thought—for a long time I had this idea that you didn't like me. That you considered me nothing more than a shallow, spoiled brat. But that didn't stop me from thinking you were the grandest thing to ever walk on Three Rivers soil."

The sound coming out of him was something between a groan and a laugh. "If I'd only known."

More tears rolled down her cheeks, only this time they were a sign of great relief. "We've both been fools, Matthew! If we'd had the courage to be honest with each other, just think of all the misery we would've been spared. You with Renee and me with Graham." She pressed her cheek to his. "But that's all in the past. And I don't ever intend to let you go, either."

He eased her head back and slowly searched her face. "This morning you made it pretty damned clear you didn't want to marry me."

Laughing now, she kissed his cheeks and chin and finally his lips. "I was mad as fire at you, Matthew. I wanted you to *ask* me to marry you, not demand it. I wanted to hear you say that you loved me and wanted me to be your wife—that you'd love me for as long as you lived."

He swept off his hat and tossed it onto the bed, then went down on one knee in front of her. "I love you, Camille, more than anything. Will you be my wife? Will you give me this baby, and more babies, and stick by my side until the end of our days?"

She went down on her knees in front of him and wrapped her arms around his neck. "Yes, Matthew! Yes, to all those things! But first there's something I need to know."

Still uncertain, he asked, "What's that? About Three Rivers? The Lost Antelope?"

Shaking her head, she smiled at him. "No. We'll figure all that out later. I just need to know what you think about the baby and if you think I deliberately got pregnant to snare you."

A puzzled frown pulled his brows together. "Deliberate? It never crossed my mind, Camille. Not once."

Her eyes were suddenly glowing with so much love it practically took his breath away. "Oh, Matthew, I can't explain it. And the doctor told me a baby can't always be explained—it just happens."

"Yeah, if you're lucky," he said softly. "And right now I have to say I'm the luckiest guy on earth."

She pressed several kisses upon his lips, then hastily began to shove off his coat that was damp from the melting snowflakes.

After she'd tossed it aside, he took her by the hands and drew the both of them to a standing position.

As he began to undress her, she kissed him fervently, her lips conveying how much she'd missed him and how much she loved and wanted him. Now that he knew the feelings that were cradled in her heart, it made everything different for Matthew. And when they were finally on the bed and he was inside her, he thought he would die from the incredible pleasure pouring through him.

A long while later, Camille and Matthew lay cuddled together beneath the warm covers and watched the snow falling beyond the bedroom window.

"I hate to think of the little calves out in this weather," she said wistfully. "But I always try to remember what Daddy used to say—Mother Nature has a way of protecting them."

"Joel was right. And I don't believe the snow will get all that deep. Tomorrow we'll spend the day making sure none of them are stuck in drifts." He rubbed his chin against the top of her head. "This evening, while we were riding back to the ranch, TooTall told me that everything with me and you was going to turn out good. I didn't believe him."

"Really? How did he know?"

"He always knows. He's Yavapai and very mystical. He knew about our baby even before I did."

Completely bemused, she raised up on her elbow and smiled down at him. "Seriously?"

Matthew nodded. "Sometimes he has visions. His mother died when he was just a little boy. Like me. I guess you could say there's a bond between us that's different from what I have with the other men."

"That's understandable." She gently pushed her fingers through his tousled curls. "Did TooTall happen to mention what the baby's sex was?"

Matthew chuckled softly, then lifted his gaze up to her face. "No. But he did talk about Red Bluff and how I would be staying here. He even made me promise to make him my ramrod. I went along just to ease his mind. But all the while I was thinking this guy is slipping off the beam."

Her eyes full of questions, she asked, "And now?"

"Now I can see how right he was about everything. I do belong here on Red Bluff, Camille. This is where you're happy and I'm happy. It's where we need to raise our children and live out our lives. I don't want you to give up The Lost Antelope. Not for me or any reason."

Her head swung back and forth. "But I don't want you to give up Three Rivers just to make me happy."

"Oh, my little darling, Red Bluff is a part of Three Rivers. And Blake and Maureen have already been planning on turning it into a larger, full-time operation. Who do you think is going to run the place for them if I don't? Together, TooTall and I will turn this ranch into the jewel of Cochise County."

Sighing with contentment, she leaned down and kissed him. "I've never been so happy."

He took her by the shoulders and pressed her down on the pillow. "I want you to stay right here until I get back." He pulled the cover up to her armpits, then climbed out of bed and reached for his clothes.

"Where are you going?" she wanted to know.

He grinned at her. "This time I'm going to cook something for you and the baby. A cowboy can cook, you know—for the woman he loves."

Her joyous laughter followed him all the way down the stairs.

Epilogue

Several weeks later, on Christmas Eve, the hacienda on Red Bluff was ablaze with lights on the inside, while on the outside, decorative lights adorned the lawn and the back courtyard. Not only was the holiday being celebrated, but this evening the last Hollister sibling had married the man of her dreams.

Inside the living room, baskets of red-and-white flowers accented with evergreen had been added to the many poinsettias, while dozens of tall, flickering candles flanked the fireplace and the windows overlooking the mountains.

Once Camille and Matthew had decided they wanted to be married on Christmas Eve, Maureen and Vivian, along with Peggy, had all pitched in to help with the planning. Camille had made a whirlwind trip to Tucson and found the perfect dress of blush pink lace that brushed the floor and exposed most of her back. Instead of a veil, she'd adorned her upswept hair with a cluster of lily of the valley blossoms.

Vivian had stood as Camille's matron of honor, while Emily-Ann and Peggy had served as her bridesmaids. Blake had acted as Matthew's best man, with Holt and TooTall being his two groomsmen.

The men had all ribbed Matthew about finally being out of his chaps and jeans. Holt had even warned the crowd that the sight of Matthew without his spurs on might just cause the ceiling to fall in. Actually, Camille had never seen him in dress clothes, and when she'd gotten her first glimpse of him in a dark Western cut suit and bolo tie with a turquoise slide, his handsome image had very nearly taken her breath away. His untamed mane of blond curls glistened like gold in the candlelight, and as Camille had gazed into his gray eyes and repeated her vows of love, she could only think how far her life had come and what a blessed circle it had made to put her at Matthew's side.

So many friends and family had traveled from Three Rivers and Dragoon to watch Camille and Matthew exchange their wedding vows that the room was bulging at the seams. Now that the matching gold bands had been exchanged and Matthew had placed a meaningful kiss on his new wife's lips, the champagne was flowing and Christmas music drifted over the joyous crowd.

"For my beautiful daughter and new son-in-law," Maureen said as she thrust a pair of fluted glasses at the newly married couple.

"Thank you, Mom, but I can't drink the champagne," Camille told her.

Maureen looked at Matthew and winked. "Just like

I've forgotten that she's carrying your baby." She forced the drink in Camille's hand. "It's ginger ale, honey. So enjoy."

Camille leaned forward and kissed her mother's cheek. "Thank you for remembering, Mom."

She laughed. "How could I forget? You two have made me so happy. And by the way, Matthew, I have a bit more good news for you. Blake has finished the negotiations for the land. If all goes smoothly he'll be signing the papers next week. Ten thousand more acres to go with the thirty-five thousand you already have here. Even if it's across the northern boundary road, it will still be Red Bluff property. Unfortunately we couldn't talk the owners of the adjoining east property into selling, but who knows, if we keep offering them a good enough price they might come around."

"That is good news," Matthew told her. "So I guess this means more barns, more cattle and cowboys, and plenty more horses for Red Bluff."

Maureen affectionately patted his arm. "More everything. I'm going to miss the heck out of working with you every day, Matthew. But I'll get over it. Especially knowing how happy you've made my daughter."

Matthew slipped his arm around the back of Camille's waist and pulled her close to his side. "I'm going to do my best to keep her that way, Maureen. As for Red Bluff, it's going to be a pleasure to help it grow."

Before Maureen could say more, Vivian rushed up and took her mother by the arm. "Mom, I hate to do this to you, but Reeva needs you in the kitchen for something."

Maureen rolled her eyes. "I told Reeva we should've

had the wedding dinner catered, but she wouldn't hear of it. She just had to do the cooking herself."

Vivian shared a knowing glance with Camille and Matthew before she said to her mother, "She was insulted that you even mentioned such a thing, Mom. Camille is the last Hollister to get married and you think she'd let some other cook do the dinner? Only over her dead body."

Vivian tugged her mother away and Matthew used the moment to draw Camille to an empty corner of the room where the noise of the wedding crowd wasn't quite so loud.

"I know, I know," Camille teased. "We should have made the trip to the courthouse in Bisbee and let the judge marry us in his chambers. I admit it would've been a lot easier and quieter."

Bringing his mouth close to her ear, he said, "And miss seeing you looking so gorgeous and having all our friends and family here? Not for anything. You deserve this celebration, my beautiful wife."

She turned her head just enough to kiss his cheek. "Have you looked in at the dining room?" she asked. "The tables are decorated with flowers and candles and crystal, and Mom brought her best flatware and china down from Three Rivers."

He smiled at her glowing face. "I could eat Reeva's prime rib off a granite plate and be just as happy."

She laughed and then looked back out at the crowd. "Peggy and Gideon and Edie seemed to be enjoying themselves. I'm glad. I want them to feel like a part of the family."

"I believe they do," Matthew commented. "And Emily-Ann seems to be especially enjoying herself. I'm glad she could make it to the wedding. I know you two have been friends forever."

"Yes. And she caught my bouquet! You know what that means," she said, her eyes twinkling suggestively.

Matthew chuckled. "Now you sound like TooTall making predictions."

"Well, Emily-Ann deserves to have someone in her life. Like we have each other."

Sighing, she turned and was about to place a kiss on Matthew's lips when Holt suddenly strolled up with a short glass of bourbon and cola in his hand.

"Uh-uh. None of that, little sis," he teased. "You're an old married woman now. You can forget the hanky-panky."

She gave her handsome brother a tight hug. "What are you doing with that stuff?" she asked, pointing to the tumbler. "In case you didn't know, you're at a wedding. You're supposed to be drinking champagne!"

He laughed and winked at Matthew. "My system couldn't stand the shock. And speaking of a shocker, we just got one from Mom a few minutes ago. Did she mention anything to you two?"

"You mean about the land purchase to add to Red Bluff?" Matthew asked, assuming that was the only thing Holt could be talking about. "She told us the deal was going through and that Blake would sign the papers in a few days."

"Actually, it's been ages since I've seen Mom this happy," Camille told her brother. "Something has definitely lifted her spirits."

Matthew cast his wife a tender look. "I like to think she's happy about us and the baby. I realize that we surprised her, but she seems to be content with having me for a son-in-law."

"Oh, there's no doubt that she's over the moon about you two and the baby. But there's something else going on," Holt said. Then, moving closer, he lowered his voice. "She just told me and Joe that Uncle Gil has just retired from the Phoenix police force. And that's not the least of it. The man is moving to Yavapai County to live."

Wide-eyed, Camille glanced at Matthew, then back to her brother. "Is this for real, Holt? Or have you been downing too much of that bourbon?"

Frowning, Holt lifted his glass, "This is my first and last. And what I'm telling you is very real. Seems as though Uncle Gil called Mom this morning to wish her a Merry Christmas. That's when he gave her the news."

"Hmm. Wonder if this has anything to do with the investigation of your father's death?" Matthew pondered out loud. "After all, the man was a detective for the police force for years."

Holt shrugged. "All of us brothers are wondering the same thing. But Mom refuses to discuss the matter with us anymore. If Uncle Gil has solving Dad's death on his mind, then he's not going to get any help from Mom. On the other hand, she seems thrilled that he's going to be living close by."

"How close?" Camille asked, picking up on the suggestive tone in Holt's voice. "On Three Rivers?"

"I have no idea. But I guess we'll find out soon enough."

Beyond Holt's shoulder, not far from the Christmas tree, Camille caught sight of Isabelle standing with Gabby and Sam. Isabelle's baby bump was clearly evident beneath her bottle-green dress, and Camille could only hope she looked that lovely once her pregnancy grew to the advanced stage. Next to her, Gabby was close to Sam's side, and as Camille studied the old cowboy from afar, she realized she'd never seen him looking so dapper in pressed jeans, a white shirt and a dark vest. Cupid had obviously struck him with an arrow, Camille thought. And considering the man's much younger fiancée, he and Gabby were a testament that love wasn't always conventional. Which made Camille wonder even more about her mother and Gil.

"Excuse me, you two," Holt spoke up. "I'd better go find Isabelle. I promised to dance with her tonight."

Camille laughed. "Where are you going to find the space to dance in this crowd?"

Holt gave her a wicked grin. "We don't need much space. As long as I have my arms around her and we sway a bit, she'll consider it dancing."

As he walked away, Camille let out a good-natured groan and Matthew chuckled.

"Wow, it's still hard for me to picture Holt married and with a baby on the way," she said fondly, "but I'm so happy for him."

"And he's happy for us," Matthew thoughtfully replied. "Our sons or daughters will be cousins close to the same age. Who would have ever guessed that would happen?"

She gave her new husband a clever smile. "Uh— TooTall might have already guessed it. You think?"

With another chuckle, Matthew plucked the glass from her hand, and after depositing it on a nearby table, he pulled her into his arms. "I think Holt had a very good idea. We need to dance."

He maneuvered her backwards and through the door leading into the dining room. The space was blessedly empty of people and Matthew took the opportunity to place a lingering kiss on her lips.

"Merry Christmas, my beautiful wife," he whispered.

She smiled up at him. "Merry Christmas, my darling husband."

He gently moved her to the music and she rested her head against his shoulder. "Matthew, do you think Mom is romantically interested in Uncle Gil?"

He was silent for so long that she finally lifted her head to see a sheepish expression on his face.

"What?" she prodded. "Tell me."

"Okay, I can't really say how Maureen feels about Gil or any man. But Holt and Chandler seem to believe she's fallen in love with the guy."

Camille regarded him with mild surprise. "Hmm. Uncle Gil? I wouldn't have expected him to be on Mom's mind. Not in that way."

"Does the idea bother you?"

Shaking her head, she touched her fingers to his cheek. "A few months ago it might have. But now that I have you and our baby on the way, I understand what love really means and how it's made my life truly whole. If Mom can find that again with Uncle Gil, then I'll be the first to congratulate her."

He rubbed his cheek against hers. "I'm very proud of you, sweetheart."

Her heart overflowing with happiness, she held him tighter. "Our baby truly is a Christmas miracle, and tonight on our wedding night, nothing is going to dim the bright star shining down on Red Bluff." She brought her lips next to his ear. "You've given me the best gift ever, Matthew. Even if I have to wait a few months to unwrap it."

"I'm glad you think so. But how am I going to find you a gift for the following Christmases that will match up to this one?"

Easing her head back, she gave him a pointed look. "You don't think we're going to stop with just one, do you?"

Laughing, he whirled her in a full circle. "Camille, living with you is going to make every day seem like Christmas."

* * * * *

COMING SOON!

We really hope you enjoyed reading this book. If you're looking for more romance, be sure to head to the shops when new books are available on

Thursday 26th December

To see which titles are coming soon, please visit

millsandboon.co.uk/nextmonth

MILLS & BOON

Coming next month

CRAZY ABOUT HER IMPOSSIBLE BOSS
Ally Blake

There was no way he wasn't fully aware she stood behind him. The man's ability to read a room was legendary. He noticed changes in temperature, pulse, breathing, tone of voice the way other people noticed being kicked in the shin.

Yet still Lucinda took a selfish moment to drink him in before making herself officially known.

For Angus Wolfe's profile was a study in staggering male beauty.

The man was all chiselled angles. Sharp jaw close shaven. Hair darkly curling and a mite overlong. Reading glasses he refused to admit he needed to wear did nothing to soften the impact of the most formidable pair of dark hazel eyes that had ever been seen.

Even the tendons in his neck were a sight to behold.

Then he shifted. Slowly. Like a big cat stretching in the sun. The lines of his charcoal suit moved with him, cut as they were to make the most of his…everything. Each one cost more than she'd spent on her car. She knew. She paid his bills.

Then she spotted his socks. Peeking out from the top of his custom-made dress shoes she saw the merest hint of a wolf motif. She'd given him those socks for Christmas.

Her heart gave a little flutter, releasing a gossamer

thread of lust that wafted from throat to belly to places less mentionable.

She squished the thing. Fast.

Angus Wolfe might be able to read a room, but if anyone dared claim that Lucinda Starling - his long-time Executive Assistant, his right-hand woman, his not-so-secret weapon – was a teeny tiny little bit in love with him, he'd have laughed till he split a kidney.

Either she kept her cards closer to her chest than she realised, or he had a blind spot when it came to her. The fact that he had no clue was a gift. And she planned to keep it that way…

Continue reading
CRAZY ABOUT HER IMPOSSIBLE BOSS
Ally Blake

Available next month
www.millsandboon.co.uk

JOIN US ON SOCIAL MEDIA!

Stay up to date with our latest releases, author news and gossip, special offers and discounts, and all the behind-the-scenes action from Mills & Boon...

 millsandboon

 millsandboonuk

 millsandboon

t might just be true love...

LET'S TALK
Romance

For exclusive extracts, competitions
and special offers, find us online:

 facebook.com/millsandboon

@MillsandBoon

@MillsandBoonUK

Get in touch on 01413 063232

For all the latest titles coming soon, visit
millsandboon.co.uk/nextmonth

MILLS & BOON
Desire

Indulge in secrets and scandal, intense drama and plenty of sizzling hot action with powerful and passionate heroes who have it all: wealth, status, good looks… everything but the right woman.